PLANE GEOMETRY

AND SUPPLEMENTS

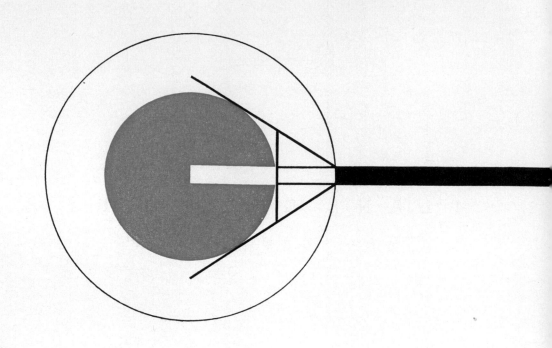

PLANE GEOMETRY

AND SUPPLEMENTS

Walter W. Hart   AUTHOR OF TEXTBOOKS FOR SECONDARY MATHEMATICS

Veryl Schult   SUPERVISING DIRECTOR, MATHEMATICS CURRICULUM
PUBLIC SCHOOLS OF WASHINGTON, D.C.

Henry Swain   DIRECTOR OF THE MATHEMATICS CURRICULUM, NEW
TRIER TOWNSHIP HIGH SCHOOL, WINNETKA, ILLINOIS

D. C. HEATH AND COMPANY • Boston

LIBRARY OF CONGRESS CATALOG CARD NUMBER: 59–5838

PREFACE

Plane Geometry and Supplements contains a course in the fundamentals of plane geometry together with supplements from plane geometry, solid geometry, trigonometry, and analytic geometry. The organization of the subject matter is apparent in the Contents (pp. viii–ix).

For a **basic course** in plane geometry omit all the supplementary optional exercises and units, marked by stars as on pages 67 and 71. The result is a substantial course, adequate for some pupils in all schools.

The aims of this course are:

1. To develop acquaintance with, some appreciation of, and ability to construct and measure the common figures of plane geometry.
2. To develop some knowledge of and some ability in the study of geometry by deductive procedures.
3. To develop some ability to reason when no mathematics is involved.

a) *The instruction in Chapter 1* was guided by two convictions:

   (1) Initial understanding of geometrical concepts by beginning pupils is acquired best through exercises in drawing and measuring geometrical figures.

   (2) Acquaintance with the meaning and the place of definitions, axioms, postulates, and proofs in deductive geometry should be allowed to develop gradually. Consequently, on pages 14–28, concepts, vocabulary, and some obvious conclusions are developed inductively. Some of the sophisticated postulates of Hilbert and Veblen are avoided. In particular, congruent figures are defined as figures that can be made to coincide by superposition. This conception can be assimilated easily by students. (See page 52.) Proofs of some obvious conclusions are omitted or are informal (§14(b), §16(e), and §17(b)). After the nature of inductive reasoning has become clear (p. 29) and such reasoning is shown to lead to uncertain conclusions (p. 30), deductive reasoning is described (pp. 31–35) and illustrated by informal proofs (pp. 37–39) and the first formal proof (p. 40).

b) *Each of Chapters 1 to 10* contains some basic plane geometry, followed by one or more optional units. Some traditional units of plane geometry (pp. 139, 190, 194, . . .) have been made optional or have been postponed. (See Chapter 11.)

(1) In each chapter, necessary new axioms, postulates, concepts, and definitions appear (pp. 51, 90, ...). Since new postulates appear in Chapters 3, 5, 6, and 10, the effect is to produce several sequences of theorems, each sequence dependent in part on a new postulate. However, to avoid uncertainty and confusion, no basic theorems are postulated.

(2) Basic theorems are proved in desirable style (pp. 40, 72, ...) but, as the course progresses, proofs become more and more incomplete to prevent mere memorization of proofs (pp. 64, 78, 92, ...).

(3) Desirable theorems that can be proved easily by use of basic theorems appear as corollaries (pp. 93, 96, 108, ...).

(4) Each basic theorem is accompanied by an adequate number of graded exercises (pp. 110, 116, ...). From time to time, footnotes appear (pp. 62, 65, 69, ...) that refer to additional exercises at the back of the book.

(5) The chapters appear in an order that is familiar to teachers—in general, in the order of difficulty.

(6) Discussion of converses (pp. 99, 115, 117), of indirect proof (p. 91), of planning demonstrations (p. 113), and of fundamental plans for proofs (pp. 57, 93, 122, ...) contribute to growth in ability to state and prove conclusions.

(7) Reviews (pp. 132, 152, 177, ...), tests (pp. 131, 149, 176, ...), and new Cumulative Guides (pp. 430–442 and 443–448) help pupils to secure and to evaluate their mastery of the subject.

The supplementary units include some from plane geometry and some that are recommended strongly by committees and by the Commission on Mathematics of the College Entrance Examination Board.

a) The basic course in plane geometry has been curtailed somewhat to provide time for recommended units from solid geometry, trigonometry, and analytic geometry. Some of the omitted units from plane geometry appear among the supplementary units.

b) The organization of the supplementary units facilitates study of such units by gifted pupils or classes of such pupils.

c) The early units of solid geometry, taught inductively, have accompanying informal demonstrations of some of the important conclusions, to be consistent with the second general aim of the course as stated on page v. Obviously any teacher who is content to have only descriptions of the solid figures and conclusions about them, or who wishes to develop such knowledge only inductively, can omit the deductive demonstrations.

d) Although the general ideals of demonstrative geometry are maintained, departures from order and formality are introduced (SG 8,

p. 58; Ex. 7, p. 61; Ex. 2, p. 87; SG 29 and SG 30, p. 105) to adapt the study of solid geometry to pupils who are younger than those to whom this subject is taught usually, and also to minimize the formality of the proofs.

e) Some demonstrations in solid geometry are no more difficult than many of those in plane geometry. Therefore reputed difficulty of proof is no argument against teaching some solid geometry during the only year in which most pupils will study geometry.

f) Special attention is directed to Chapter 12 in which the theorems concerning mensuration of the common solids appear. Many of these formulas are included in junior high school mathematics, where efforts are made to provide experiential backgrounds for understanding them. To do less or only as much in the present course in geometry is not justifiable. Therefore demonstrations of the important conclusions, either formal or informal, are included. The demonstrations in Chapter 12 are an appropriate climax and challenge at the close of the course. Obviously any teacher who prefers to omit these proofs can do so.

g) The optional units from analytic geometry are included for three reasons:

(1) To give exploratory experience in this branch of mathematics.

(2) To develop in particular the formulas for the coordinates of the mid-point of a segment and the formula for the length of the segment between two points that are described by their coordinates, referred to rectangular axes. These formulas are interesting as such, and can be used to prove analytically some theorems of plane geometry.

(3) To correlate the algebraic and the geometric study of certain loci (pp. 335–345).

h) Study of some or of all of these supplementary units by gifted pupils or classes of such pupils is recommended strongly. Further discussion of these units and procedures for using them appear in the Teacher's Manual. The presence of these units in the book does not alter the fact that the book contains a realistic basic course in plane geometry that can be taught in one school year.

W. W. H.
V. S.
H. S.

CONTENTS

Plane Geometry
AND SUPPLEMENTS

INTRODUCTION

Man-made objects often have shapes that are called *geometric solids*. You are acquainted with the shapes that are represented by the drawings below. These are called *solids* even though the objects having these forms may be hollow.

Thus: Tennis balls and bowling balls are spherical even though the former are hollow and the latter are not.

A *rectangular solid* consists of six plane surfaces that are bounded by squares or rectangles.

The *circular cylinder* shown consists of two plane surfaces that are enclosed by circles and a *curved surface* that meets the plane surfaces in the circles.

A *sphere* is entirely a curved surface.

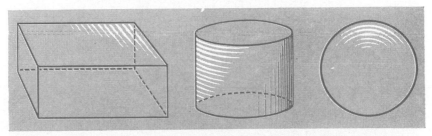

RECTANGULAR SOLID   CIRCULAR CYLINDER   SPHERE

Squares and rectangles are formed by straight lines that meet at points. The study of squares, rectangles, circles, and other combinations of points and lines that lie on a plane surface is called *plane geometry*. The study of solid figures is called *solid geometry*.

 Geometric figures are evident in the Atlas Intercontinental Ballistic Missile, its launching pad, and gantry tower at Cape Canaveral, Florida.
CONVAIR

1

Origins of

The study of geometry began when people first noticed the shapes of objects about them.

A stretched-out finger of a hand, twigs of trees, tall trees that had grown close together in a thick forest, blades of grass, threads of a spider web—these gave the idea of a *straight line*.

Marks between layers of some rocks, falling rain, the tall trees mentioned above—these gave the idea of *parallel lines*.

An arm bent at the elbow, crossing paths on a field, the ever-changing direction during the day of the shadow of a pole cast by the sun—these gave the idea of an *angle*.

The outline of the full moon, of the rising or setting sun, of the pupil of an eye, the cross sections of some fruits and berries—these made early people aware of the *circle*. They discovered that an animal, tied to a stake in the ground, when it moved around the stake made a circular path on the ground. This fact suggested to some inventive genius that he could draw this curved line on the ground if he held one end of a stick stationary

Top: Sap is being taken from a Georgia pine forest.
Bottom: Diatoms and diffraction rings have geometric shapes.

PHOTO BY U. S. FOREST SERVICE

CARNEGIE INSTITUTION OF WASHINGTON AND PROFESSOR
M. E. HUFFORD, INDIANA UNIVERSITY

Geometry

and dragged the other end around it on the ground. It was only a short step from this to drawing a circle on stone or wood by some tool that was the forerunner of our pair of compasses.

Men who lived where snow fell could see in some snowflakes beautiful and complicated figures made of lines. Others found interesting figures consisting of lines when they examined spider webs, honeycombs, and other natural objects.

Many kinds of fruit and some pebbles suggested the *sphere*. In the course of time scientists decided that the earth is approximately a sphere.

Tall trees easily suggested the *circular cylinder*.

The fact that geometrical shapes appear in nature led the Greek philosopher Plato to say, "God eternally geometrizes."

1. During the year, try to find for your notebook pictures showing geometrical forms in natural objects.

Top: A spider web suggests lines and polygons.
Bottom: Snowflakes are basically hexagonal in shape.

THE AMERICAN MUSEUM
OF NATURAL HISTORY

3

Ancient

Geometrical figures are found in the architectural remains of Babylonia, Assyria, Persia, Egypt, Greece, and Rome.

By 2000 B.C. the city of Babylon had a system of streets parallel to the river Euphrates, crossed at right angles by other parallel streets. The large city contained as many as 250 towers, vast temples, and houses two and three stories high.

The pyramids of Ancient Egypt were built of huge blocks of stone cut on geometrical lines. In the British Museum there is a papyrus copied about 1700 B.C. by an Egyptian scribe called Ahmes. This manuscript contains, among mathematical problems and solutions, the rules for measuring certain geometrical figures. The rule for finding the area of a triangle is incorrect; that for the area of a circle, while remarkably good, is less accurate than one given later by Archimedes.

The Greek historian Herodotus said that the Egyptians had to resurvey some of their land often because landmarks were destroyed by floods of the river Nile. This may have led the

Parallel columns in the Forum of ancient Rome.

Egyptian pyramids.

The Nashville, Tennessee, reproduction of the ancient Greek Parthenon.

A. DEVANEY, INC., N. Y.

EWING GALLOWAY. N. Y.

TENNESSEE CONSERVATION DEPARTMENT PHOTO

Geometry

Greeks to use as a suitable name for the subject the word *ge-ometry*, from their word *gē*, meaning the earth, and *metron*, meaning measure, so that *geometry* referred to measuring the earth.

Thales of Miletus (600 B.C.) became acquainted with geometry when he traveled in Egypt. He taught his friends what he had learned about geometry and, with them, made new discoveries in the subject. The Greeks became interested in geometry for its own sake as well as for its usefulness. Between 600 and 300 B.C., they not only extended knowledge of geometry but developed it into a science by systematizing and organizing it and by insisting upon proofs of what appeared to be true.

About 300 B.C. Euclid, a Greek teacher of mathematics at the university at Alexandria, gathered the elementary parts of geometry in thirteen booklets, Euclid's *Elements*. These have been the models for subsequent books on elementary geometry.

Your teacher will give you references to books in which other historical facts about geometry can be found.

A portion of an ancient Greek theater
on the Gulf of Aegina.

Bas relief at Persepolis.

Palace at Knossos in Crete.

Geometry

Even though knowledge of geometry has grown greatly since the days of Euclid, elementary parts of the subject are still taught because they are useful.

Engineers and designers of both practical and artistic objects start with sketches of the machinery, the building, the highway, the airplane, the dress, or the linoleum pattern which they are called upon to design. Often they must make drawings from which they can secure measurements. When that becomes necessary, they use information and skills based on facts which they learned while studying geometry.

Draftsmen, taking the preliminary drawings and measurements, prepare finished drawings that are as accurate as possible, not only of the object as a whole but of parts of it so that workmen can produce the object that has been designed.

Thus, the plans for an elaborate home or for an office building will include accurate drawings of the layout of the heating, plumbing, and electrical systems, and detailed drawings of the doors, windows, and cabinet work to be installed in the building.

Scale drawings must be made before the manufacture of such scientific instruments as those pictured below.
Left: The mechanical arms and hands used in a radiation test cell.
Right: 200-in. mirror disk for the telescope at Mt. Palomar.

STANDARD OIL CO. (N. J.)

CORNING GLASS WORKS

Today

Such drawings are called mechanical drawings, although they are far from being mechanical. The draftsmen must use methods and information that are included in courses in plane and solid geometry or in higher geometry for the study of which a knowledge of elementary geometry is necessary.

Geometrical drawings are used to help explain many kinds of problems that occur in science, engineering, navigation, and industry.

Geometry is the subject on which numerical trigonometry is based. Trigonometry is fundamental in the study and practices of surveying, navigation, astronomy, and higher mathematics.

In daily work in industry, on a farm, and in a home, knowledge of geometry can be used. Fields not only look better but can be worked better if they are laid out in certain geometrical forms and on geometrical lines. In a home, curtains, floor coverings, table and bed linen all look better when they have certain geometrical shapes and when they fit the places where they are to be used.

Geometrical forms are the basis of much modern furniture and many home appliances.

CORNING GLASS WORKS

CORNING GLASS WORKS

Why Study

A beginner in geometry is said to have asked Euclid, "What shall I profit by learning these things?"

Euclid, calling to him a servant, said, "Give him three pence since he must make gain out of what he learns."

Why should you study geometry?

First, for the fun of it, just as you play or dance for fun rather than for any physical benefit you may get from it; for the fun of learning about the oldest science in the world, for the fun of learning what millions before you have learned, and for the fun of studying something that uses your ability to think as well as your ability to remember.

Second, study geometry for the possible use you may have for it in later life. This may be only the ability to recognize and to appreciate the beauty of geometry in the world about you, but it may be knowledge and skill that you will use in some trade or vocation, or in the study of college mathematics, science, or technology.

Geometric figures appear in many aspects of life:

Industry — gear wheels, trusses, and smokestacks.

Agriculture — layout of fields on a truck farm.

Geometry?

Third, study geometry for certain indirect benefits you can derive from studying it. Geometry, as taught, emphasizes logical thinking. This kind of thinking distinguishes normal human beings from animals, and adults from children. It is the kind of thinking that enables us to use old experiences as guides to new experiences. It is the opposite of thinking by "trial and error." No other subject in the high school curriculum gives such training so well as geometry.

There are other indirect benefits. These include training in exact use of English, in public speaking, in perseverance and in originality in solving problems—especially mathematical ones, of course—in the use of drawing instruments, and in neat, orderly ways of preparing and presenting solutions of problems. These by-products become yours as results of the way in which geometry is taught and studied, the way in which your class is conducted, and the way in which you prepare your lessons.

"Like most every other subject of human interest, mathematics is just as easy or as difficult as we choose to make it."   John Perry

Sports — archery.

World's Fair — atomium, the symbol of the Brussels fair.

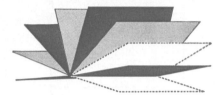

LINES—ANGLES—PLANES

In earlier courses in mathematics you have learned some facts about lines and angles. In this chapter you will review and extend that knowledge and explore some facts about planes.

Previously you learned facts about geometrical figures by drawing and measuring the figures.

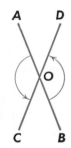

Thus: If straight lines *AB* and *CD* cross, or intersect, you *see* that angle *AOC* equals angle *BOD*, or you can measure them and reach the same conclusion. If you do that with several figures, you decide that angles such as *AOC* and *BOD* always are equal. This method of reasoning is called *inductive reasoning*. The conclusion is uncertain because it depends on the accuracy of the drawing and measuring.

Before the end of this chapter you will be introduced to a kind of reasoning (deductive) that gives more dependable conclusions. When such reasoning is employed, it is necessary to know the meanings of the geometric figures, to know what we assume about them, and to remember and use what we prove about them.

Top: Styling Buildings at the General Motors Technical Center.
Center: Interior of San Gabriel High School, San Gabriel, California.
Bottom: Exterior of San Gabriel High School, San Gabriel, California.

1. You probably can draw and describe some geometrical figures, can tell some facts about them, and can compute some perimeters, areas, and volumes.

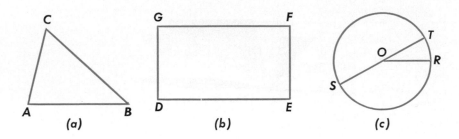

(a) (b) (c)

1. (a) What is each of the figures above called?
  (b) Using the letters on it, name each figure.

2. What kinds of lines appear in the figures?

3. In figure (a) what do lines AB and AC form?

4. (a) In figure (b) what kind of lines are DE and GF?
  What kind of lines are DG and EF?
  (b) How does DE compare in length with GF?

5. In figure (a) what kind of angle is at each of the vertices A, B, and C?

6. In figure (b) what kind of angle is at each vertex?

7. In figure (c) what do we call:
  (a) Point O? (b) OR? (c) ST?

8. What tool or instrument is used to draw figure (c)?

9. (a) Name places in your classroom where you see a plane (or flat) surface.
  (b) How many dimensions does each such surface have?
  (c) What are the dimensions called?

10. (a) What geometrical shape does a chalk box have?
  (b) Name another object that has the same shape.
  (c) How many dimensions does that shape have?
  (d) What are those dimensions called?

11. (a) What geometrical shape does a coffee can have?
  (b) Name some other object having that same shape.

12. (a) What geometrical shape does a baseball have?
  (b) Name another object that has that same shape.

13. (a) Approximately, what is the shape of the earth?
  (b) Draw a figure to represent the earth. Place on it points to mark the North Pole and South Pole and a line to represent the Equator.

2. Some **geometrical figures** and their names are recalled to you by the exercises that appear on page 12. These figures consist of points, lines, and surfaces. In the geometry that you will study this year, exact definitions (or descriptions) of geometrical figures must be given.

A **definition** of a geometrical figure or of a relation between figures is a description of it by means of figures or of words whose meanings are known. Clearly then we must start with some figures and words that we do not define.

We shall not define *point, line, straight line, surface,* or *plane.* These are our **undefined geometrical concepts.** As aids to thinking about them:

(*a*) We *represent a point* by a small dot, and name it by a capital letter printed beside it, as point *A*.

(*b*) We agree that a line consists of or is a set of points. We *represent a line* by a mark made by a pen, a sharp pencil, or a piece of crayon. We *name* it by some points of it, as line *BCDE*.

(*c*) We name a *straight line* by two points of it, as line *FG*, or by a small letter placed near it, as line *m*. The two arrowheads on *FG* indicate that *FG* runs on and on in each of two directions.

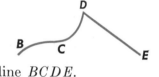

A point *P* of a line *m* separates the line into *two parts*, on opposite sides of *P*, as parts *PR* and *PS*.

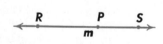

(*d*) The *surface* of an object is the part of the object that we can touch.   A surface, also, consists of or is a set of points. A *plane surface* is smooth and flat, like the surface of a mirror.

(*e*) We think of lines as having *one dimension* and a plane as having *two* dimensions. **In plane** geometry, **all the points and lines of each figure lie in one and in only one plane.** Plane geometry is two-dimensional geometry.

3. Drawings *suggest* some *agreements* about points and straight lines.

1. (*a*) Through a point *O* draw:
   Horizontal line *AOP*
   Vertical line *BOS*
   Oblique lines *COR* and *DOT*
   (*b*) What do the arrowheads suggest?
   (*c*) How many straight lines can be drawn on a plane through a point of the plane?

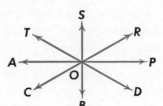

2. (*a*) Draw a straight line *AB* through two points *A* and *B*.

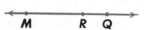

   (*b*) Can you draw more than one straight line through both *A* and *B?*

3. (*a*) On straight line *MQ* place point *R* *between* *M* and *Q.*

   (*b*) Points *M*, *Q*, and *R* are in the **order** *MRQ.*

4. (*a*) On straight line *AB* place point *D* so that *B* is between *A* and *D.*
   Points like *D* are on *AB* *extended.*

   (*b*) If point *A* is between points *E* and *B* of line *AB*, then points like *E* are on *BA* extended.
   (*c*) *AB* can be extended in each of the two directions.

5. (*a*) Draw straight line *RS* with dotted parts to represent the extensions of *RS*.

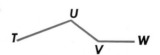

   (*b*) *Segment RS* consists of points *R* and *S*, and the points of line *RS* between *R* and *S.*

6. (*a*) In a plane draw a line *TUVW* that consists of three connected segments— *TU*, *UV*, and *VW.*
   (*b*) *TUVW* is a *broken* line.

7. (*a*) In a plane draw a line *XYZW* no part of which is straight.
   (*b*) *XYZW* is a *curved* line.

8. How many end points:
   (*a*) Has a line?   (*b*) Has a segment?

9. (*a*) Draw a line *CD*. On it place point *E* between *C* and *D*; also, place *F* on *CD* between *C* and *E.*
   (*b*) Is there a limit to the number of points that can be placed on *CD* between *C* and *D?*

1. (*a*) On a plane draw a straight line and also a curved line through points D, E, and F.

   (*b*) Points D, E, and F are *points of intersection* of the two lines.

2. (*a*) Draw straight lines FG and HK intersecting at P.

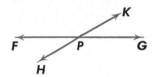

   (*b*) How many points of intersection can two straight lines have?

3. (*a*) Through a point O draw a straight line ROP, using a dotted line for the part OR. Erase the dotted part OR.

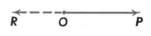

   (*b*) OP is a *ray*. It consists of point O and all points of line ROP at the right side of point O.

   (*c*) What does the arrowhead at P suggest?

4. **Definitions.** (*a*) A **straight line segment** or simply a **segment** is a set of points consisting of two points of a straight line and the points between them. (Ex. 5, p. 14)

(*b*) A **broken line** consists of two or more connected straight-line segments in a plane. (Ex. 6, p. 14)

(*c*) A **curved line** in a plane is a line of which no part is straight. (Ex. 7, p. 14)

(*d*) A **simple closed line** in a plane is a line which can be followed continuously from any point of it back to that point without passing through any point of it more than once. It encloses a part of the plane called the **interior** of the closed line.

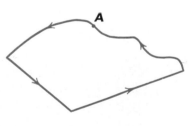

(*e*) Two **intersecting lines** have one or more points that are in both of them (Ex. 1, p. 15). We say that such points are **common points** or **points of intersection**.

(*f*) A **ray** is a set of points consisting of a point of a straight line, called its **origin**, and all the points of the line on one side of the origin (Ex. 3(*b*), p. 15). A ray extends infinitely far (on and on) in one direction from its origin.

5. The exercises on pages 14 and 15 also help you to understand the following statements. These statements *have not been proved*. They are suggested by the drawings. Such assumed geometrical statements are called **postulates.**

(*a*) *One and only one straight line can be drawn through two points*, as line *AB* in Ex. 2, p. 14.

(*b*) Two *straight lines can* **intersect** *in only one point*, as in Ex. 2, p. 15. *P* is the **point of intersection.**

(*c*) Sometimes we must use more of the straight line of which a given segment is a part, so we agree that:
A segment can be extended in each of two directions. (Ex. 4, page 14)

6. *Hereafter*, when a line is mentioned, a straight line is meant. Since a straight line is infinitely long, we can draw only a part of it. We really draw a segment.

7. Often two segments must be compared. With compasses take *radius CD* by placing one point of the compasses on *C* and the other on *D*. Keeping the *legs* of the compasses unchanged, place one point of the compasses on *E* and see where the other will

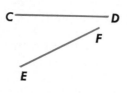

fall on *EF*. If the other point falls on *F*, then **CD equals EF.** If the other falls between *E* and *F*, then **CD is less than** (<) **EF.** If the other falls on *EF* extended, then **CD is greater than** (>) **EF.**

1. On the adjoining figure, using compasses:
    (*a*) Compare *YX* with *YW*.
    (*b*) Compare *YX* with *XW*.
    (*c*) Compare *XW* with *ZW*.

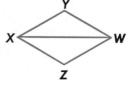

2. (*a*) On a line *RS* place point *L*. With compasses take radius *HJ*. On *RS* find *M* to the right of *L* so that *LM = HJ*.
    (*b*) Similarly find *N* to the right of *M* so that *MN = JK*. Now *LN = HJ + JK*.
    (*c*) Compare *HK* with *LN*, or *HJ + JK*.

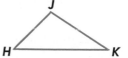

3. (*a*) On a ray *OT*, with compasses locate point *C* so that *OC* equals twice *HK* of Ex. 2.
    (*b*) On a line *AB* place point *D*. With compasses locate point *E* on ray *DB* so that *DE* equals 3*JK* of Ex. 2.

1. (*a*) Compare AC with CB as suggested in §7.

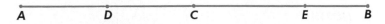

(*b*) If $AC = CB$, then C *bisects* AB, and C is the *mid-point* of AB. Does D bisect AC?

(*c*) Is E the *mid-point* of CB?

2. Draw a segment MN. Try to bisect it freehand. Then test the two parts to see whether you did bisect MN.

8. The exercises on pages 16 and 17 teach:

(*a*) **Two segments are equal or congruent if they can be made to coincide,** as in §7, p. 16.

(*b*) **One segment is less than another** *if it equals a part of the other.* (§7)

(*c*) *On a line, in one direction from a point of the line, there is one and only one segment equal to a given segment.* (Ex. 2(*a*), p. 16) It can be laid off by means of compasses.

(*d*) The **shortest distance** or **distance** between two points is the segment between the points, as HK in Ex. 2(*c*), p. 16.

(*e*) A **point bisects a segment** when it separates the segment into two equal segments, as in Ex. 1(*a*), p. 17. The point is the mid-point of the segment.

(*f*) *A segment has one and only one mid-point.* The way to locate this mid-point will be taught later.

9. **To measure a segment.**

AB is nearer to $2\frac{3}{8}$ in. than to $2\frac{1}{2}$ in. We say that AB is $2\frac{3}{8}$ in. *correct to the nearest* $\frac{1}{8}$ in.

AB is nearer to $2\frac{7}{16}$ in. than to $2\frac{6}{16}$ in., or $2\frac{3}{8}$ in. We say that AB is $2\frac{7}{16}$ in. *correct to the nearest* $\frac{1}{16}$ in.

Both measures are correct. The second is said to be *more precise* than the first because it is correct to the smaller unit of length. When measuring a segment, express the length correct to the smallest unit of length that appears on the scale (ruler). Here $3\frac{1}{2}$ in. means $3\frac{1}{2}$ in. correct to the nearest $\frac{1}{16}$ in.

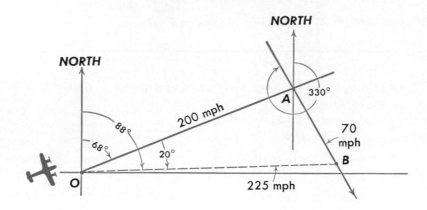

DRAWING TO FIND THE DRIFT ANGLE

The drawing above is a kind that appears in a book on navigation for airplane pilots. It is used as an aid in solving the following problem.

A private airplane is flying at an air speed of 200 miles an hour on a course that makes an angle of 68 degrees with the North-South direction. This much is indicated by the segment *OA* of the drawing.

A wind of 70 miles an hour is blowing from the direction that makes an angle of 330 degrees with the North-South direction, the angle being measured in the direction in which the hands of a clock turn. This much is indicated by the segment *AB* of the drawing.

Under these conditions, the wind will cause the airplane to *drift* south of the direction in which it is *headed*. The resulting path the plane actually flies, or *track* as it is called, is indicated by the segment *OB*.

Measurements indicate that this track makes an angle of 88 degrees with the North-South direction, and that the airplane moves at about 225 miles an hour.

The *angle of drift* is 20 degrees south.

This is one of the ways in which a knowledge of angles is important in the training and work of airplane pilots. Illustrations of use of angles in trades and professions such as pattern making, architecture, carpentry, surveying, and engineering could be given. You will learn about angles while studying the following pages.

10. An **angle** consists of two rays that have the same origin, as angle AOB ($\angle AOB$).

$\angle AOB$ may also be called $\angle O$ or $\angle 1$. O is the *vertex* of $\angle AOB$; OA and OB are the *sides*. OA is the *initial side* and OB the *terminal side*.

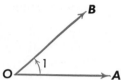

If a ray starts from the position of OA and turns about O in the *counterclockwise* direction until it reaches OB, it passes over the **interior** of $\angle AOB$.

Since the sides are rays, they extend on and on from the vertex, so the *size* of an angle does not depend on the apparent lengths of its sides.

1. $\angle DPF = \angle 1 + \angle 2$.
  (*a*) What is $\angle EPF + \angle FPG$?
  (*b*) What is $\angle 1 + \angle 2 + \angle 3$?
  (*c*) What is $\angle DPG - \angle FPG$?

2. (*a*) On tracing paper take a copy of $\angle RST$. Place the copy on $\angle XYZ$ so that S is on Y and SR is on YX.
  (*b*) If ST falls on YZ, $\angle S = \angle Y$.
  (*c*) If ST falls in the interior of $\angle XYZ$, then $\angle S < \angle Y$.
       How does $\angle S$ compare with $\angle Y$?

3. With tracing paper, compare $\angle MNO$ and $\angle ONP$.
  If $\angle MNO = \angle ONP$, then NO *bisects* $\angle MNP$.

11. (*a*) **Two angles are equal or congruent** if they can be made to coincide, as $\angle S$ and $\angle Y$ in Ex. 2(*b*), above.

(*b*) **An angle is less than another** if the terminal side of the first falls in the interior of the other when the initial side of the first is placed on the initial side of the other. (Ex. 2(*c*))

(*c*) **A ray bisects an angle** if it separates the angle into two equal angles, as NO in Ex. 3. The ray is the **bisector** of the angle.

(*d*) *An angle has one and only one bisector.*

Note to teacher. See the *Teacher's Manual.*

12. **Adjacent angles** are two angles that have the same vertex and a common side between them, as $\angle AOC$ and $\angle COB$.

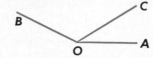

1. (*a*) Is $\angle 3$ adjacent to $\angle 4$? Why?
   (*b*) Is $\angle 6$ adjacent to $\angle 4$? Why?
   (*c*) Name three angles that are adjacent to $\angle 5$.

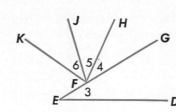

2. (*a*) Draw a line XOY. Place your Geometry Tool with one corner at point O and one edge on OY.
   (*b*) From O draw OZ upward along the adjoining edge of the tool.
   (*c*) Compare $\angle YOZ$ and $\angle ZOX$ by using the tool.

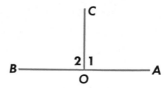

If $\angle YOZ = \angle ZOX$, then each is a *right angle*, and OZ is *perpendicular to* XY.

3. (*a*) Draw a horizontal line m, and mark three points of it by the letters A, B, and C.
   (*b*) Above m, draw perpendiculars to m at A, B, and C.
   (*c*) What kind of angle does each perpendicular form with m?

4. (*a*) Draw an oblique line n. Place point P on one side of it and point R on the other side of it.
   (*b*) As in Ex. 2, draw a line *from* P perpendicular to n.
   (*c*) Draw a perpendicular to n from R.

13. (*a*) If one straight line or ray makes two equal adjacent angles with another line, each of the angles is a **right angle.**

(*b*) Two lines or segments are **perpendicular** ($\perp$) if they form at least one right angle. $OC \perp BOA$ if $\angle 1$ or $\angle 2$ is a right angle.

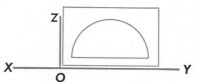

(*c*) *All right angles are equal.*

5. (*a*) What kind of angles are $\angle 1$ and $\angle 2$ in §13?
   (*b*) $\angle AOB = \angle 1 + \angle 2$. How large then is $\angle AOB$?

$\angle AOB$ is called a *straight angle*. Observe that OA and OB form a straight line.

14. (*a*) A **straight angle** is an angle whose sides lie on opposite sides of its vertex in a straight line, as ∠ *AOB* in Ex. 5, p. 20.

(*b*) *A straight angle equals two right angles.*

(*c*) *All straight angles are equal* since all right angles are equal and each straight angle is equal to two right angles.

(*d*) An **acute angle** is an angle less than a right angle, as ∠ *RST*.

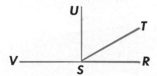 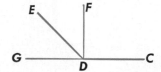

(*e*) An **obtuse angle** is an angle greater than one right angle and less than a straight angle, as ∠ *CDE*.

1. In the figure for Ex. 2, p. 20, what kind of angles are:
   (*a*) ∠ *YOZ?*   (*b*) ∠ *ZOX?*   (*c*) ∠ *YOX?*

2. What kind of angle is formed by the hands of a clock:
   (*a*) When it is three o'clock?
   (*b*) When it is one o'clock?
   (*c*) When it is four o'clock?
   (*d*) When it is six o'clock?

3. At what angle do streets usually cross?

4. Do you see any right angles in your classroom? Where?

15. The common unit for measuring an angle is a small angle commonly called a degree (°), but more properly called an angle-degree. An **angle-degree** is one ninetieth of a right angle, as ∠ *RNS*.
Therefore 1 rt. ∠ = 90°; 1 st. ∠ = 180°.
Degrees are divided into smaller units.
1° = 60 minutes; 1 minute = 60 seconds.

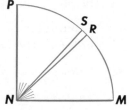

Note. Remember that these are not minutes or seconds of time.

5. How many degrees are there in each of the angles named in Ex. 2?

6. (*a*) In one hour, through how many degrees does the hour hand of a clock move?
   (*b*) Through how many degrees does the minute hand move?

CORNING GLASS WORKS

16. (*a*) A **circle** is the set of all points of a plane that are at a given distance from a given point of the plane. The given point is the **center** of the circle, as *O*. The symbol for the word *circle* is ⊙. Thus ⊙ *ARBC* refers to the *closed curved line* at the right; ⊙ *O* refers to the circle whose center is point *O*.

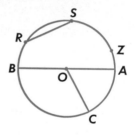

(*b*) The **radius** of a circle is the segment that joins the center to any point of the circle, as radii (rā′dǐ-ī) *OA*, *OB*, *OC*.

(*c*) A **chord** of a circle is the segment that joins two points of the circle, as chord *RS* above.

(*d*) A **diameter** of a circle is a chord of the circle through the center of the circle, as diameter *AOB*.

(*e*) *A diameter of a circle equals two radii of the circle.*

(*f*) *In a plane with any point as center and any radius, there is a circle on the plane.* It is drawn by means of compasses.

17. (*a*) **Equal circles** are circles that have equal radii. Such circles can be made to coincide.

(*b*) *All radii and all diameters of the same circle or of equal circles are equal.*

18. (*a*) An **arc** (⌒) of a circle is the part of the circle between two points of the circle, as **minor arc** *XZ* and **major arc** *XYZ*. When an arc is named by two letters, the minor arc between the points is meant.

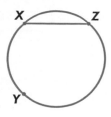

(*b*) Two **arcs are equal** (or congruent) if they can be made to coincide.

(*c*) A diameter of a circle separates the circle into two equal arcs called **semicircles,** as $\overset{\frown}{ADB}$ and $\overset{\frown}{ACB}$ below.

19. Two perpendicular diameters *AOB* and *COD* form four right angles at the center of the circle. They separate the circle into four equal arcs—$\overset{\frown}{AC}$, $\overset{\frown}{CB}$, $\overset{\frown}{BD}$, and $\overset{\frown}{DA}$. If ∠*AOC* were divided into its 90 angle-degrees, these equal angles at the center of the circle would separate $\overset{\frown}{AC}$ into 90 equal arcs, properly called **arc-degrees.** If the other right angles were divided simi-

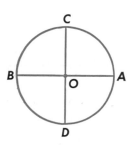

larly, the whole circle would be divided into 360 arc-degrees. *These arc-degrees are used to measure arcs on this circle and on all equal circles.*

20. *The number of angle-degrees in an angle with vertex at the center of a circle equals the number of arc-degrees in the arc of the circle that is cut out by the angle.*

Thus: If ∠*PRS* contains 60 angle-degrees, then arc *PS* contains 60 arc-degrees.

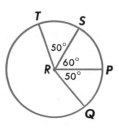

Arc-degrees and angle-degrees are usually referred to simply as degrees, *but remember* that angle-degrees are meant when the measure of an angle is given, and arc-degrees, when the measure of an arc is given.

Thus: ∠*Z* = 45° means that ∠*Z* = 45 angle-degrees;
$\overset{\frown}{XY}$ = 75° means that $\overset{\frown}{XY}$ = 75 arc-degrees.

1. In the figure for §20 give the measure of:
 (*a*) $\overset{\frown}{PS}$ (*b*) $\overset{\frown}{ST}$ (*c*) $\overset{\frown}{SQ}$ (*d*) $\overset{\frown}{QPT}$

2. How does $\overset{\frown}{ST}$ compare with $\overset{\frown}{QP}$?

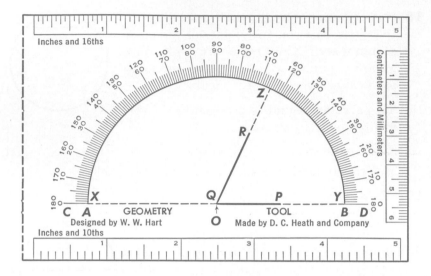

21. The tool for measuring angles and arcs is a *protractor*. The semicircular part of your Geometry Tool is one form of protractor.

The center of the semicircle is point *O*. The diameter of it is *AOB*.

The semicircle is marked off into 180 arc-degrees which are numbered from *A* toward *B* and also from *B* toward *A*.

If radii were drawn from the ends of the arc-degrees on the semicircle they would separate the straight angle *AOB* into its 180 angle-degrees. This is proved later.

22. **To measure** ∠*PQR*. Place the protractor with its center *O* on vertex *Q* of ∠*PQR*, with diameter *AOB* on side *QP*, and with side *QR* inside the semicircular cutout of the protractor.

QR, extended if necessary, cuts the protractor at *Z*.

∠*PQR* starts from *OB*. Therefore we find the measure of ∠*PQR* on the scale that starts from *B*. This is the outer scale.

Therefore   ∠*PQR* = 65°.

∠*XQR* starts from *AO*. Therefore we use the scale that goes between *A* and *Z*, namely, the inner scale.

Therefore   ∠*XQR* = 115°.

23. **To draw an angle of given size.** Use the figure on page 24. Suppose that you are to construct at point Q on a line XY an angle of 65°, having QY as its *initial side*.

Place the protractor with O on Q, and AOB on XY. On the *outer scale* find 65, which is midway between 60 and 70.
Place a point at Z, at the 65° mark.
Draw QZ. Then $\angle YQZ = 65°$.

1. (*a*) On thin paper, make a tracing of each of the following angles and extend their sides.

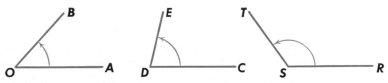

(*b*) Measure each of the angles on your tracing.

2. The adjoining drawing appears in a book for navigators of airplanes.
   (*a*) Make a tracing of this drawing on a large piece of paper.
   (*b*) Measure $\angle 1$, $\angle 2$, and $\angle 3$.
   (*c*) How large is $\angle 5$, $\angle 4$?

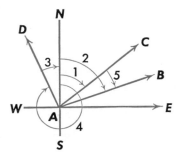

3. Make a tracing of the figure in §16, p. 22.
   (*a*) Measure $\angle AOC$. $\angle BOC$.
   (*b*) How large is $\overset{\frown}{AC}$? $\overset{\frown}{BC}$?

4. (*a*) Draw a segment AB, about 3 in. long. On it place a point C between A and B.
   (*b*) From C, draw CD above AB, making $\angle BCD = 60°$.
   (*c*) From C, draw CE below AB, making $\angle BCE = 45°$.

5. (*a*) Draw an oblique line MN. On it place point L between M and N.
   (*b*) To the right of MN, draw LP, making $\angle NLP = 75°$.
   (*c*) To the right of MN, draw LR, making $\angle MLR = 80°$.

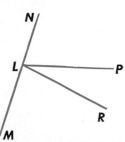

6. (*a*) Draw a vertical segment YZ. On it place point X between Y and Z.
   (*b*) From X, draw XW at the right of YZ, making $\angle YXW = 50°$.
   (*c*) From X, draw XR at the left of YZ, making $\angle YXR = 100°$.

24. **Complementary angles** are two angles whose sum is a right angle, or 90°. Each of the angles is the **complement** of the other. If $OC \perp OA$, then $\angle 1$ and $\angle 2$ must be complementary because $\angle 1 + \angle 2 = \angle AOC$, and $\angle AOC$ is a right angle.

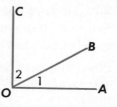

Note. Learn the correct spelling of *complementary*.

1. What is the complement of an angle that measures:
   (a) 25°?   (b) 60°?   (c) 81°?   (d) $x°$?

2. What angle equals its complement?

3. Are angles of 25° and 75° complementary? Why?

4. Draw a right angle RST. From S draw a ray that separates $\angle RST$ into two angles. What kind of angles are the two parts of $\angle RST$?

5. Draw any acute $\angle DEF$. With a square-cornered card, draw from E a ray EG forming a complement of $\angle DEF$.

6. (a) If $NO \perp NM$ and $NQ \perp NP$, how large are $\angle 1$ and $\angle 3$ when $\angle 2 = 50°$? How then do $\angle 1$ and $\angle 3$ compare?
   (b) Do part (a) if $\angle 2 = 60°$.
   (c) Complete the following sentence:
   Complements of the same angle are . . . .

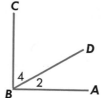

7. Suppose that $SP \perp SR$ and $BC \perp BA$.
   (a) If $\angle 1 = 30°$ and $\angle 2 = 30°$, how large are $\angle 3$ and $\angle 4$?
   (b) How then do $\angle 3$ and $\angle 4$ compare?
   (c) Do parts (a) and (b) if $\angle 1$ and $\angle 2$ each equal 50°.
   (d) Complete the following sentence:
   Complements of equal angles are . . . .

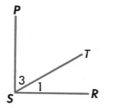

8. Draw two adjacent angles that are not complementary.

9. (a) Draw two adjacent angles that are complementary.
   (b) What kind of angle is formed by their exterior sides?

10. Draw two complementary angles that are not adjacent.

11. What angle is twice its complement?

Suggestion. Let x = the number of degrees in the complement.

12. What angle exceeds its complement by 20°?

25. *Complements of the same angle or of equal angles are equal.*

26. Supplementary angles are two angles whose sum is a straight angle, or 180°. Each of the angles is the **supplement** of the other. If COA is a straight line, then $\angle 1$ and $\angle 2$ must be supplementary because $\angle 1 + \angle 2 = \angle COA$, and $\angle COA$ is a straight angle.

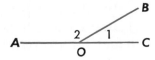

1. What is the supplement of an angle that measures:
    (a) 80°?   (b) 45°?   (c) 110°?   (d) $x°$?

2. What is the supplement of a right angle?

3. XY and ZW are intersecting straight lines. Name two angles that are supplements:
    (a) Of $\angle 2$ (b) Of $\angle 3$ (c) Of $\angle 4$

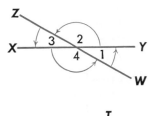

4. (a) In the figure for Ex. 3, if $\angle 4 = 120°$, how large are $\angle 3$ and $\angle 1$? How then do they compare?
    (b) Do part (a) if $\angle 4 = 150°$.

5. Let QSR and PNM be straight lines.
    (a) If $\angle 3$ and $\angle 1$ each equal 60°, how large are $\angle 4$ and $\angle 2$? How then must $\angle 4$ and $\angle 2$ compare?
    (b) Do part (a) if $\angle 1$ and $\angle 3$ each measure 75°.
    (c) Complete the following sentence: *Supplements of equal angles are . . . .*

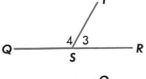

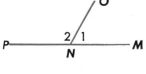

6. (a) Let $\angle CDE = 110°$ and $\angle EDF = 70°$.
    (b) What angle equals $\angle CDE + \angle EDF$?
    (c) What kind of angle is $\angle CDF$?
    (d) What kind of line is line CDF?
    (e) Do parts (b), (c), and (d) if $\angle CDE = 100°$ and $\angle EDF = 80°$.

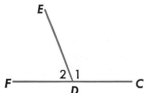

27. The preceding exercises suggest:

(a) *If two adjacent angles have their exterior sides in a straight line, they are supplementary.* (§14(a); §26)

(b) *Supplements of the same angle or of equal angles are equal.* (Ex. 4 and 5 above)

(c) *If two adjacent angles are supplementary, their exterior sides lie in a straight line.* (Ex. 6 above)

28. Vertical angles are the opposite angles formed when two straight lines intersect.

If CA and BD are straight lines, $\angle 1$ and $\angle 2$ are vertical angles; also $\angle 3$ and $\angle 4$ are vertical angles.

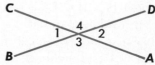

1. (a) How do you think $\angle 1$ compares with $\angle 2$?
   (b) Convince yourself by using transparent paper, or by making a large tracing of the figure and measuring $\angle 1$ and $\angle 2$.

2. Compare $\angle 3$ and $\angle 4$.

3. (a) Recall §27(a). If $\angle 2 = 50°$, how large is $\angle 3$?
   (b) If $\angle 2 = 50°$, how large is $\angle 4$?
   (c) How must $\angle 3$ compare with $\angle 4$?

4. If $\angle 1 = 80°$, compare $\angle 3$ and $\angle 4$.

5. A proof that $\angle 3 = \angle 4$.
   (a) $\angle 3$ is a supplement of $\angle 2$.   (Tell why, using §27(a).)
   (b) $\angle 4$ is a supplement of $\angle 2$.   (Tell why.)
   (c) Therefore $\angle 3 = \angle 4$.   (Tell why, using §27(b).)

6. Complete and memorize the following statement:
   If two straight lines intersect, vertical angles . . . .

7. In the figure at the right, using the angles that measure 30° and 150°, decide how large each of the other angles must be, without measuring them.
   Suggestion. Use §27 and Ex. 6.

8. $XY \perp ZW$, and one angle is 30° as marked. Without measuring them, decide how large each of the other angles of the figure must be.
   Suggestion. Use facts about right angles, complementary angles, and vertical angles.

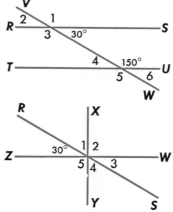

9. If two straight lines intersect so that one of the angles formed by them is a right angle, how large is each of the other angles?

29. The foregoing exercises suggest:

(a) *When two straight lines intersect, the vertical angles formed are equal,* as in Ex. 1 to 6.

(b) *The total angle around a point in a plane equals two straight angles, or 360°.* (Ex. 9)

30. You reached conclusions in many exercises on the preceding pages after you observed results to be true in geometrical figures in which certain conditions were met.

Thus: In Ex. 6, p. 26, you decide that *complements of the same angle are equal* because this fact is observed when the "same angle" measures 50° and when it measures 60°.

In Ex. 1, 2, 3, and 4, p. 28, you become convinced that *vertical* angles are equal when two straight lines intersect because you find them to be equal in the figures you study.

This kind of reasoning is called *inductive reasoning.* It is used when the facts are not mathematical as well as when they are mathematical.

Thus: A physician discovered that one of his patients had headaches after eating bread but not after eating other foods. He assumed that his patient was allergic to bread, and that the patient was allergic to wheat. However, the patient was not allergic to cake made from wheat flour. He found the patient had headaches after eating rye bread. He decided that the patient was allergic to an ingredient that was in bread and not in cake, namely yeast.

A child discovers that his finger hurts if he touches a hot coffeepot. If he decides that his finger will hurt if he touches a coffeepot, he is wrong, because it is not the coffeepot but the heat in it that causes the discomfort. If he decides that his finger will hurt if he touches any hot vessel he is right.

This second illustration shows that the conditions must be analyzed to make sure that an observed effect is associated with the proper cause. After deciding on a conclusion, the conclusion should be checked by examining other instances of it, as was done by the physician. A faulty conclusion is indicated if a single exception to it can be found.

What conclusion may be suggested by each of the following statements? Is the conclusion a true one?

1. All cows observed on an automobile trip had black and white markings.
2. No cream rises to the top of bottles of milk bought at a certain store.

31. In geometry, *you may be misled by the appearances of a figure.*

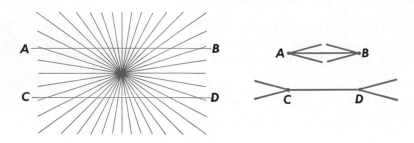

Thus: In the left-hand figure above, the many lines radiating from a point between AB and CD *make it appear* that AB and CD are curved lines. Are they?

In the right-hand figure above, does AB appear equal to CD? Test them to see whether they are equal.

In the adjoining figure, are AB and CD straight lines? Test them in some way.

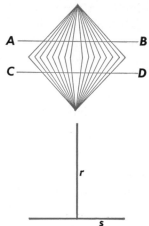

In the figure at the right, do segments r and s have the same length? After you have decided, test them in some way.

These examples illustrate how we may be led to a wrong conclusion if we depend on appearances in a drawing.

For this reason, in arriving at conclusions from a drawing it is important to examine more than one drawing in which the conditions described in the problem occur and to be careful not to put into the drawing any conditions which are not part of the problem. Make the figures as general as possible.

Thus: If a problem concerns an angle, and does not specify what kind of angle, do not draw a right angle. A right angle has special characteristics which may mislead you. Instead, draw an acute angle and also draw an obtuse angle if it is permitted by the conditions of the problem.

32. For other reasons as well as those considered on pages 29 and 30, it is customary to study geometry and other parts of mathematics principally by reasoning that is called **deductive reasoning.**

In elementary geometry the procedure consists of two parts:

(*a*) *As a foundation:*

    (1) Assume as true some statements about mathematical quantities, such as:

        If equals be added to equals, then the sums are equal.

        Such assumed truths are called **axioms.**

    (2) Accept some *undefined geometrical concepts*, such as the concepts of a point and a straight line. This is necessary since definitions must be expressed by means of ones already known.

    (3) Assume as true some statements about geometrical concepts, such as:

        One and only one straight line contains both of two given points.

        Such statements are called **postulates.** Some of them add meaning to the undefined concepts. Some of the postulates that we shall use can be proved.

(*b*) *Thereafter:*

    (1) Define all other geometrical concepts by ones previously assumed or known, as:

        An angle consists of two rays that have a common origin.

        Two angles are complementary if their sum is a right angle.

        To assist you, there is on pages 430 to 442 of this book a list of the concepts that appear in this textbook, arranged in the order in which they occur, with references to the pages where they first appear.

    (2) Prove all other statements about geometrical figures. Some illustrations will appear soon.

33. Deductive reasoning is used also when the facts concerned are not mathematical. A discussion of reasoning about non-mathematical conditions appears on pages 373 through 386. This can be studied now.

34. An **axiom** is a statement about numbers and measurable geometrical figures (such as segments, angles, arcs, and others to be introduced) that is assumed to be true. The following axioms are sufficient for the present.

Ax. 1. *Quantities that are equal to the same quantity or to equal quantities are equal to each other.*
Thus: If $\angle A = \angle B$ and $\angle C = \angle B$, then $\angle A = \angle C$.
If segment XY = segment MN,
segment ZW = segment PQ,
and segment MN = segment PQ,
then segment XY = segment ZW.

Ax. 2. *A quantity may be substituted for its equal in an equation or an inequality.*
Thus: If $\angle A + \angle B = 90°$ and $\angle A = \angle D$,
then $\angle D + \angle B = 90°$.

Ax. 3. *If equals are added to equals, their sums are equal.*
Thus: If $AB = CD$, and $BE = DF$,
then $AB + BE = CD + DF$.

Ax. 4. *If equals are subtracted from equals, the remainders are equal.*
Thus: If $x + 15 = 90$,
then $x + 15 - 15 = 90 - 15$.

Ax. 5. *If equals are multiplied by equals, the products are equal.* In particular, *doubles of equals are equal.*
Thus: If $\angle M = \angle N$, then $2\angle M = 2\angle N$.

Ax. 6. *If equals are divided by equals, the quotients are equal.* In particular, *halves of equals are equal.*
Thus: If segment AB = segment CD,
then $\frac{1}{2}AB = \frac{1}{2}CD$.

Ax. 7. *The whole of any measurable geometrical figure is equal to the sum of its parts.*
Thus: $\angle AOB = \angle AOC + \angle COB$.

Ax. 8. *The whole of any measurable geometrical figure is greater than any of its parts.*
Thus: $\angle AOB$ is greater than $\angle AOC$.
$\angle AOB$ is also greater than $\angle COB$.

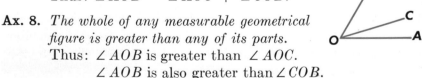

35. It is not always easy to give definitions of nonmathematical words and concepts.

Thus: What is a path? One dictionary states: *A path is a way or road.* And then it states that *a way is a path or road;* and *a road is a path or way.*
Unless one knows what one of the three concepts *path, way,* or *road* is, the dictionary fails to give any help in understanding what the other two are.

This illustration shows that any set of definitions must start with some words and concepts that are accepted as known without definition. These are the *undefined terms* and *concepts.* The undefined terms, ideas, and concepts of nonmathematical character are not listed easily, and this increases the difficulty of defining other words, ideas, and concepts of such character.

Try to give a definition of each of the following:

1. A book **2.** A *hit* in baseball

3. A chair **4.** An automobile

36. A *good definition* has three characteristics.

(*a*) It tells the nearest *known group* of objects to which a new object belongs.
Thus: A square is a rectangle—

(*b*) It tells enough but not more than enough to distinguish the new object from all others of its group.
Thus: A square is a rectangle *having two adjacent sides equal;*
not   A square is a rectangle *having four sides equal and four right angles.*
The *italicized* part of the second definition contains more than is necessary because a rectangle already has four right angles, and because we can prove that four sides of a square must be equal after we know that two adjacent sides are equal.

(*c*) A definition is reversible, or can be turned around.
Thus: A square is a rectangle having two adjacent sides equal.
A rectangle having two adjacent sides equal is a square.

37. A **postulate** is a statement about geometrical concepts that is accepted without proof. The postulates that have appeared so far in this book are summarized on this page and the next. They were introduced by intuitive exercises so that they would appear reasonable to you. Some of them are so obvious that you would consider proofs of them unnecessary, as Postulate 3. Some are assumed even in an advanced course in geometry. Some you can prove now, as Postulates 9, 10, 12, and 13.

Read these postulates carefully, looking back, if necessary, to the section reference if any postulate is not clear to you. After each is clear to you, learn it so that you can repeat it correctly when it is needed as an authority in a proof.

Post.   1. *One and only one straight line contains both of two given points. (§5(a))*

Post.   2. *A segment can be extended in each of two directions on it. (§5(c))*

Post.   3. *Two straight lines intersect in only one point. (§5(b))*

Post.   4. *On a line, in one direction from a point of the line, there is one and only one segment equal to a given segment. (§8(c))*

Post.   5. *On a plane the shortest line between two points is the line segment between the two points (§8(d)).* It is the **distance** between the two points.

Post.   6. *A segment has one and only one mid-point. (§8(f))*

Post.   7. *An angle has one and only one bisector. (§11(d))*

Post.   8. *All right angles are equal. (§13(c))*

Post.   9. *A straight angle equals two right angles. (§14(b))*

Post. 10. *All straight angles are equal. (§14(c))*

Post. 11. *In a plane with any point as center and any segment as radius there is one and only one circle on the plane (§16(f)).* Compasses are used to draw the circle.

Post. 12. *A diameter equals two radii. (§16(e))*

Post. 13. *All radii and all diameters of the same circle or of equal circles are equal.* (§17(b))

Post. 14. *The number of degrees in an angle with vertex at the center of a circle equals the number of degrees in the arc of the circle that is cut out by the angle.* (§20)

Post. 15. *Complements of the same angle or of equal angles are equal.* (§25)

Post. 16. *If two adjacent angles have their exterior sides in a straight line, they are supplementary.* (§27(a))

Post. 17. *Supplements of the same angle or of equal angles are equal.* (§27(b))

Post. 18. *If two adjacent angles are supplementary, their exterior sides lie in a straight line.* (§27(c))

Post. 19. *When two straight lines intersect, vertical angles formed are equal.* (§29(a))

Post. 20. *The sum of all the successive adjacent angles in a plane around a point is two straight angles or 360°.* (§29(b))

The following *optional exercises* illustrate proofs of some of the "postulates" which we have assumed earlier.

★**1.** Prove Postulate 9 by using the definitions of a straight angle, a right angle, and axioms.

Proof. BOA is a st. line, since
$\angle BOA$ is a st. $\angle$. (§14(a))
Let CO make $\angle 1 = \angle 2$. (§11(d))
$\angle BOA = \angle 1 + \angle 2$ (Ax. 7)
$\angle 1$ and $\angle 2$ are rt. $\angle$ (§13(a))
$\therefore \angle BOA = 2$ rt. $\angle$ (Ax. 2)

★**2.** Prove Postulate 12.

★**3.** Prove Postulate 13, using the definitions of radius, diameter, and equal circles.

★**4.** Prove Postulate 15, using the definition of the complement of an angle, Postulate 8, and Axiom 4.

★**5.** Prove Postulate 17.

★**6.** Prove Postulate 20, using Axiom 7.

1. Turn to the list of concepts that appears on pages 430 to 442 in this book. Before each concept are the page number and the section number where the concept is introduced. Without looking back to the section number:
   (a) Where possible draw a figure to illustrate each concept through §37.
   (b) Give the verbal definition of each concept.

2. How many straight lines can be drawn through two points?

3. In how many points can two straight lines intersect?

4. What is the complement of 65°? The supplement of 65°?

5. How large must each of the angles 1, 2, and 3 be, in the adjoining figure, if AB and CD are straight lines?

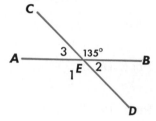

6. (a) Draw two intersecting lines that form an angle of 40°.
   (b) Without measuring them, tell how large each of the other angles formed by these lines must be.

7. (a) Test ∠4 and ∠5 at the right to see whether they are equal angles.
   (b) If ∠4 = ∠5 what do we call line YW?

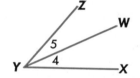

8. How many degrees are there in:
   (a) The complement of a right angle?
   (b) The supplement of a right angle?

9. $SU \perp ST$ and RST is a straight line.
   (a) What kind of angles are ∠1 and ∠2?
   (b) What kind of angles are ∠1 and ∠3?
   (c) Find the difference between ∠3 and ∠2.

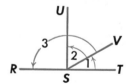

10. MN and PQ are straight lines.
    (a) What kind of angles are ∠5 and ∠6?
       What kind of angles are ∠7 and ∠6?
       What then must be true of ∠5 and ∠7?
    (b) How does ∠6 compare with ∠8? Why?

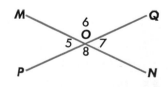

38. In the following exercises you can prove the statement that is given or can prove that your answer to a question is correct by quoting a definition, an axiom, or a postulate, as is done in the illustrative exercise.

Illustrative exercise. If segment AB = segment CD, and if segment RS = segment CD, does $AB = RS$?

Statement. $AB = RS$

Authority. If quantities (AB and RS) are equal to the same quantity (CD) they are equal to each other. (Ax. 1)

For the following exercises, if a figure is not given, draw one that represents the statements. Then answer the question, if one is asked, and give your reason for believing that your answer is correct. If a true statement is made, give the reason why it must be true.

1. $\angle A = \angle B$ and $\angle X = \angle B$. Does $\angle A = \angle X$?

2. $MN = RS$, $XY = TU$, and $RS = TU$. What must be true about MN and XY?

3. Segments x and y are equal; also segments r and s are equal.
   (a) Prove that $x + r = y + s$.
   (b) Prove that $x - r = y - s$.
   (c) Prove that $3x = 3y$.
   (d) Prove that $\frac{2}{3}r = \frac{2}{3}s$.
   (e) Prove that $3x + \frac{2}{3}s = 3y + \frac{2}{3}r$.

4. (a) OC bisects $\angle AOB$ and OB bisects $\angle COR$. How must $\angle 1$ compare with $\angle 3$?
   (b) How does $\angle COR$ compare with $\angle AOB$?
   (c) Prove $\angle AOB = \angle 1 + \angle 2$.
   (d) Prove $\angle AOR = \angle 1 + \angle 2 + \angle 3$.

5. ZYW is a straight line. $XY \perp ZW$
   (a) What kind of angles are $\angle 4$ and $\angle 5$?
   (b) How does $\angle 4$ compare with $\angle 5$?
   (c) What kind of angle is $\angle WYZ$?

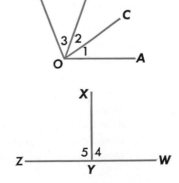

For the following exercises be sure to give your reason for believing your answer is correct.

1. MN, MR, and MP are radii of the same circle. How do they compare in length? (Draw a figure.)

2. $\angle C$ is a complement of $\angle R$, and $\angle D$ is a complement of $\angle R$. Compare $\angle C$ and $\angle D$.

3. Suppose $\angle 2 = \angle 3$. How does $\angle 1 + \angle 2$ compare with $\angle 1 + \angle 3$?

4. Roads x and y are two different roads from village A to village B.
   (a) You know that road x is a straight road. Can road y be a straight road?
   (b) Which road is the longer?

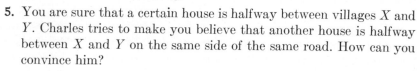

5. You are sure that a certain house is halfway between villages X and Y. Charles tries to make you believe that another house is halfway between X and Y on the same side of the same road. How can you convince him?

6. Straight highways c and d cross at village N. Do they ever cross again?

7. $x + y = 24$. $x = 7$. Give an equation for the value of y.

8. Three straight roads connect villages A, B, and C in pairs. Is AC longer or shorter than $AB + BC$?

9. At the right, suppose that $\angle 1$ and $\angle 2$ are supplementary. Is the figure drawn correctly? If not, how should it be drawn?

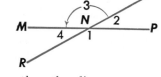

10. MNP and RNS are straight lines.
    (a) Compare $\angle 4$ and $\angle 2$.
    (b) What kind of angles are $\angle 1$ and $\angle 2$?
    (c) What is the sum of $\measuredangle$ 1, 2, 3, and 4?

11. At the right below, CDE is a straight line; the other lines are rays from point D.
    (a) Prove $\angle EDG$ and $\angle GDC$ are supplementary.
    (b) Are $\measuredangle$ 6 and 8 adjacent angles?
    (c) What angle is adjacent to $\angle 9$?
    (d) Suppose that $\measuredangle$ 7 and 8 are complementary and also that $\measuredangle$ 6 and 7 are complementary. Compare $\angle 6$ and $\angle 8$.

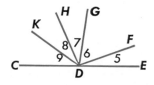

39. The lines in the figures below are straight lines. These exercises illustrate longer proofs.

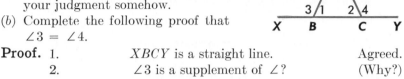

1. Assume that $\angle 1 = \angle 2$.
   (a) Does $\angle 3$ appear equal to $\angle 4$? Check your judgment somehow.
   (b) Complete the following proof that $\angle 3 = \angle 4$.

   Proof. 1. $XBCY$ is a straight line.   Agreed.

   2. $\angle 3$ is a supplement of $\angle$?   (Why?)

   3. $\angle 4$ is a supplement of $\angle$?   (Why?)

   4. $\angle 1 = \angle 2$ Agreed.

   5.   Therefore $\angle 3 = \angle$?   (Why?)

40. **How such proofs are discovered.** Consider Ex. 1. We are to prove that $\angle 3 = \angle 4$.

Ask: What do I know about $\angle 3$ that connects it with either $\angle 1$ or $\angle 2$, which, we are told, are equal?
The answer is that $\angle 3$ is a supplement of $\angle 1$.
Next ask: What do I know about $\angle 4$?
The answer is that $\angle 4$ is a supplement of $\angle 2$.
Next ask: What do I know about $\angle 1$ and $\angle 2$?
The answer is that $\angle 1 = \angle 2$ by agreement.
You should now recall that supplements of equal angles are equal. Therefore $\angle 3 = \angle 4$.

2. In the figure on the right, assume that $\angle 2 = \angle 6$.

   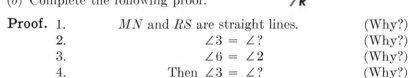

   (a) Does $\angle 3$ appear equal to $\angle 6$? Check your judgment somehow.

   (b) Complete the following proof.

   Proof. 1. MN and RS are straight lines.   (Why?)

   2. $\angle 3 = \angle$?   (Why?)

   3. $\angle 6 = \angle 2$ (Why?)

   4.   Then $\angle 3 = \angle$?   (Why?)

3. In the figure for Ex. 2, still assume $\angle 2 = \angle 6$. Complete the following proof that $\angle 7 = \angle 3$.

   Proof. 1. $\angle 7 = \angle$?   (Why?)

   2. $\angle 3 = \angle$?   (Why?)

   3. $\angle 2 = \angle 6$ (Why?)

   4.   Then $\angle 7 = \angle$?   (Why?)

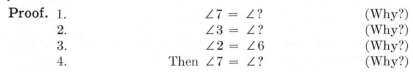

41. A **theorem** is a mathematical statement that is to be proved or has been proved. Every theorem can be expressed by a sentence that has one clause beginning with *if* and a second clause beginning with *then*, as:

If two straight lines intersect, then the vertical angles formed are equal.

The *if* clause is the **hypothesis,** *containing what is known or assumed.* The *then* clause is the **conclusion,** *containing what is to be proved.* The word *then* often is omitted.

42. A **formal proof** of the theorem:

If two straight lines intersect, vertical angles formed are equal.

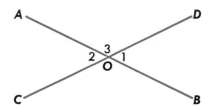

Hypothesis. Straight lines AB and CD intersect at O, forming vertical angles $\angle 1$ and $\angle 2$.

Conclusion. $\angle 1 = \angle 2$

Proof.

Statements	Authorities
1. AB is a straight line.	1. By hypothesis.
2. ∴ $\angle 1$ is a supp. of $\angle 3$.	2. If two adjacent ⩘ have their exterior sides in a st. line, they are supplementary.
3. CD is a straight line.	3. By hypothesis.
4. ∴ $\angle 2$ is a supp. of $\angle 3$.	4. Reason 2 above.
5. ∴ $\angle 1 = \angle 2$	5. Supplements of the same angle are equal.

Beside each statement is the authority for its correctness. The authority may be a statement in the hypothesis, a definition, an axiom, a postulate, or a previously proved theorem.

Each authority should be written in full, using only abbreviations that are clear.

Illustrative exercise.

Hypothesis. ABX, ACY, and BC are straight lines. $\angle 1 = \angle 2$

   Conclusion. $\angle 3 = \angle 4$

   Proof.

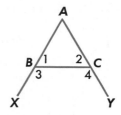

Statements	Authorities
1. ABX is a st. line.	1. By hypothesis.
2. ∴ $\angle 3$ is supp. of $\angle 1$.	2. Tell why in full. (Post. 16)
3. ACY is a st. line.	3. Tell why.
4. ∴ $\angle 4$ is supp. of $\angle 2$.	4. Tell why.
5. $\angle 1 = \angle 2$.	5. Tell why.
6. ∴ $\angle 3 = \angle 4$.	6. Post. 17

For each exercise, draw the figure, copy the hypothesis and conclusion, and write the full proof. For Ex. 2 through 8, the hypothesis includes that below the figure, and the special hypothesis of the exercise.

1. Hyp. AX, AY, and ZW are all straight lines. $\angle 1 = \angle 2$
   Con. $\angle 5 = \angle 6$

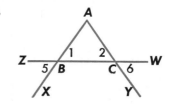

2. Hyp. $\angle 3 = \angle 5$
   Con. $\angle 1 = \angle 7$

3. Hyp. $\angle 3 = \angle 5$
   Con. $\angle 4 = \angle 6$

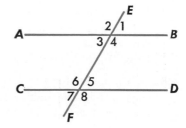

4. Hyp. $\angle 3 = \angle 5$
   Con. $\angle 2 = \angle 8$

5. Hyp. $\angle 1 = \angle 5$
   Con. $\angle 3 = \angle 5$

6. Hyp. $\angle 1 = \angle 5$
   Con. $\angle 2 = \angle 6$

7. Hyp. $\angle 3 = \angle 7$
   Con. $\angle 4 = \angle 8$

Hypothesis. AB and CD are straight lines, cut by EF.

8. Hyp. $\angle 2$ is supp. of $\angle 7$.
   Con. $\angle 1 = \angle 7$

Note. §395 and §396 can be read now.

1. In the adjoining figure assume that ∠ABC = ∠BAC, that AD bisects ∠BAC, and that BD bisects ∠ABC. Prove that ∠1 = ∠2.

2. In the figure for Exercise 1 assume that ∠BAC = ∠ABC, and ∠1 = ∠2.
   Prove that ∠3 = ∠4.

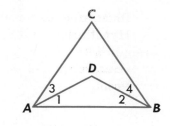

3. In the adjoining figure assume that ∠XZY is a right angle and that angles 1 and 3 are complementary.
   Prove that ∠3 = ∠2.

4. In the figure for Ex. 3, assume that ∠3 = ∠2 and that angles 1 and 3 are complementary.
   Prove that ∠XZY is a right angle.

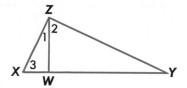

5. In the adjoining figure assume that BC ⊥ BA and that BD ⊥ BE.
   Prove that ∠1 + ∠2 = ∠2 + ∠3.

6. If the sum of the complement and the supplement of an angle is 130°, how large is the angle?

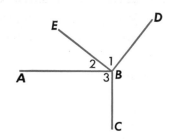

Suggestions. Let x = the number of degrees in the angle. Form and solve an equation.

7. In the adjoining figure assume that ∠1 = ∠2 and that DABE is a straight line.
   Prove that ∠3 = ∠4.

★8. In the figure for Ex. 7, assume also that ∠3 is one half ∠1. Find the number of degrees in ∠4.

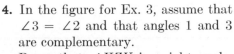

9. In the adjoining figure assume that line XSY bisects ∠RST.
   Prove that ∠RSY = ∠TSY.

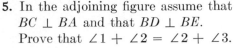

10. In the adjoining figure assume that ∠ABC + ∠BCD equals 180°, that BE bisects ∠ABC, and that CE bisects ∠BCD.
    Prove that ∠2 and ∠3 are complementary.

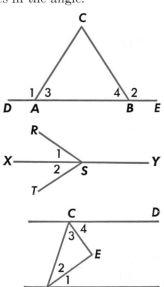

1. **Hyp.** NP bisects $\angle MNO$.

   $RNS \perp NP$

   Con. $\angle 3 = \angle 4$

   Suggestion. Read §40 again. What kind of
   angle is $\angle RNP$? What then, do you
   know about $\angle 3$ and $\angle 1$?

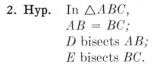

2. **Hyp.** In $\triangle ABC$,

   $AB = BC$;

   D bisects AB;

   E bisects BC.

   Con. $AD = CE$

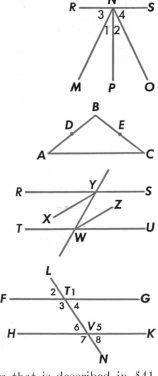

3. **Hyp.** $\angle UWY = \angle WYR$,

   WZ bisects $\angle UWY$,

   XY bisects $\angle WYR$.

   Con. $\angle XYW = \angle YWZ$

4. **Hyp.** $\angle 1$ and $\angle 8$ are
   supplementary.

   Con. $\angle 2 = \angle 8$

5. **Hyp.** $\angle 1$ and $\angle 8$ are
   supplementary.

   Con. $\angle 3$ and $\angle 6$ are
   supplementary.

6. State Ex. 2 in words in the *if, then* form that is described in §41,
   p. 40. Do not refer by letters to the figure in Ex. 2.

7. If the supplement of an angle equals four times the complement of
   the angle, how large is the angle?

8. If two straight lines intersect so that one of the smaller angles formed
   equals 30°, how large is each of the other angles?

9. **Hyp.** $\angle MNP = \angle NPQ$,

   NR bisects $\angle MNP$,

   PS bisects $\angle NPQ$.

   Con. $\angle 1 = \angle 2$

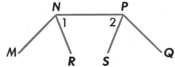

10. If the sum of the supplement of an angle and three times the com-
    plement is 250°, how large is the angle?

11. Draw a figure like that for Ex. 4.

    (*a*) Write the hypothesis, conclusion, and proof for the following
       statement:

    *If angles 4 and 5 are supplementary, then angles 2 and 7 are supple-
    mentary.*

    ★(*b*) If $\angle 5$ is 64° larger than $\angle 4$, how large is each of the angles in
       the figure?

1.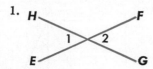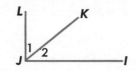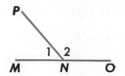

(a) What kind of angle-pair is formed by ∠1 and ∠2 in each of the figures above if all the lines are straight lines?

(b) In each of these figures how large is ∠2 if ∠1 measures 50°? Give in full the reason for each answer.

2. Assume: ∠XYZ = 55°, ∠YXZ = 55°, RX ⊥ XY, SY ⊥ XY

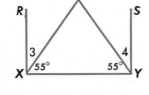

(a) How does ∠3 appear to compare with ∠4?

(b) By a method used in experimental or inductive geometry, satisfy yourself that your answer in part (a) is correct.

(c) By the methods used in demonstrative geometry, prove that your answer in part (a) is correct.

3. What kind of reasoning is employed in demonstrative geometry?

4. (a) What is a definition? Give an illustration.

(b) Why are a few concepts necessarily undefined?

(c) What concepts have we left undefined?

5. What kinds of statements may be given as reasons or authorities for statements in a proof in geometry?

6. (a) What is a theorem?

(b) What is the hypothesis of a theorem?

(c) What is the conclusion of a theorem?

7. (a) Prove the conclusion stated below for the figure as it is described in the hypothesis.

Hypothesis. ABCD is a straight line.
∠3 = ∠4
Conclusion. ∠1 = ∠2

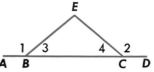

(b) Extend EB through B to F and EC through C to G. What angles of the resulting figure appear to be equal? Prove your conclusion.

8. What angle is 20° less than its complement?

9. What angle is 20° less than its supplement?

10. What angle is 30° less than its supplement?

SOME RELATED SOLID GEOMETRY

43. From time to time hereafter, we shall refer to figures that do not lie wholly in one plane. These are the figures of **solid geometry** or **three-dimensional geometry.**

44. A plane has been described loosely (§2(d)) as a surface that is smooth and flat. We accept it as an undefined concept. Two postulates and some theorems that are suggested by the following exercises will furnish more adequate understanding of the concept of a plane.

A card may be used to represent a part of a plane, also a drawing like that at the right. The plane in the figure is called plane *MNRS*.

1. (*a*) If you draw a line *AB* through two points *A* and *B* on a card, where will all the points of *AB* lie?

   (*b*) Part (*a*) suggests: *If a line joins two points of a plane, it lies wholly.* . . . Also: *A plane must extend infinitely far in all directions on the plane from a point on the plane.*

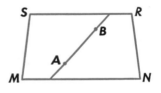

2. (*a*) Have two pupils hold three pencils with points up, so that the points do not all lie in one straight line. Such points are called **noncollinear points.** Can you place a card so that it will touch all three points?

   (*b*) Can more than one card be in that position at one time?

   (*c*) Parts (*a*) and (*b*) suggest: *Three non-collinear points lie in one.* . . .

3. (*a*) Hold a pencil below a card *ABCD*. Hold the pencil stationary. Rotate the card about *AB*, without moving *AB*, until the card touches the point of the pencil.

   (*b*) In how many positions of the card can it touch the point of the pencil when the point and *AB* are stationary?

   (*c*) Parts (*a*) and (*b*) suggest: *Through a line and a point that is not on the line, one* . . .

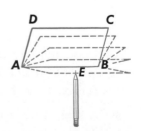

1. (a) Let AB be one edge of a card $ABCD$. Holding AB stationary, turn the card so that it takes the positions $ABCD$, $ABEF$, $ABGH$.

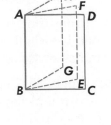

 (b) In how many such positions can the card be placed?

 (c) Parts (a) and (b) suggest: *Through a given straight line, there can be ...*

2. (a) Let AB and AC represent two pencils placed on the top of your desk so that their points meet. Can you place a card so that it will be in contact with both pencils?

 (b) Can more than one card be in that position at one time?

 (c) Parts (a) and (b) suggest: *Through two intersecting lines, there can be ....*

3. (a) Place a card $ABCD$ on the top of your desk. Can you hold a card $XYZW$ so that all points of one edge of it will touch $ABCD$? If you can, then $XYZW$ intersects $ABCD$ in YZ. What is YZ?

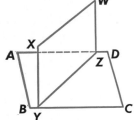

 (b) Part (a) suggests: *If two planes intersect, their intersection is a ....*

45. Some definitions, postulates, and theorems of solid geometry will be introduced in optional sections of this book—some of them intuitively, and some by informal or formal proofs. Summaries of the statements of them appear in numbered sections such as those on page 47. A complete summary appears on pages 443 through 448, where each statement is accompanied by its original section number and the number of the page where it appeared for the first time. This list will help you to review and use the statements from solid geometry when you need them.

46. The exercises on pages 45 and 46 suggest the following conclusions.

SG1. (Post.) *The straight line through two points of a plane lies wholly in the plane.* (Ex. 1, p. 45.)

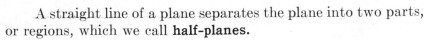

A straight line of a plane separates the plane into two parts, or regions, which we call **half-planes.**

SG 2. *A plane extends infinitely far in every direction on it.* (Consequence of SG 1.)

SG 3. **(Post.)** *Three noncollinear points lie in one and only one plane.* (Ex. 2, p. 45.)
We say: Three **noncollinear points determine** a plane.

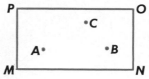

SG 4. *A line and a point that is not on it determine a plane.* (Ex. 3.)
Informal proof. Let *A* and *B* be any two points of line *AB* and *C* be any point that is not on *AB*. Then *A*,

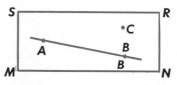

B, and *C* lie in one and only one plane (SG 3). All of *AB* lies in that plane (SG 1). Therefore *AB* and *C* lie in one and only one plane, or they determine a plane.

SG 5. *An infinite number of planes contain a given straight line.* (Ex. 1, p. 46.)
Informal proof. *AB* and any point *X* that is not on *AB* determine a plane, as *ABCD* (SG 4). Since there are infinitely many points like *X* not on *ABCD*, there are infinitely many planes containing *AB* and point *X*.

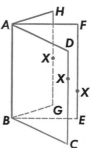

SG 6. *Two intersecting straight lines determine a plane.* (Ex. 2.)
Informal proof. Let *AB* and *CD* intersect at *O*. Then *AB* and *C* determine a plane (SG 4). All of line

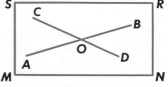

COD lies in that plane (SG 1). Therefore *AB* and *CD* lie in one and only one plane.

SG 7. *If two planes intersect, their intersection is a straight line.* (Ex. 3.)
Informal proof. If points *B* and *E* lie in plane *AD* and also in plane *GK*, then *BE* must lie in both

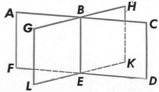

planes (SG 1). If any point other than those of *BE* were in both planes, the two planes would coincide (SG 4).

CHAPTER 2

TRIANGLES—CONGRUENCE

Triangles are fundamental figures in geometry and in applications of geometry.

A most common and important use of triangles is illustrated in the pictures on the opposite page. You see that triangles are formed by pieces of the structure. These triangles brace the structure, or keep it rigid. Triangles are used in this way in the frames of houses, in trusses of roofs, on bridges, on gates, and on some packing crates.

This use of triangles depends on a property of them called *congruence*. In general, two or more triangles are congruent when they are exactly alike in shape and size.

The conditions that cause two triangles to be congruent and some consequences of congruence are developed in this chapter.

Triangles are used to brace a tower for high tension wires. Modified triangles are used in trusses for the roof of the Exhibition Hall at Turin.

TOP: H. ARMSTRONG ROBERTS   BOTTOM: G. E. KIDDER SMITH, NEW YORK

TOP: FENESTRA, INC. BOTTOM: NEWS BUREAU, GENERAL ELECTRIC COMPANY, SCHENECTADY, NEW YORK

Top: Isosceles triangles are important elements in the design of a recreation building in Elizabethtown, Pa. *Bottom:* This circular exhaust tower is part of a million-dollar jet engine combustion laboratory in Evendale, Ohio

47. A **triangle** (△) is a geometrical figure consisting of three points that do not lie on the same straight line and the segments that join these points by pairs, as △*ABC*.

A, B, and C are **vertices** of △*ABC*.

AB, AC, and BC are the **sides** of △*ABC*.

∠*A*, ∠*B*, and ∠*C* are the **angles** of △*ABC*.

∠*B* is *opposite* side AC, AC is opposite ∠*B*.

∠*B* is *included* by sides AB and BC.

Side AB is included by ∠*A* and ∠*B*.

The **parts** of a triangle are its sides and angles.

48. Frequently, from now on, figures will be *constructed* with compasses and a straight edge. When compasses are not used, we shall direct you to *draw* or to *sketch* the figure.

In theory the segments and angles in plane geometry are not measured. However, to assist your teacher in checking your drawings or constructions, the lengths of segments and sizes of angles will be given at times. The lengths of the segments will be approximate lengths taken from a ruler or from your Geometry Tool. The sizes of the angles will be the approximate sizes obtained by using the protractor of your Geometry Tool.

49. **Post 21.** *An arc can be drawn from a point as center so that it will intersect a given line or a given circle in two points,* as in the following figures.

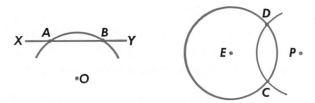

Thus: With adequate radius, an arc can be drawn from a point O as center to cut XY in points A and B, or from P as center, to cut or intersect circle E in points C and D.

Often we need only one of the points of intersection so *we draw an arc that intersects a line or a circle in a point.*

1. (a) Draw $\triangle ABC$ having $AB = 4$ in., $\angle A = 50°$, and $AC = 3$ in.; also $\triangle DEF$ having $DE = 4$ in., $\angle D = 50°$, and $DF = 3$ in.
   (b) Compare your triangles by cutting one from the paper and placing it on the other.
   (c) Compare your triangles with those made by other pupils of your class. What appears to be true?

2. Let $\triangle RST$ have $RS = 4$ in., $ST = 6$ in., and $\angle S = 60°$. Let $\triangle NMP$ have $NM = 4$ in., $MP = 6$ in., and $\angle M = 60°$.
   (a) How should these triangles compare in shape and size?
   (b) If $\triangle RST$ were placed on $\triangle PMN$, what should happen?

3. Suppose that you and a boy in England each draw accurately a $\triangle XYZ$ having $XY = 6$ in., $\angle Y = 80°$, and $YZ = 5$ in.
   (a) How will your triangles compare in shape and size?
   (b) How would your side XZ compare with his?

4. Try to state in words the fact about triangles that is suggested by Exercises 1, 2, and 3.

5. (a) Draw a $\triangle ABC$ having $AB = 5$ in., $\angle A = 60°$, and $AC = 3$ in. Draw a $\triangle XYZ$ having $XY = 4$ in., $\angle X = 60°$, and $XZ = 3$ in.
   (b) Compare *these* triangles as in Ex. 1(*b*).

50. Congruent figures are figures that can be made to coincide by placing one on the other. Such figures have the same shape and size. The symbol for *is congruent to* is $\cong$.

The part $\smile$ of this symbol is the letter S turned forward on its face. S is the first letter of the word *similar* which refers to similarity in shape.

Thus: $\triangle ABC \cong \triangle DEF$ means $\triangle ABC$ is congruent to $\triangle DEF$.

51. Exercises 1 to 3 teach *inductively* the theorem that is stated in §52 on the following page.

You have become convinced of the truth of this theorem by placing one of your triangles on another and finding that they coincide. The word **superpose** means *place upon*.

Many teachers assume this theorem as a postulate; others have it proved by *imaginary superposition* as is done on page 53. The proof is based on the following postulate.

Post. 22. *Any geometrical figure can be moved about without changing the shape, the size, or the relative positions of its parts.*

Note to teacher. See comments for p. 52 in the *Teacher's Manual.*

52. *If two triangles have two sides and the included angle of one equal respectively to two sides and the included angle of the other, the triangles are congruent.*

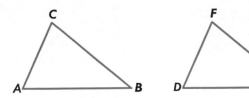

Hypothesis.   In $\triangle ABC$ and $\triangle DEF$,
$$AC = DF,\ AB = DE,\ \angle A = \angle D.$$
Conclusion. $\triangle ABC \cong \triangle DEF$
Optional proof by superposition.

Statements	Authorities
1. Place $\triangle ABC$ on $\triangle DEF$ so that point A is on point D and side AB is on side DE.	1. A geometrical figure can be moved without changing the shape, the size, etc.
2. $\qquad AB = DE$	2. By hypothesis.
3. $\qquad \therefore\ B$ will fall on E.	3. Equal segments can be made to coincide.
4. $\qquad \angle A = \angle D$	4. By hypothesis.
5. $\qquad \therefore\ AC$ will fall on DF.	5. Equal angles can be made to coincide.
6. $\qquad AC = DF$	6. By hypothesis.
7. $\qquad \therefore\ C$ will fall on F.	7. Authority 3.
8. $\quad \therefore\ BC$ will coincide with EF.	8. Only one segment can be drawn between two points.
9. $\qquad \therefore\ \triangle ABC \cong \triangle DEF$	9. Geometrical figures are congruent if they can be made to coincide.

Advice to pupils. Learn the statement of the theorem because you must give it frequently as an authority for a statement in a proof. It may be abbreviated by s.a.s. = s.a.s.

★**1.** Draw two triangles that satisfy the hypothesis of §52 but have a different shape and different letters from those above.
Prove your triangles are congruent.

Illustrative exercise.

Hypothesis. O bisects BC, $\angle B = 80°$, $\angle C = 80°$, $AB = DC$.

Conclusion. $\triangle ABO \cong \triangle DCO$

Plan of proof. Prove the triangles congruent by §52.

Proof.

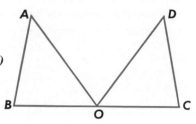

Statements	Authorities
In $\triangle ABO$ and $\triangle DCO$:	
1.　　　$AB = DC$ ✓	1. By hypothesis.
2.　　$\angle B = 80°$, $\angle C = 80°$	2. By hypothesis.
3.　　∴　$\angle B = \angle C$ ✓	3. Angles equal to the same angle are equal. (§34, Ax. 1)
4.　　　O bisects BC.	4. By hypothesis.
5.　　∴　$BO = CO$ ✓	5. A pt. that bisects a segment separates the segment into two equal segments. (§8(e))
6.　　∴　$\triangle ABO \cong \triangle DCO$	6. s.a.s. = s.a.s. (Write the theorem in full.)

Remarks. The **proper authority,** in full or abbreviated, must be written opposite each statement of the proof. Above:

1. For Step 1, "By hypothesis" is correct because the hypothesis includes the agreement that $AB = DC$.
   For Steps 2 and 4, the authorities are correct for like reasons.

2. For Step 3, think: Angles ($\angle B$, $\angle C$) equal to the same angle (80°) are equal to each other ($\angle B = \angle C$). The authority is correct only because you have Step 2.

3. For Step 5, the authority is correct because, from Step 4, you know O bisects BC. (§8(e))

4. For Step 6, the three checked statements direct attention to equalities of "two sides and the included angle" that permit us to say that $\triangle ABO$ is congruent to $\triangle DCO$. Three equalities such as those checked are always necessary as proof that two triangles are congruent.

53. For proofs like those on page 54, ask yourself systematically *what you know* or *can prove* about each angle and each side of one of the triangles.

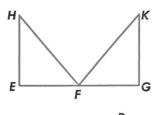

1. Hyp. $\angle E = 90°$, $\angle G = 90°$
$HE = KG$
F bisects EG.
   Con. $\triangle HEF \cong \triangle KGF$

2. Hyp. M bisects LN.
M bisects PR.
   Con. $\triangle PML \cong \triangle NMR$

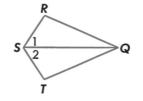

3. Hyp. $RS = ST$
SQ bisects $\angle TSR$.
   Con. $\triangle QSR \cong \triangle QST$
Note. $SQ = SQ$. For authority you may write *Identical*, meaning any quantity equals itself.

4. Hyp. $XY \perp ZW$
Y bisects ZW.
   Con. $\triangle WYX \cong \triangle ZYX$

5. Hyp. $AD \perp AC$, $CE \perp AC$
$AD = CE$, B bisects AC.
   Con. $\triangle ABD \cong \triangle CBE$

6. Hyp. GK bisects $\angle FGH$.
$FG = GH$
   Con. $\triangle GFK \cong \triangle GHK$

7. Hyp. $\angle 1 = 50°$, $\angle 4 = 50°$
$PQ = RS$
   Con. $\triangle RQS \cong \triangle PQS$

8. Hyp. $XY = XZ$, $YR = ZS$
$\angle Y = 50°$, $\angle Z = 50°$
   Con. $\triangle ZXS \cong \triangle YXR$

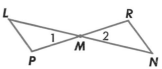

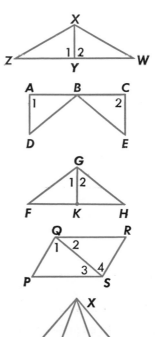

54. On page 54 you proved that
△*ABO* ≅ △ *DCO*.

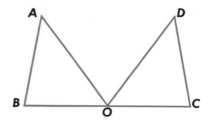

How does *AO* compare with *DO?*

Check your judgment by using tracing paper.

A better way to answer the question follows.

Since △*ABO* ≅ △*DCO*, then △*ABO* could be made to coincide with △*DCO*, with *AB* falling on *DC*, *BO* on *CO*, and ∠*B* coinciding with ∠*C*. Since *A* would be on *D*, and *O* of △*ABO* would be on *O* of △*DCO*, then *AO* would coincide with *DO*. Therefore *AO* must equal *DO*.

AO and *DO* are called **corresponding sides** of the triangles. Notice that *AO* is opposite ∠*B* and *DO* is opposite ∠*C*. These two angles were used as equals in proving the triangles congruent.

Similarly ∠*A* is opposite *BO*, and ∠*D* is opposite *CO*. *BO* and *CO* were used as equals in proving the triangles congruent. Therefore ∠*A* and ∠*D* are **corresponding angles** of these congruent triangles and would coincide if the triangles were made to coincide. Therefore ∠*A* = ∠*D*.

55. (*a*) **Corresponding sides** of congruent triangles lie opposite equal angles of the triangles.

(*b*) **Corresponding angles** of congruent triangles lie opposite equal sides of the triangles.

(*c*) *Corresponding sides and corresponding angles of congruent triangles are equal.*

1. (*a*) In the figure above, when △*ABO* was proved congruent to △*DCO*, what side did *AB* equal?
(*b*) What angle lies opposite *AB?*
(*c*) What angle lies opposite *DC?*
(*d*) What two angles then must be equal?

2. (*a*) On page 53, what side must *BC* equal? Why?
(*b*) What angle must ∠*B* equal? Why?
(*c*) What angle must ∠*C* equal? Why?

56. Fundamental Plan 1. *To prove two segments are equal or two angles are equal, try to show that they are corresponding parts of congruent triangles.*

Illustrative exercise.

Hyp. BC and AD are straight lines.
$AB = DC$, O bisects BC.
$\angle B = 90°$, $\angle C = 90°$

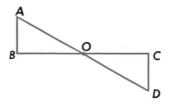

Con. $AO = DO$

Plan. Prove AO and DO correspond-ing sides of congruent △.

Proof.

Statements	Authorities
In △ABO and △DCO:	
1. $AB = DC$ √	1. By hypothesis.
2. O bisects BC.	2. By hypothesis.
3. ∴ $BO = CO$ √	3. Give def. of bisect.
4. $\angle B = 90°$, $\angle C = 90°$	4. By hypothesis.
5. ∴ $\angle B - \angle C$ √	5. Give Ax. 1, p. 32.
6. ∴ △$ABO \cong$ △DCO	6. Give §52 in full.
7. AO and DO are corres. sides of △ABO and △DCO.	7. §55(*a*)
8. ∴ $AO = DO$	8. Give §55(*c*) in full.

1. In the figure for §56:
   (*a*) What angle must equal $\angle A$? Why?
   (*b*) What angle must equal $\angle AOB$? Why?

Do the following exercises as above.

2. **Hyp.** $MN = NP$
   NO bisects $\angle PNM$.
   Con. (*a*) $MO = PO$
   (*b*) $\angle M = \angle P$

3. **Hyp.** $AB = AC$
   AD bisects $\angle BAC$.
   Con. (*a*) $DB = DC$
   (*b*) $\angle B = \angle C$

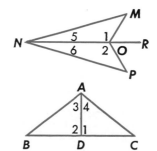

1. **Hyp.** $AB = CD$
   $\angle 1 = \angle 2$
   Con.   (a) $\angle A = \angle C$
   (b) $AD = BC$

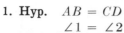

2. **Hyp.** $RSTUV$ has five equal sides.
   $\angle R = \angle T$
   Con.   (a) $VS = US$
   (b) $\angle RSV = ?$

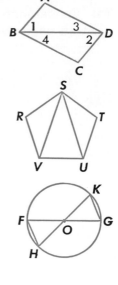

3. **Hyp.** FG and HK are diameters of circle O.
   Con.   (a) $FH = ?$
   (b) $\angle H = ?$
   (c) $\angle F = ?$

4. (a) If $MO = OP$ and $\angle 1 = \angle 2$, how does MN compare with NP?
      Prove your conclusion.
   (b) How does $\angle 5$ compare with $\angle 6$?
      Prove your conclusion.

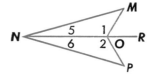

5. BD bisects $\angle ABC$, and $AB = BE$.
   (a) What does $\angle A$ equal? Prove your conclusion.
   (b) What does AD equal? Prove your conclusion.

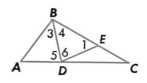

6. Let $RS = RT$ and $RX = RY$.
   (a) Does $SY = XT$? Prove it.
   (b) What does $\angle S$ equal? Why?
   (c) What does $\angle 7$ equal? Why?

Suggestion. Prove $\triangle RSY \cong RTX$.

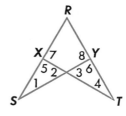

★**SG 8.** A line (AOB) is perpendicular to a plane $(MNRS)$, if it is perpendicular to every line (CO) in the plane, through its intersection (O) with the plane. Draw this figure and prove that any point (C) on the plane is equidistant from A and B if $OA = OB$.

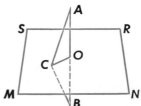

1. Draw $\triangle ABC$ having $BC = 4$ in., $\angle B = 70°$, and $\angle C = 50°$.
   Draw $\triangle ZYX$ having $XY = 4$ in., $\angle X = 70°$, and $\angle Y = 50°$.

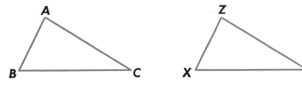

Compare a tracing of $\triangle ABC$ with $\triangle XYZ$.
What do you discover?

Note. If the triangles fail to be alike in shape and size, draw them again
very carefully with a sharp pencil.

2. Compare the tracing of your $\triangle ABC$ with one of the triangles made
   by another pupil of your class. What do you discover?

3. If you draw a $\triangle DEF$ having $DE = 5$ in., $\angle D = 60°$, and $\angle E = 80°$,
   how should your triangle compare with a $\triangle RST$ made by a boy in
   England, having $RS = 5$ in., $\angle R = 60°$, and $\angle S = 80°$?

4. Express as a theorem like that on page 53 the fact that is suggested
   by Exercises 1 to 3.

57. The foregoing exercises teach inductively the theorem that
is stated in §58, p. 60.

Some teachers prefer to accept this theorem, also, as a
postulate. Others have their pupils read and understand the
optional proof by superposition that appears on page 60.

Advice to pupils. (*a*) Be guided by your teacher's preference
about reading the proof.

(*b*) Learn the statement of the theorem as it appears in
§58 because you must quote it frequently as the authority that
two triangles are congruent.

5. In the triangles drawn for Exercise 1, what side of $\triangle ZYX$ corresponds
   to side AB of $\triangle ABC$?
   Should these sides be equal? Why?
   Test them somehow to see whether they are equal.

6. How should $\angle A$ compare with $\angle Z$? Why?
   Test them somehow to see whether they are equal.

7. How should AC compare with ZY? Why?
   Suppose that AC fails to equal ZY. What explanation for the failure
   may there be?

Note. Read §394, p. 376 at this time.

58. *If two triangles have two angles and the included side of one equal respectively to two angles and the included side of the other, they are congruent.*

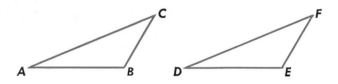

Hypothesis.   In $\triangle ABC$ and $\triangle DEF$,

$$\angle A = \angle D, \ \angle B = \angle E, \ AB = DE.$$

Conclusion. $\triangle ABC \cong \triangle DEF$

Optional proof by superposition.

Statements	Authorities
1. Place $\triangle ABC$ on $\triangle DEF$ so that point A falls on point D and AB falls on DE.	1. Any geometrical figure can be moved about without changing the shape, the size, or the relative positions of its parts.
2. $AB = DE$	2. By hypothesis.
3. $\therefore$ B will fall on E.	3. Equal segments can be made to coincide.
4. $\angle A = \angle D$	4. By hypothesis.
5. $\therefore$ AC will fall on DF, C falling somewhere on DF.	5. Equal angles can be made to coincide.
6. Similarly BC will fall on EF, C falling somewhere on EF.	6. See Steps 4 and 5.
7. $\therefore$ C must fall on F.	7. Two straight lines intersect at only one point.
8. $\therefore$ $\triangle ABC \cong \triangle DEF$	8. Geometrical figures are congruent if they can be made to coincide.

Note. This theorem may be abbreviated by writing a.s.a. = a.s.a.

★1. Prove your mastery of §58 by drawing two triangles that meet the conditions of the theorem but have a different shape and different letters from those above. Write the hypothesis and conclusion, and then write the proof for your triangles.

Do the exercises on this page in the form used for those on pages 55 and 58.

1. Hyp. $\angle 1 = 60°$, $\angle 2 = 60°$
  $\angle 3 = 25°$, $\angle 4 = 25°$
 Con.   (a) $\triangle ABD \cong \triangle CDB$
  (b) $\angle A = \angle C$

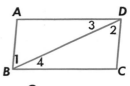

2. Hyp. EF bisects $\angle GEH$.
  EF bisects $\angle GFH$.
 Con.   (a) $\triangle EFG \cong \triangle EFH$
  (b) $EG = EH$

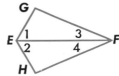

3. Hyp. NQ bisects $\angle MNP$.
  $NQ \perp MP$
 Con.   (a) $MN = ?$
  (b) $\angle M = ?$
  (c) $MQ = ?$

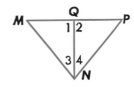

4. Hyp. O bisects XW.
  $\angle XOY = \angle WOZ$
  $YX \perp XW$, $ZW \perp XW$
 Con.   (a) $YO = ZO$
  (b) $YX = ?$

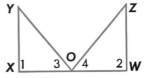

5. Hyp. $\angle 5 = 30°$, $\angle 6 = 30°$
  $\angle 1 = 120°$, $\angle 2 = 120°$
 Con.   (a) $RS = ?$
  (b) $SO = ?$
  (c) $\angle S = ?$

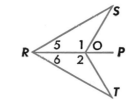

6. Hyp. R bisects BC.
  $\angle 1 = 60°$, $\angle 2 = 60°$
  $\angle B = 70°$, $\angle C = \angle 70°$
 Con.   (a) $RS = ?$ $BS = ?$
  (b) If $\angle S = 50°$,   how
   large is $\angle T$?

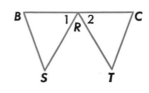

★7 (SG). The drawing at the right represents a **rectangular solid.** On each face, each angle is a right angle and the opposite sides are equal.

Copy this drawing. Prove:

(a) $AF = DG$ (b) $EG = HF$

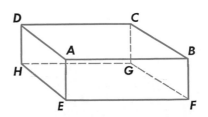

1. *To obtain the distance AB across a river.*
   (1) On one side of the river, lay off $BO \perp AB$. Extend BO to C, making $OC = BO$.
   (2) Lay off $CE \perp BOC$.
   (3) By *sighting*, find D on CE, in line with O and A.
   (4) Measure CD. Prove $AB = CD$.

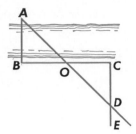

2. *Making and using a homemade surveying instrument to find the distance KH across a pond.*
   (1) By a bolt and nut, attach a movable rod GN to the top of a rod GK.
   (2) Stand it at point K. Hold KG upright (or plumb) with G at eye level.
   (3) Adjust $\angle KGN$ so that you can sight along GN to H. Tighten nut.
   (4) Without changing $\angle KGN$, turn the instrument about line KG until GN points toward a point, F, on HK extended.
   (5) Measure KF. Prove $KF = KH$.

3. **Hyp.** $YW = YR$
              $ZW \perp YWX$
              $XR \perp YRZ$
   Con.   (a) $XR = ZW$
              (b) $\angle X = ?$
              (c) $XY = ?$

4. **Hyp.** $EG = EH$, $\angle 1 = \angle 3$,
              $\angle 4 = \angle 6$
   Con.   (a) $ED = EF$
              (b) $DG = HF$
              (c) $\angle D = ?$

★5 **(SG).** Assume that $\odot O$ lies in plane MN, that OA is perpendicular to MN at O, and that points B, C, and D are any points of $\odot O$. Prove that $AB = AC = AD$.

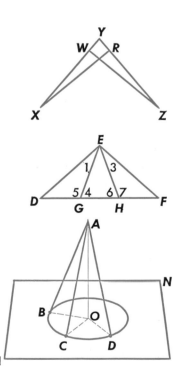

Suggestion. Recall when a line is perpendicular to a plane. (Given in SG 8, p. 58.)

Note. Ex. 1 through Ex. 20, pp. 387–388, can be done now.

59. (*a*) A **scalene triangle** is a triangle having three unequal sides.

(*b*) An **isosceles triangle** is a triangle having two equal sides, as $\triangle ABC$ if $AB = AC$.

The **vertex of an isosceles triangle** is the point in which the equal sides meet, as vertex A.

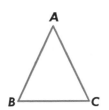

The **vertex angle** is the angle formed by the two equal sides, as $\angle A$.

The **base** of an isosceles triangle is the side that is opposite the vertex, as side BC.

The **base angles** of an isosceles triangle are the angles at the ends of the base, as $\angle B$ and $\angle C$.

1. (*a*) Draw a triangle ABC having AB and AC each 3 in. long and $\angle A = 40°$.

(*b*) Compare $\angle B$ with $\angle C$ by using tracing paper, and also by measuring them.

2. Do Ex. 1, changing $\angle A$ to 50°.

63

60. *If two sides of a triangle are equal, the angles opposite the equal sides are equal.*

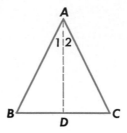

Hypothesis.   In $\triangle ABC$, $AB = AC$.

Conclusion. $\angle B = \angle C$

Plan. Use Fundamental Plan 1.

Proof.

Statements	Authorities
1. Let AD be the bisector of $\angle BAC$, meeting BC at D.	1. An angle has a bisector. (Post. 7, p. 34)
2. $\triangle BDA \cong \triangle CDA$	2. Prove in full.
3. $\therefore$ $\angle B = \angle C$	3. Why?

Note. This theorem usually is stated:
  The base angles of an isosceles triangle are equal.

61. A **corollary (Cor.)** is a theorem that is an easily proved consequence of another theorem. Be prepared to give the details of the proof, however.

62. An **equilateral triangle** has three equal sides.

63. Cor. *An equilateral triangle is equiangular.*

Hypothesis. In $\triangle XYZ$, $XY = YZ = XZ$.

Conclusion. $\angle X = \angle Y = \angle Z$

Proof. 1.   Since $XY = XZ$, $\angle Z = \angle Y$.   §60
       2.   Since $XY = YZ$, $\angle Z = \angle X$.   Why?
       3. $\therefore$ $\angle X = \angle Y = \angle Z$ Ax. 1, p. 32

Note. See Ex. 13, p. 81. It can be done now. It avoids the construction of bisector AD above.

1. **Hyp.** In $\triangle ABC$, $AB = AC$, $BD = DC$.
   Con. (a) $\angle BAD = \angle DAC$, or AD bisects $\angle BAC$.
   (b) $\angle BDA = \angle ADC$, or $AD \perp BC$.

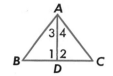

2. **Hyp.** In $\triangle EFG$, $EF = EG$, $FH = KG$.
   Con. (a) $EH = EK$
   (b) $\angle EHF = \angle EKG$

3. **Hyp.** In $\triangle MNP$, $MN = MP$, $NO = OP$, $\angle 1 = \angle 2$.
   Con. (a) $RO = SO$
   (b) $NR = PS$

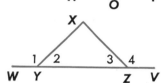

4. **Hyp.** In $\triangle XYZ$, $XY = XZ$, $\angle 2 = 75°$.
   Con. $\angle 1 = ?$ $\angle 3 = ?$ $\angle 4 = ?$

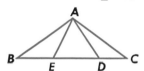

5. **Hyp.** In $\triangle ABC$, $AB = AC$, $BD = CE$.
   Con. (a) $AD = AE$
   (b) $\angle BDA = \angle AEC$

Suggestion. Prove $\triangle ABD \cong \triangle ACE$.

6. **Hyp.** In $\triangle FGH$, $FG = FH$.
   K bisects FG.
   L bisects FH.
   Con. $GL = HK$

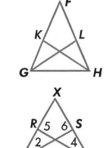

7. **Hyp.** In $\triangle XYZ$, $XY = XZ$.
   YS bisects $\angle XYZ$.
   ZR bisects $\angle XZY$.
   Con. (a) $YS = ZR$
   (b) $\angle 5 = \angle 6$

Note. Ex. 21 through Ex. 25, pp. 388 and 389, can be done now.

64. **An important experiment.** (a) Using compasses, construct $\triangle ABC$ having $AB = 4$ in., $AC = 2.5$ in., and $BC = 3$ in.
(b) Compare your triangle with those made by other pupils.
(c) What theorem is suggested by your comparisons?

65. *If two triangles have the three sides of one equal respectively to the three sides of the other, the triangles are congruent.*

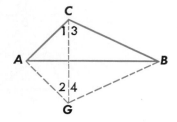 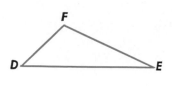

Hypothesis.   In $\triangle ABC$ and $\triangle DEF$,
$$AB = DE, \ AC = DF, \text{ and } BC = EF.$$

Conclusion. $\triangle ABC \cong \triangle DEF$

Plan. First prove $\angle ACB = \angle F$; then use s.a.s. = s.a.s.

Proof.

Statements	Authorities
1. Place $\triangle DEF$ with D on A, DE on AB, and F at G, on the opposite side of AB from C. Draw CG.	1. (a) Post. 22, p. 52 (b) Equal segments can be made to coincide. (c) Post. 1, p. 34
2. In $\triangle ACG$, $AC = AG$.	2. Ax. 1, p. 32
3. ∴ $\angle 1 = ?$	3. Why?
4. Similarly, $\angle 3 = ?$	4. Give the proof.
5. ∴ $\angle 1 + \angle 3 = \angle 2 + \angle 4$	5. Ax. 3, p. 32
6. ∴ $\angle ACB = \angle AGB = \angle DFE$ In $\triangle ABC$ and $\triangle DEF$:	6. Ax. 7, Ax. 2, p. 32
7. $AC = ?$ √	7. Why?
8. $BC = ?$ √	8. Why?
9. $\angle ACB = \angle DFE$ √	9. Step 6.
10. ∴ $\triangle ABC \cong \triangle DEF$	10. Why?

Note 1. Be prepared to give the full reason wherever "Why?" or only a section number or the number of an axiom appears.

Note 2. This theorem is referred to by s.s.s. = s.s.s.

1. Hyp. $AB = DC$
  $BC = AD$
  Con. (a) $\triangle ABD \cong \triangle BCD$
  (b) $\angle A = \angle C$
  (c) $\angle ABD = \angle BDC$

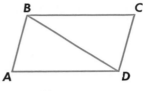

2. Hyp. $XY = WY$
  $XZ = WZ$
  Con. (a) YZ bisects $\angle WYX$.
  (b) YZ bisects $\angle WZX$.
  (c) $\angle X = \angle W$

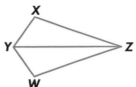

3. Hyp. $MP = MR$
  $NP = NR$
  Con. (a) $\triangle MNP \cong \triangle MNR$
  (b) MO bisects $\angle RMP$.
  ★(c) MNO bisects $\angle RNP$.

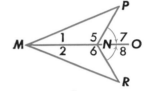

4. Hyp. $EF = HG$
  $EG = HF$
  Con. (a) $\angle E = \angle H$
  (b) $\angle EGF = ?$
  (c) $\angle EFG = ?$

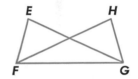

5. Hyp. In $\triangle RST$, $SR = ST$.
  $RU = UT$
  Con. (a) SU bisects $\angle RST$.
  (b) $SU \perp RT$

Suggestion. Prove $\angle 3 = \angle 4$,
  also $\angle 1 = \angle 2$.

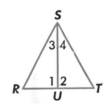

★**6.** Prove that two equilateral triangles are congruent if a side of one equals a side of the other.

Suggestion. Draw the necessary triangles; write the hypothesis and conclusion, and then write the proof.

★**7. Hyp.** AZ, BY, and CX are straight lines through point O.
  $AO = OZ, BO = OY, CO = OX$
  Con. $\triangle ABC \cong \triangle ZYX$

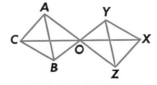

Suggestion. First prove $AB = YZ$, using $\triangle ABO$ and YZO; then $BC = YX$, and then $AC = ZX$. Then prove $\triangle ABC \cong \triangle ZYX$.

66. Planning a longer proof by analysis.

Illustration.

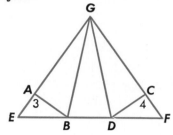

Hyp. $GE = GF$, $AE = CF$
           $AB \perp GE$, $CD \perp GF$

Con. $GB = GD$

Analysis. 1. $GB = GD$ if
             $\triangle GBE \cong \triangle GDF$.

2. In these triangles, $GE = GF$ and $\angle E = \angle F$. $\triangle GBE \cong GDF$ if $BE = DF$.

3. Does $BE = DF$? Yes, if $\triangle ABE \cong \triangle CDF$.

4. We know that $\angle 3 = \angle 4$, $\angle E = \angle F$, and $AE = CF$.
             $\therefore \triangle ABE$ is congruent to $\triangle CDF$.

5. Reversing the foregoing steps, we have the following plan.

   Plan. 1. Prove $\triangle ABE \cong \triangle CDF$ to get $BE = DF$.
            2. Prove $\triangle GBE \cong \triangle GDF$ to get $GB = GD$.
   Write out the proof using only this plan.

   We make the *analysis* to find a *plan*.

1. What is the fundamental plan for proving:
   (*a*) Two segments equal?   (*b*) Two angles equal?

   By an analysis like that above, find a plan for proving each of the following exercises. Then prove the exercise.

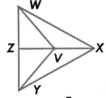

2. Hyp. $\triangle XYW$ is isosceles.
           $\triangle VYW$ is isosceles.
   Con.   (*a*) $\angle YXV = \angle WXV$
           (*b*) $YZ = WZ$

3. Hyp. $CD = DE = EF = FG = GC$
           R bisects FC.
           S bisects FD.
           $\angle G = \angle E$
   Con. $CS = DR$

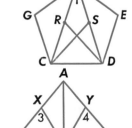

4. Hyp. $AO \perp BC$
           $BO = CO$
           $\angle 1 = \angle 2$
   Con.   (*a*) $XO = YO$
           (*b*) $\angle 3 = \angle 4$

1. **Hyp.** $MN = MO$
        NH bisects $\angle MNO$.
        OG bisects $\angle MON$.
   Con. (a) $NH = OG$
        (b) $GK = HK$

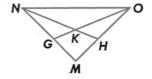

2. A figure is said to be *rigid* if its shape cannot be changed without changing the size of its angles or sides.
   Why is a triangle rigid when its three sides have fixed lengths?

3. If a side of a crate is made by nailing four boards to two upright boards as in the adjoining figure, how can the side be made rigid by nailing another board to the side?

4. If two sides of a triangle and the segment drawn to the midpoint of one of them from the opposite vertex are equal respectively to two sides and the corresponding segment in another triangle, the two triangles are congruent.

★5. **Hyp.** $DB = DC$
        R bisects DB.
        S bisects DC.
   Con. (a) $\triangle BCT$ is isosceles.
        (b) DT bisects $\angle BDC$.

★6. **Hyp.** $MN = MP$
        O bisects NP.
        $\angle NOQ = \angle POR$
   Con. $RN = QP$

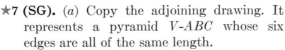

★7 (SG). (a) Copy the adjoining drawing. It represents a pyramid $V\text{-}ABC$ whose six edges are all of the same length.
   (b) How many *faces* has this pyramid?
   (c) Prove that the faces are enclosed by congruent triangles.

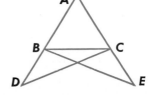

8. Draw $\triangle ABC$ having $AB = AC$.
   Extend AB to D, and AC to E, making $BD = CE$. Draw BE and CD. Without using §60 prove:
   (a) $\triangle ACD \cong \triangle ABE$
   (b) $\triangle CBD \cong \triangle CBE$
   (c) $\angle CBD = \angle BCE$
   (d) $\angle ABC = \angle ACB$

Note. Exercises 26 through 32, p. 389, can be done now.

67. Recall that theorems can be expressed in the *if-then* form. The *if-clause* is the hypothesis, and the *then-clause* is the conclusion. (See §41.)

A theorem like:

The base angles of an isosceles triangle are equal

can be expressed in the *if-then* form in the following manner.

If a triangle is isosceles, then its base angles are equal.

When a theorem is expressed in this manner, draw a figure that includes all lines named in the theorem, describe in the hypothesis the lines and points named in the *if-clause* and, in the conclusion, state what is to be proved, guided by the *then-clause.*

Prove exercises 1 *through* 8.

1. If X is any point on the perpendicular to a segment RS at the mid-point of the segment, then $XR = XS$.

2. If MN is the bisector of the vertex angle M of isosceles triangle PMQ meeting PQ at N, then N bisects PQ.

3. If the opposite sides of a *quadrilateral* (four-sided figure) $ABCD$ are equal, then the *diagonal DB* separates the quadrilateral into two congruent triangles.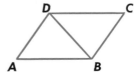

4. If the equal sides of an isosceles triangle are extended through the vertices of the base angles, then the extensions form equal angles with the base.

5. If BA, one of the equal sides of isosceles $\triangle BAC$, is extended through the vertex A to a point D and side CA is extended through A to a point E so that $AD = AE$, then DC equals EB and $\angle E = \angle D$.

6. If ZX and WY, perpendiculars to a segment XY at its end points X and Y, are equal, and if O is the mid-point of XY, then $ZO = WO$.

7. If the diagonals XY and ZW of a quadrilateral $XWYZ$ bisect each other, then the opposite sides of the quadrilateral are equal.

8. If $\triangle ABC$ and $\triangle XYZ$ have $AB = XY$, $\angle A = \angle X$, and $\angle B = \angle Y$, and if P bisects BC and Q bisects YZ, then $AP = XQ$.

9. Express in the *if-then* form the theorem that appears as Exercise 2, p. 67.

10. Express in the *if-then* form the theorem that appears as Exercise 3, p. 57.

SG 9. A *regular square pyramid* is represented by the adjoining drawing. Its base is enclosed by a square, which, as you know, has four equal sides. The lines that join the vertices of its base, A, B, C, and D, to the vertex, V, of the pyramid are equal.

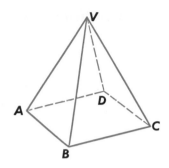

Note. AD, DC, and VD are drawn with dotted lines because they are in the background, and would not be visible.

1. What kind of triangle is $\triangle VAB$?
2. What can you prove about $\angle VAB$ and $\angle VBA$?
3. Prove $\triangle VAB \cong \triangle VBC \cong \triangle VAD \cong \triangle VDC$.
4. What other pairs of angles besides those in Ex. 2 are equal?
5. To what angles is $\angle AVB$ equal?
6. (a) Draw a large figure like that above. On the *face AVB*, draw the line from V to the mid-point R of AB.
   (b) Prove $\triangle AVR$ congruent to $\triangle BVR$.
   (c) How does VR divide $\angle AVB$? Prove it.
   (d) At what angle does VR meet AB? Prove it.
7. (a) Also, on face VBC, draw VS to the mid-point of BC.
   (b) What can you prove about VS?
   (c) How does VS appear to compare with VR? Prove your conclusion.
8. On face VCD draw VT to the mid-point T of CD, and on face VDA draw VW to the mid-point W of AD. State and prove conclusions about VT and VW.
9. Draw AC and BD in the figure above. Since $ABCD$ is a square, prove $AC = BD$.

SG 10. A *right circular cone* has its base enclosed by a circle, and its vertex in the line that is perpendicular to the base at the center of the base.

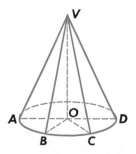

10. If A, B, C, . . . are points on the circle, prove $VA = VB = VC$, ... (See SG 8, p. 58.)
11. Prove that VA, VB, VC, . . . make equal angles with VO.

1. Draw a horizontal segment *CD about* 3 in. long. By means of compasses, locate *E* above *CD* so that $CE = DE = 2.5$ in.; also locate *F* below *CD* so that $CF = DF = 2$ in. Draw *EF* intersecting *CD* at *G*. How does *EF* appear to cross *CD?*

68. The **perpendicular-bisector** of a segment is the line that bisects and is perpendicular to the segment.

69. *If each of two points is equidistant from the ends of a segment, the two points determine the perpendicular-bisector of the segment.*

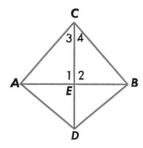

Hypothesis. $AC = BC$, $AD = BD$

Conclusion. CD is the perpendicular-bisector of AB.

Analysis and Plan. $AE = EB$ and $\angle 1 = \angle 2$ if $\triangle AEC \cong \triangle BEC$. To prove $\triangle AEC \cong \triangle BEC$, first prove $\angle 3 = \angle 4$ by proving $\triangle ACD \cong \triangle BCD$.

Proof.

Statements	Authorities
1. $\qquad \triangle ACD \cong \triangle BCD$	1. Full proof?
2. $\qquad \therefore \quad \angle 3 = \angle 4$	2. Why?
3. $\qquad \therefore \quad \triangle AEC \cong \triangle BCE$	3. Full proof?
4. $\qquad \therefore \quad AE = ?$	4. Why?
5. $\qquad$ and $\quad \angle 1 = ?$	5. Why?
6. $\therefore \quad \angle 1$ and $\angle 2$ are rt. $\angle$s.	6. §13(*a*), p. 20
7. $\therefore \quad CD$ is the $\perp$-bis. of AB.	7. Why?

2. In a quadrilateral *ABCD* if $AB = BC$ and $AD = DC$, then BD must bisect AC, $\angle ABC$, and $\angle ADC$.

Note. Ex. 33 through Ex. 36, p. 390, can be done now.

GEOMETRICAL CONSTRUCTIONS ARE THE BASIS OF MECHANICAL DRAWINGS SUCH AS THE ONE ABOVE SHOWN TO A CLASS IN AUTOMOTIVE DESIGN.

THE FUNDAMENTAL CONSTRUCTIONS

70. Since the days of Plato theoretical plane geometry has been restricted to figures that can be constructed by means of an *unmarked straight edge and compasses alone*.

Note. In spite of the above agreement, lengths of segments will be specified often in the construction exercises, so that the figures drawn by all the pupils of the class will be approximately congruent, to assist the teacher in checking.

71. *A segment equal to a given segment can be laid off on a line, from a point of the line.* (Post. 4, p. 34)

Given. Segment a and line XY containing point P.

Required. To construct on XY a segment PR equal to a.

Construction	Authorities
1. On compasses take radius a.	1. See §7, p. 16.
2. With P as center and radius a, draw an arc cutting XY at R.	2. Post. 21, p. 51.

Statement. $PR = a$ Why?

72. We have postulated that an angle has one and only one bisector (Post. 7, p. 34). A method for constructing the bisector of an angle follows.

73. An angle can be bisected.

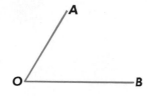 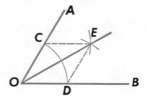

Given. $\angle BOA$

Required. To bisect $\angle BOA$.

Construction	Authorities
1. With O as center and any radius, draw an arc cutting OA at C and OB at D.	1. A circle can be drawn with any point as center and any segment as radius.
2. With a radius more than $\frac{1}{2}CD$, draw arcs from C and D as centers, intersecting at E.	2. Post. 21, p. 51
3. Draw OE.	3. Post. 1, p. 34

Statement. OE bisects $\angle BOA$.

Plan. Prove $\angle COE$ and $\angle DOE$ corres. $\angle\!\!\!\angle$ of cong. $\triangle\!\!\!\triangle$.

Proof.

Statements	Authorities
1. Draw CE and DE. In $\triangle OCE$ and $\triangle ODE$:	1. A segment can be drawn between two points.
2. $OE = ?$ √	2. A quantity equals itself.
3. $OC = OD$ √	3. Post. 13, p. 35.
4. $CE = DE$ √	4. See Authority 3.
5. ∴ $\triangle OCE \cong \triangle ODE$	5. Why?
6. ∴ $\angle COE = \angle DOE$	6. Why?
7. ∴ OE bisects $\angle BOA$.	7. Why?

1. Draw a scalene triangle. Bisect each of its angles.

74. *The perpendicular-bisector of a segment can be constructed.*

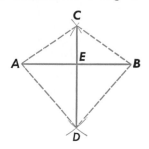

Given. Segment AB

Required. To construct the perpendicular-bisector of AB.

Construction	Authorities
1. With radius more than $\frac{1}{2}AB$, and A and B as centers, draw arcs above AB, intersecting at C.	1. Why possible?
2. With radius more than $\frac{1}{2}AB$, and A and B as centers, draw arcs below AB, intersecting at D.	2. Why possible?
3. Draw CD.	3. Why possible?

Statement. CD is the perpendicular-bisector of AB.

Plan. Use §69, p. 72.

Proof.

Statements	Authorities
1. Draw CA, CB, DA, and DB.	1. Why possible?
2. $CA = CB$ $DA = DB$	2. Why?
3. $\therefore$ CD is $\perp$-bis. of AB.	3. Why?

1. Draw a horizontal segment, a vertical segment, and an oblique segment. Construct the perpendicular-bisector of each of the segments.
2. Draw a reasonably large scalene triangle. Construct the perpendicular-bisector of each of its sides. What happens?
3. Draw a segment *about* 4 in. long, without measuring it. Divide it into four equal segments.

75. *A perpendicular to a line can be constructed at any point of the line.*

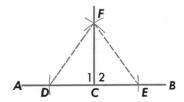

Given. Point C on line AB.

Required. To construct a perpendicular to AB at C.

Construction	Authorities
1. With C as center and any radius draw arcs cutting AB at D and E.	1. Post. 21, p. 51
2. With radius longer than CD, draw arcs from D and E as centers, intersecting at F.	2. Why possible?
3. Draw CF.	3. Why possible?

Statement. $CF \perp AB$ at C.

Analysis and Plan. $CF \perp AB$ if $\angle 1 = \angle 2$. Draw FD and FE. Prove $\triangle FDC \cong \triangle FEC$.

Proof. Left to the pupil.

Discussion. This construction is always possible.

76. *On a plane one and only one perpendicular can be drawn to a line at a point of the line.*

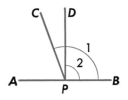

Informal proof. If CP and DP were both perpendicular to AB at P, then $\angle 1$ and $\angle 2$ would both be right angles, and equal. But $\angle 1$ is greater than $\angle 2$ (Ax. 8, p. 32). Therefore only DP (or CP) is $\perp AB$ at P.

Note. In the figure, DP is the perpendicular to AB at P.

1. Draw a horizontal segment. Construct a perpendicular to it:
   (*a*) At a point that is not near one end of it.
   (*b*) At one end of it. (See Post. 2, p. 34.)
2. Construct an angle: (*a*) Of 45°   (*b*) Of 135°

77. *A perpendicular can be constructed to a line from a point that is not on the line.*

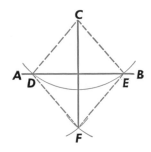

Given. Line AB and point C that is not on AB.

Required. To construct a perpendicular to AB from C.

Construction	Authorities
1. With C as center and a radius that is long enough, draw an arc cutting AB at D and E.	1. Possible?
2. With D and E as centers and equal radii, greater than $\frac{1}{2}DE$, draw arcs intersecting at F.	2. Possible?
3. $\qquad\qquad$ Draw CF.	3. Possible?

Statement. $\qquad\qquad CF \perp AB$

Plan of proof. Use §69, p. 72.

Proof.

Statements	Authorities
1. $\qquad$ Draw CD, CE, FD, and FE.	1. Why possible?
2. $\qquad\quad CD = CE, FE = ?$	2. Why?
3. $\quad \therefore \quad CF$ is the $\perp$-bis. of DE.	3. Why?
4. $\qquad\quad \therefore \quad CF \perp AB$	4. Why?

78. It will be proved in §106, p. 108, that only one perpendicular can be drawn to a line from a point that is not on the line.

79. **The distance from a point to a line** is the segment perpendicular to the line from the point; as CO at the right.

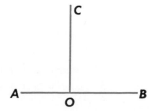

80. *At a point of a line in a plane a line can be constructed that makes a given angle with the given line.*

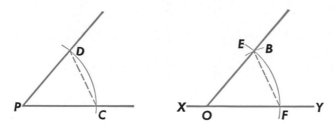

Given. $\angle P$ and point O on line XY.

Required. To construct a line from O that makes with XY an angle equal to $\angle P$.

Construction	Authorities
1. With P as center and any radius, draw an arc cutting the sides of $\angle P$ at C and D.	1. Post. 21, p. 51
2. With O as center and PC as radius, draw an arc EF, cutting XY at F.	2. Why possible?
3. With F as center and CD as radius, draw an arc cutting arc EF at B.	3. Why possible?
4. Draw OB.	4. Why possible?

Statement. $\angle FOB = \angle P$

Plan. Draw CD and FB. Prove $\triangle FOB \cong \triangle CPD$.

Proof. Left to the pupil.

1. Construct $\triangle ABC$ having AB equal to a given segment m and $\angle A$ and B equal to the angles given at the right.

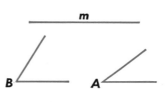

2. Construct $\triangle DEF$, having DE 3 in. long, $\angle D = \angle B$ of Exercise 1, and DF 2.5 in. long.

3. Construct isosceles $\triangle XYZ$ having XY and XZ each 2.5 in. long and $\angle X$ equal to $\angle B$ of Exercise 1.

4. Repeat both parts of Exercise 1, p. 76:
   (*a*) Starting with a vertical segment
   (*b*) Starting with an oblique segment

1. (*a*) Draw a $\triangle ABC$ of *reasonably* large size.

    (*b*) *Construct* a $\triangle RST$ congruent to $\triangle ABC$, using:

        (1) The first congruence theorem

        (2) The second congruence theorem

        (3) The third congruence theorem

2. Given segment AB.

A   B

Construct $\triangle MNO$ having $MN = AB$, $\angle M = 90°$, and $\angle N = 45°$.

3. Given segments RS and XY.

R   S

X   Y

    (*a*) Construct the equilateral triangle whose sides all equal XY.

    (*b*) Construct the isosceles triangle ABC having $AB = AC = RS$, and $BC = XY$.

    (*c*) Construct the isosceles triangle MNO having $MO = RS$, and $MN = NO = XY$.

    (*d*) Can you construct $\triangle DEF$ having $DE = XY$, $\angle D = 90°$, and $DF = RS$?

4. (*a*) Draw a large isosceles triangle. Bisect the vertex angle.

    (*b*) Where does the bisector appear to meet the base?

    (*c*) Prove the conclusion you reach in part (*b*).

5. (*a*) Construct AB perpendicular to XY at a point B of XY.

    (*b*) On XY place C and D on opposite sides of B so that $BC = BD$. Draw AC and AD.

    (*c*) What appears to be true about AC and AD?

    (*d*) Prove the fact observed in part (*c*).

6. (*a*) Draw a large acute $\angle ABC$ and construct BD bisecting it.

    (*b*) At O on BD construct XY perpendicular to BD, meeting AB at Y and BC at X.

    (*c*) What appears true of BX and BY? Prove it.

    (*d*) How does XO appear to compare with YO? Prove it.

7. (*a*) Draw a horizontal segment CD 3 in. long. Locate E above CD, 2.5 in. from C and 2.5 in. from D. Locate F below CD, 2 in. from C and 2 in. from D. Draw EF, meeting CD at G.

    (*b*) What must be true of CG?

8. (*a*) Construct $\triangle RST$ having $RS = 1.5$ in., $ST = 2.5$ in., and $RT = 2$ in.

    (*b*) With compasses find X, the mid-point of RT.

    (*c*) Draw SX. Extend it to Y so that $XY = SX$. Draw TY.

    (*d*) Prove $\triangle RSX \cong \triangle YXT$.

81. (*a*) An **altitude** of a triangle is the segment from a vertex of the triangle perpendicular to the opposite side or the opposite side extended; as *AD* in △*ABC*. *BC* is called the **base** of the triangle for that altitude.

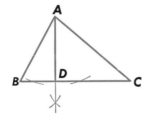 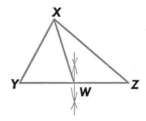

(*b*) A **median** of a triangle is the segment from a vertex of the triangle to the mid-point of the opposite side, as *XW* in △*XYZ*.

1. (*a*) Draw a reasonably large triangle. Construct the *three* altitudes of the triangle. Extend them if necessary so that they will intersect. What happens?
   (*b*) Do part (*a*) in a triangle that has one obtuse angle.
   (*c*) What conclusion is suggested by parts (*a*) and (*b*)?

2. (*a*) Draw a large triangle. Construct the *three* medians of the triangle. What happens?
   (*b*) Do part (*a*) in a second triangle.
   (*c*) What tentative conclusion is suggested by parts (*a*) and (*b*)?

3. (*a*) Construct △*ABC* having *AB* = 2 in., *BC* = 2.5 in., and *AC* = 3 in.
   (*b*) Construct the altitude *BD* to *AC* from *B*. Measure it correct to the nearest .1 in.
   (*c*) Construct the median *BE* to *AC* from *B*. Measure it.
   (*d*) Construct the bisector *BF* of ∠*ABC*, meeting *AC* at *F*. Measure *BF*.
   (*e*) Of the segments *BD*, *BE*, and *BF*, which is the shortest?

4. (*a*) Draw a large △*ABC*. Construct △*XYZ* so that it will be congruent to △*ABC*, so that *XY* corresponds to *AB*, and *YZ* to *BC*.
   (*b*) Construct the median *AD* in △*ABC*. Construct the median in △*XYZ* from the vertex of the angle that equals ∠*A*.
   (*c*) Prove that the two medians are equal.
   (*d*) State the theorem that you have proved in part (*c*).

5. (*a*) Construct △*RST* congruent to △*ABC* of Ex. 3(*a*).
   (*b*) Construct the altitude *SX* of △*RST* that corresponds to altitude *BD* of Ex. 3(*b*). Measure it.
   (*c*) How does *SX* compare with *BD*?

1. Draw a segment near the lower edge of a piece of paper. Construct the perpendicular-bisector of the segment.
2. What is: (*a*) An axiom? (*b*) A postulate? (*c*) A theorem?
3. What are congruent triangles?
4. What is the superposition postulate?
5. What are corresponding sides of congruent triangles?
6. What are corresponding angles of congruent triangles?
7. What is Fundamental Plan 1?
8. What is a median of a triangle?
9. What is an altitude of a triangle?
10. If the median is drawn to the base of an isosceles triangle, what facts can be proved about it?
11. Place point X on a line AB and a point Y above AB. Construct the perpendicular to AB at X and the one from Y.
12. (*a*) Draw any $\triangle ABC$ of convenient size. Construct $\triangle DEF$ congruent to $\triangle ABC$, so that DE and AB are corresponding sides, and also EF and BC.

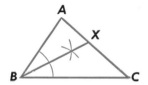 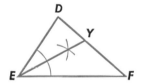

(*b*) Construct BX bisecting $\angle CBA$, meeting AC at X, and EY bisecting $\angle FED$, meeting DF at Y.
(*c*) How does BX appear to compare with EY?
(*d*) State and prove the tentative conclusion you reach in part (*c*).
13. The theorem in §60, p. 64 was proved by using the bisector of the vertex angle, which was assumed in Post. 7, p. 34, to exist. The theorem can be proved as follows, without using the bisector of the vertex angle.

Hypothesis.   In $\triangle BAC$, $BA = BC$.

Conclusion. $\angle CAB = \angle ACB$

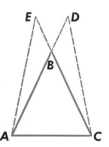

Construction. Extend AB to D and CB to E so that $BD = BE$. Draw AE and CD.

Plan. Prove:
(1) $\triangle CBD \cong \triangle ABE$ (2) $\triangle ACD \cong \triangle ACE$ (3) $\angle CAB = \angle ACB$

1. (a) Construct an isosceles △ABC.
   (b) Construct DB ⊥ BC and EC ⊥ BC. Make BD = CE.
   (c) Draw DA and EA.
   (d) How does DA appear to compare with EA?
   (e) Prove the tentative conclusion stated in part (d).

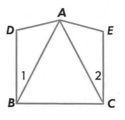

Suggestion. First compare ∠1 and ∠2.

   (f) Prove other facts that you observe about the figure.

2. (a) Construct the adjoining figure having ∠AOB any acute angle with AO and BO extended so that OC = OA, and OD = OB.

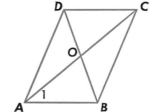

   (b) State a tentative conclusion:
   (1) About AD and BC.
   (2) About DC and AB.
   (3) About ∠BAO, and about ∠DCO.
   (c) Prove your tentative conclusions.

3. (a) Draw any △ABC.
   (b) Construct △XYZ, having ∠X = ∠A, XY = AB, and XZ = AC.

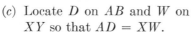
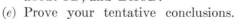

   (c) Locate D on AB and W on XY so that AD = XW.
   (d) State tentative conclusions about CD, and ∠ACD.
   (e) Prove your tentative conclusions.

4. (a) Construct any isosceles △ABC.
   (b) Locate X and Z on BC so that BX = CZ.
   (c) Construct XY ⊥ BC, meeting AB at Y, and ZW ⊥ BC, meeting AC at W.

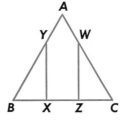

   (d) State tentative conclusions about XY and ∠BYX.
   (e) Prove your tentative conclusions.

★5. (SG) The adjoining figure represents a pyramid whose edges are all equal.
   (a) What kind of triangle encloses each face?
   (b) State and prove a conclusion about the medians of the face triangles ABC and ACD.

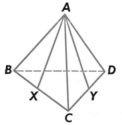
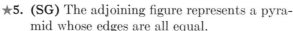

1. Without using a protractor construct $\triangle XYZ$ having XY 2 in. in length, $\angle Y$ equal to 90°, and $\angle X = 45°$.

2. Construct an isosceles triangle having its vertex angle equal to a given acute $\angle A$ and the including sides equal to a given segment m.

Suggestion. Draw an acute angle, A, of reasonably large size, and an unmeasured segment, m.

3. If all the sides of $ABCDEF$ are equal and $\angle F = \angle D$, then BE must be the perpendicular-bisector of AC.

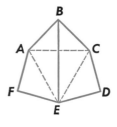

Suggestion. Draw AE and CE. Prove them equal. Then use §69, p. 72.

4. (a) Construct a large isosceles triangle. Construct the median to the base of the triangle.

   (b) What angle does the median appear to make with the base of the triangle?

   (c) Prove the tentative conclusion reached in part (b).

5. If $\triangle RST$ is equilateral and its sides are extended so that $SA = TB = RC$, then $\triangle ABC$ must be equilateral.

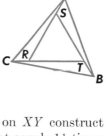

6. (a) Construct an isosceles $\triangle ABC$ on one side of base BC and isosceles $\triangle BDC$ on the other side of BC.

   (b) Prove that AD bisects $\angle BAC$ and also $\angle BDC$.

7. Given an acute $\angle B$ and a line XY. At point O on XY construct above XY a line that makes with XY an angle that equals $1\frac{1}{2}$ times $\angle B$.

8. In any quadrilateral $RSTU$, if $RS = ST$ and $RU = UT$, then SU is perpendicular to RT.

9. (a) Construct the adjoining figure so that $XO = YO$, $\angle SXO = \angle RYO$, and with SOY and ROX straight lines.

   (b) How does SX appear to compare with RY?

   (c) Prove the tentative conclusion suggested by part (b).

   (d) Prove $SO = RO$ and $\angle S = \angle R$.

10. If the median to the base of a triangle is perpendicular to the base, then the triangle must be isosceles.

Draw the figure. State the hypothesis and conclusion and prove the theorem.

PERPENDICULAR LINES AND PLANES

Experimental approach. 1. Draw two intersecting straight lines OA and OB on a piece of paper on the top of your desk.

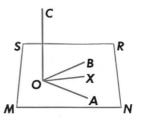

2. Can you hold a pencil (CO) at O so that it will be perpendicular to OB but not perpendicular to OA?

3. Can you hold CO perpendicular to OA and OB? If you can, what angle does CO appear to make with any other line OX that you draw on your paper? This suggests:

SG 11. *If a straight line is perpendicular to each of two intersecting lines at their point of intersection, it is perpendicular to any line in their plane through their intersection.*

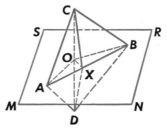

Hypothesis. OA and OB determine plane $MNRS$.
$$CO \perp OA, \ CO \perp OB$$
OX is any other line in $MNRS$ through O.

Conclusion. $CO \perp OX$

Plan. 1. Extend CO to D making $OD = CO$. Let AB cut OX at X.

2. Prove $XC = XD$ as follows:
   (a) Prove $\triangle AOC \cong \triangle AOD$. $\therefore AC = AD$
   (b) Similarly prove $BC = BD$.
   (c) Prove $\triangle ABC \cong \triangle ABD$, and $\therefore \angle CAB = \angle DAB$.
   (d) Prove $\triangle CAX \cong \triangle DAX$, and $\therefore XC = XD$.
3. Prove $XO \perp COD$, and $\therefore CO \perp OX$.

SG 12. *If a line is perpendicular to each of two intersecting lines at their point of intersection, it is perpendicular to their plane.*

This theorem is a consequence of SG 8, p. 58, and SG 11. (Why?)

1. The theorem at the bottom of page 84 justifies *a procedure* for erecting
a post perpendicular to a floor at a
point of the floor.

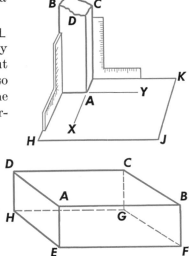

   Place the post so that edge $AD \perp$
any line AX on the floor, doing so by
using a carpenter's square. Without
changing rt. $\angle XAD$, tip the post so
that $AD \perp$ any other line AY on the
floor HJK. Why is edge AD then perpendicular to the floor?

2. Prove that edge AE of a rectangular solid must be perpendicular to
faces $EFGH$ and $ABCD$.

3. To what faces of the solid AG must
edge AB be perpendicular?

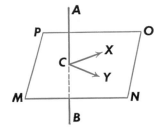

SG 13. *Through a point of a line,
there can be a plane perpendicular
to the line.*

Informal proof. In any plane that contains line ACB, take $CX \perp ACB$ at C.
In any other plane that contains AB,
take $CY \perp AB$ at C. CX and CY determine plane XCY. (Why?)
    $ACB \perp$ plane XCY. (Why?)

SG 14. *Through a point that is not on a given line, there can be
a plane that is perpendicular to the line.*

Informal proof. In the plane ABX
(where X is the given point) take $XC \perp$
AB at C. In any other plane through
AB, take $CY \perp AB$ at C. Then CX
and CY determine plane XCY. (Why?)
    $\therefore ACB \perp$ plane XCY or plane
$XCY \perp AB$. (Why?)

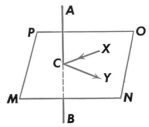

SG 15. It can be proved:

(a) *Through a point of a line, there can be only one plane that is
perpendicular to the line.*

(b) *Through a point that is not on a given line, there can be only
one plane that is perpendicular to the line.*

SG 16. Three kinds of angles that can be formed by two planes are represented by the following drawings.

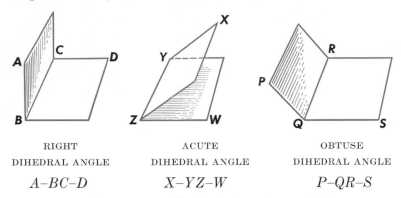

RIGHT	ACUTE	OBTUSE
DIHEDRAL ANGLE	DIHEDRAL ANGLE	DIHEDRAL ANGLE
A–BC–D	X–YZ–W	P–QR–S

Note. In $\angle A$–BC–D, ABC represents the **half-plane** on one side of *edge BC*. *BC*, a line, is infinitely long.
Half-plane ABC extends *infinitely far on ABC away from BC* at all points on infinitely-long *BC*.

1. Hold the front cover of your book so that, in turn, it makes an angle of each of these three kinds with the front page of your book.

SG 17. A **dihedral angle** consists of two half-planes that have a common **edge.** The **faces** of the angle are the two half-planes. The size of the angle does not depend on the extent of its edge or of its faces.

2. Decide where two walls of your classroom make a dihedral angle. What kind of dihedral angle do they form?

SG 18. The **plane angle** of a dihedral angle is the angle formed by two rays, one in each plane, each perpendicular to the edge of the dihedral angle at the same point.

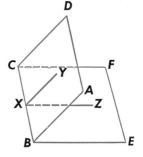

Note. On $ABCD$, $XY \perp BC$ at X. On $EBCF$, $XZ \perp BC$ at X. Then $\angle ZXY$ is the plane angle of dihedral $\angle E$–BC–A.

3. What kind of plane angle does $\angle ZXY$ above appear to be?

4. Draw an obtuse dihedral angle with its edge and faces lettered as above, and with lines XY and XZ drawn on the faces as above. Answer again the question that appears in Ex. 3.

SG 19. A **dihedral angle** is **acute, right,** or **obtuse** according as its plane angle is acute, right, or obtuse.

(b) Two **planes** are **perpendicular** when they form a right dihedral angle.

1. (a) Hold a pencil (AB) perpendicular to a piece of paper ($MNPR$) on the top of your desk. Place a card against the pencil to represent a plane $XZYW$ that contains the pencil, intersecting plane $MNPR$ in line YZ.

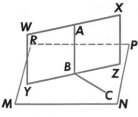

(b) What kind of dihedral angle does the card appear to make with the paper on your desk?

(c) State a tentative conclusion suggested by parts (a) and (b).

2. **Informal proof** of Ex. 1(c).

Hyp. $AB \perp$ plane $MNPR$, plane $YZXW$ contains AB.
Plane $YZXW$ intersects $MNPR$ in line YZ.

Con.   Plane $YZXW \perp$ plane $MNPR$.

Plan. Prove dihedral angle X–YZ–N is a right dihedral angle.

Proof. 1. In $MNPR$, draw $BC \perp YZ$ at B.

2. Since $AB \perp YZ$ and $BC \perp YZ$, then $\angle ABC$ is the plane angle of dihedral $\angle X$–YZ–N.   (Why?)

3.   Since $AB \perp MNPR$, $\angle ABC$ = ?   (Why?)

4.   ∴   dihedral $\angle X$–YZ–N is ——.   (Why?)

5.   ∴   plane $YZXW$ is ——.   (Why?)

SG 20. Ex. 1 suggests and Ex. 2 proves:

If a line is perpendicular to a plane, then any plane that contains the line is perpendicular to the plane.

3. On rectangular solid AG:

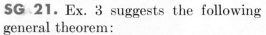

(a) $\angle AEF$ = rt. $\angle$, $\angle AEH$ = ?

(b) ∴ AE _?_ plane $EFGH$. (Why?)

(c) ∴   plane $AEFB$ _?_ plane $EFGH$. (Why?)

(d) Also plane $AEHD$ _?_ plane _?_. (Why?)

(e) At what angle does face $ABCD$ meet $AEHD$?

SG 21. Ex. 3 suggests the following general theorem:

Each face of a rectangular solid is perpendicular to the faces that it meets.

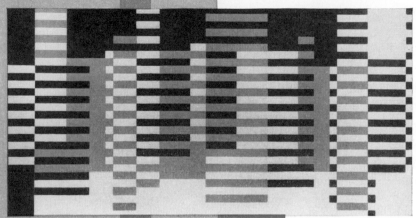

JOSEF ALBERS

STEED BROS.

H. ARMSTRONG ROBERTS, PHILADELPHIA

CHAPTER 3

PARALLELISM

You can see parallel lines in edges of door frames and of doors, in the ten-yard lines of a football field, in lanes in a turnpike, in patterns in some kinds of linoleum, and in modern design. You can see that opposite walls of your room are parallel, that the ceiling is parallel to the floor, that the cuts between slices of a loaf of sliced bread are in parallel planes.

By this time you know that such lines and planes are not lines or planes in the strict mathematical sense, but you recognize that there is something about them that you think of as *parallelism*.

Because parallel lines and planes are so useful and so pleasing artistically, it is desirable to learn the mathematical description of them, and to learn some of the consequences when such lines or planes appear in geometrical figures.

Such information appears in Chapter 3. Some of the proofs are a new kind used not only in mathematics but in reasoning when the facts are not mathematical.

 Parallel lines are used in modern painting—"City," by Josef Albers; architecture—Nativity Church in El Monte, California; and engineering—the layout of the New Jersey Turnpike.

82. Coplanar lines are lines that are in the same plane.

1. In your classroom: (*a*) Find two coplanar lines that intersect.
   (*b*) Find two coplanar lines that will not meet no matter how far they are extended.
   (*c*) Find two lines that are not coplanar. Can they ever intersect?

83. (*a*) **Parallel lines** are coplanar lines that do not intersect no matter how far they are extended, as *AB* and *CD*. The symbol for *is parallel to* is ∥, and for *is not parallel to* is ∦.

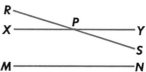

(*b*) Therefore two coplanar lines either intersect or are parallel.

(*c*) **Skew lines** are two straight lines that are not coplanar. They cannot meet. (SG 6, p. 47)

84. Although we cannot test two lines by following them to see whether they intersect, no matter how far extended, we are inclined to believe that parallel lines do exist. We assume:

Post. 23. *Through a point in a plane there is one and only one parallel to a line of the plane.*

Thus: If line *XY* through *P* is parallel to line *MN*, then any other line through *P* is not parallel to *MN*.

85. *If two lines are parallel to a third line, all in the same plane, the lines are parallel to each other.*

Hyp. *AB* ∥ *CD*, *EF* ∥ *CD*
AB, *CD*, and *EF* are coplanar.

Con. *AB* ∥ *EF*

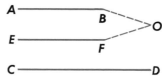

Informal Proof. 1. Assume that *AB* ∦ *EF*.
2. Then *AB* must meet *EF* at a point *O*. Why?
3. Then both *AB* and *EF*, through *O*, would be parallel to *CD*.
4. But only one line through *O* can be parallel to *CD*.
5. Therefore the assumption in Step 1 must be wrong.
6.   That is, *AB* ∥ *EF*.

86. The proof in §85 is an **indirect proof.** Notice:

1. The proof starts by assuming the negative of the desired conclusion. (Step 1)

2. Logical consequences of the hypothesis and the assumption (Steps 2 and 3) lead to a contradiction. (Step 4)

3. Since there must be an error somewhere, we conclude that the assumption is false. Therefore the negative of it, the desired conclusion, is true. (Steps 5, 6)

Such reasoning occurs often when no mathematics is involved. It is based on the following assumed principle of logic.

Principle. *If the negative of a statement logically produces a contradiction, then the statement itself must be true.*

Thus: A pupil, missing her geometry textbook, is sure that she brought it to school. Hoping it is in her last classroom, she considers the negative possibilities.
"Is it in my locker?" She finds that it is not.
"Is it in my desk?" She finds that it is not.
She decides that it must be at her seat in her last class.

In such cases, the reasoning is based on considering in turn the various possibilities. For more discussion, see pp. 381, 382.

87. **Definitions** needed for the study of parallel lines.

If two straight lines, AB and CD, are cut by a third line EF, then EF is called a **transversal** of AB and CD and:

    ∡ 3, 4, 5, and 6 are **interior** angles.

    ∡ 1, 2, 7, and 8 are **exterior** angles.

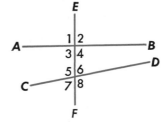

    ∡ 3 and 6 are **alternate-interior** angles; also ∡ 5 and 4.

    ∡ 1 and 8 are **alternate-exterior** angles; also ∡ 2 and 7.

    ∡ 2 and 6 are **corresponding angles;** also ∡ 1 and 5, ∡ 3 and 7, and ∡ 4 and 8.

    ∡ 4 and 6 are interior angles on the same side of the transversal; also ∡ 3 and 5.

88. If a side BC of a $\triangle ABC$ is extended through one vertex, an **exterior angle** of $\triangle ABC$ is formed, as exterior angle DCA of $\triangle ABC$. Two such angles can be formed at each vertex. $\angle A$ and $\angle B$ of $\triangle ABC$ are the **nonadjacent interior angles** associated with exterior $\angle DCA$.

1. By means of tracing paper, compare $\angle DCA$:
   (*a*) With nonadjacent $\angle A$ (*b*) With $\angle B$

2. State a tentative conclusion suggested by Ex. 1.

89. *An exterior angle of a triangle is greater than either nonadjacent interior angle of the triangle.*

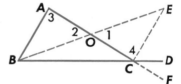

Hypothesis. BC of $\triangle ABC$ is extended to D forming exterior $\angle DCA$.

Conclusion.   (1) $\angle DCA > \angle A$
                   (2) $\angle DCA > \angle B$

Plan. Prove $\angle DCA >$ an angle that equals $\angle A$.

Proof.

	Statements	Authorities
1.	Bisect AC, marking the mid-point O. Draw BO. Extend BO to E, making $OE = BO$. Draw CE.	1. Possible?
2.	$\triangle COE \cong \triangle ABO$	2. Prove this.
3.	$\therefore \quad \angle 4 = ?$	3. Why?
4.	$\angle DCA > \angle 4$	4. Ax. 8, p. 32
5.	$\therefore \quad \angle DCA > ?$	5. Ax. 2, p. 32
6.	Similarly, $\angle BCF > \angle B$	6. Prove in full.*
7.	$\angle DCA = \angle BCF$	7. Why?
8.	$\therefore \quad \angle DCA > \angle B$	8. Why?

*__Note.__ To prove Step 6, bisect BC, marking the mid-point R. Draw AR and extend it to S so that $RS = AR$. Draw CS. Then prove steps like Steps 2–5 above.

90. *If a transversal of two coplanar lines makes a pair of alternate-interior angles equal, the two lines are parallel.*

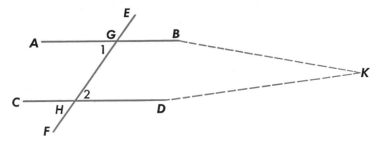

Hypothesis. *AB* and *CD* are coplanar. *EF* cuts *AB* at *G* and *CD* at *H*, making $\angle 1 = \angle 2$.

Conclusion. $AB \parallel CD$

Proof.

Statements	Authorities
1. Suppose $AB \not\parallel CD$.	1. A supposition.
2. $\therefore$ AB meets CD at a point K.	2. §83(b)
3. $\angle 1$ is an exterior $\angle$ of $\triangle GHK$.	3. §88
4. $\therefore$ $\angle 1 > \angle 2$	4. Why?
5. But $\angle 1 = \angle 2$.	5. Why?
6. $\therefore$ $AB \parallel CD$	6. §86, p. 91

91. **Fundamental Plan 2. To prove that two coplanar lines are parallel, try to prove that a transversal of them makes a pair of alternate interior angles equal.**

92. **Cor. 1.** *If a transversal of two coplanar lines makes a pair of corresponding angles equal, the two lines are parallel.*

Hyp.   *EF* cuts *AB* and *CD* so that $\angle 2 = \angle 6$.

Con. $AB \parallel CD$

Plan.   Prove $\angle 3 = \angle 6$. Use §90.

93. **Cor. 2.** *If a transversal of two coplanar lines makes a pair of interior angles on the same side of the transversal supplementary, the two lines are parallel.*

94. **Cor. 3.** *If two coplanar lines are perpendicular to the same line, they are parallel.*

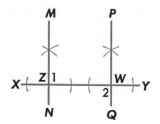

Hyp.   *MN* and *PQ* are coplanar.
         MN ⊥ *XY*, *PQ* ⊥ *XY*
Con.   *MN* ‖ *PQ*
(Plan and proof left to the pupil.)

In the following exercises, the lines are all coplanar.

1. In the adjoining figure, is *AB* ‖ *CD*:
    (a) If ∠4 = 60° and ∠5 = 60°?
    (b) If ∠3 = 150° and ∠7 = 150°?
    (c) If ∠1 = 75° and ∠5 = 75°?
    (d) If ∠5 = 30° and ∠3 = 150°?
    (e) If ∠4 = 80° and ∠6 = 100°?

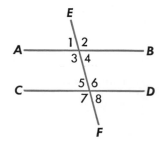

2. Prove that *AB* ‖ *CD* above, if
    ∠1 = 50° and ∠7 = 130°.

3. Prove that *AB* ‖ *CD* if ∠2 = 140° and ∠7 = 140°.

4. If many lines are drawn perpendicular to the straight edge of a piece of paper, what kind of lines must they be?

5. Prove this exercise.
    Hyp.   *AB* = *CD*
             AD = *BC*
    Con.   *AB* ‖ *CD*
             AD ‖ *BC*

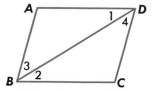

6. Draw a line *XY*. At points *A*, *B*, and *C* of *XY*, construct perpendiculars to *XY*. What kind of lines are these perpendiculars?

7. Construct △*ABC* having *AB* = *AC*. Construct *BD* so that ∠*CBD* = ∠*ABC*. What kind of lines are *BD* and *AC*?

8. If segments *MN* and *PQ* bisect each other at a point *O*, then *MQ* ‖ *NP*.

9. If alternate-exterior angles are equal when two coplanar lines are cut by a transversal, the lines are parallel.

10. If exterior angles on the same side of the transversal are supplementary when a transversal cuts two coplanar lines, the lines are parallel.

11. Six principal theorems for proving two lines are parallel appear on pages 93 and 94. Read them again and learn them.

95. *Through a point that is not on a given line, to construct a parallel to the line.*

Given. AB and point C not on AB.

Required. To construct a line through C parallel to AB.
Suggestion. Draw any line EF through C intersecting AB at G. In the plane of A, B, and C construct $\angle 2 = \angle 1$ by the method taught in §80, p. 78. Then prove $MN \parallel AB$.

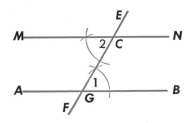

1. Given point O not on line FG. Through O construct OW perpendicular to FG. At O construct HK perpendicular to OW in plane OFG. What kind of lines are HK and FG? Why?

2. Given an acute $\angle XYZ$. On YZ place points A, B, and C so that $YA = 1$ in., $YB = 1.5$ in., and $YC = 2$ in.
   (a) Through A construct AD parallel to YX.
   (b) Through B and C construct parallels to YX.
   (c) What kind of lines are the three constructed lines?

3. (a) In the adjoining plane figure, if $\angle CRS$ and $\angle RSB$ each equal $100°$, what kind of lines are AB and CD?
   (b) If SX bisects $\angle RSB$ and RT bisects $\angle CRS$, prove SX parallel to RT.

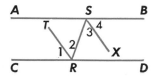

4. If a pair of equal corresponding angles made by a transversal of two coplanar lines are bisected, then the bisectors must be parallel.

96. An important experiment.

(a) On a line XY, place A and C about $1\frac{1}{2}$ in. apart. Construct AB parallel to CD. (§94)

(b) Draw EF cutting AB at G and CD at H.

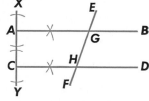

(c) Compare a tracing of $\angle AGH$ with $\angle GHD$; also a tracing of $\angle HGB$ with $\angle CHG$.

(d) What appears true?

(e) Express as a theorem the conclusion you reach in Part (d)

5. In the figure for §96, compare also a pair of corresponding angles formed by EF with AB and CD. Express your conclusion as a theorem.

97. If two parallel lines are cut by a transversal, alternate-interior angles are equal.

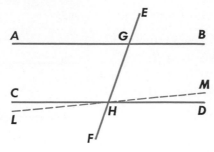

Hypothesis. $AB \parallel CD$. EF cuts AB at G and CD at H.

Conclusion. $\angle AGH = \angle GHD$

Plan. Prove $\angle GHD$ coincides with an angle equal to $\angle AGH$.

Proof.

Statements	Authorities
1. Imagine line LHM through H drawn so that $\angle GHM = \angle AGH$.	1. §80, p. 78
2. Then $LHM \parallel AGB$.	2. §90, p. 93
3. But $CHD \parallel AGB$.	3. Why?
4. ∴ LHM coincides with CHD.	4. Post. 23, p. 90
5. ∴ $\angle GHD = \angle GHM$	5. §11(a), p. 19
6. ∴ $\angle GHD = \angle AGH$	6. Why?

98. **Cor. 1.** *If two parallels are cut by a transversal, corresponding angles are equal.*

Hyp. $AB \parallel CD$. EF cuts them in G and H respectively.

Con. $\angle 2 = \angle 6$

Plan.   Use §97 and Ax. 1.

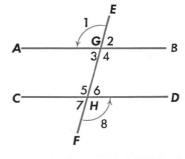

99. **Cor. 2.** *If two parallels are cut by a transversal, interior angles on the same side of the transversal are supplementary.*

Prove. $\angle 4 + \angle 6 = 1$ st. $\angle$, if $AB \parallel CD$.

100. **Cor. 3.** *If a line is perpendicular to one of two parallels, it is perpendicular to the other also, if all the lines are coplanar.*

Hyp. $XY \parallel ST$, $WR \perp XY$

Con. $WR \perp ST$

Plan. Prove $\angle 2$ is a rt. $\angle$.

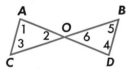

101. **Cor. 4.** *If two coplanar angles have their sides respectively parallel, they are equal if the corresponding sides extend in the same directions from their vertices, or in the opposite directions.*

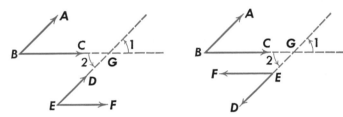

Hyp. Coplanar $\angle CBA$ and FED have $BA \parallel ED$ and $BC \parallel EF$, with the directions of corresponding sides indicated.

Con. $\angle CBA = \angle FED$

Plan. Extend the sides as on the drawing. Prove $\angle CBA$ and $\angle FED$ equal to the same angle or to equal angles.

1. In the figure for §98, p. 96, how large is each of the other angles when $\angle 3$ is 70°?

2. Construct $\triangle RST$ having $RS = RT$. Extend SR through R to point Y. Construct RX parallel to ST. Prove RX bisects $\angle TRY$.

3. **Hyp.** $AC \parallel BD$
      $AO = DO$
   Con. $CO = BO$
   Plan. Use Fundamental Plan 1.

4. If a line is parallel to the base of an isosceles triangle, cutting the equal sides, it makes equal angles with the sides of the triangle.

5. In the figure for Ex. 3, if $AC \parallel BD$ and $AC = BD$, prove that O bisects AD and also bisects BC.

6. For §101, draw a figure in which $ED \parallel BA$, extending in the same direction from the vertices of their angles, and $EF \parallel BC$, but extending in opposite directions from the vertices of their angles. Decide on and prove a conclusion about $\angle FED$ and CBA.

1. MN, joining points on two parallels, is bisected by point O. PQ, drawn through O, is terminated by the parallels.
   Prove that O bisects PQ.

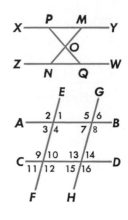

2. In the adjoining figure, $AB \parallel CD$ and $EF \parallel GH$. Prove:
   (a) $\angle 2 = \angle 13$
   (b) $\angle 8 = \angle 12$
   (c) $\angle 3 + \angle 13 =$ one st. $\angle$
   (d) $\angle 6$ is supp. to $\angle 9$
   (e) If $\angle 6 = 80°$, how large is $\angle 15$? $\angle 10$? $\angle 2$?
   (f) If $\angle 4 = 120°$, how large is $\angle 10$? $\angle 13$?

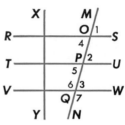

3. Construct coplanar lines RS, TU, and VW each perpendicular to XY; also, NM cutting RS, TU, and VW in points O, P, and Q.
   (a) What kind of lines are RS, TU, and VW? Why?
   (b) How do $\angle$ 1, 2, and 3 compare?
   (c) Compare $\angle 4$ and $\angle 5$.
   (d) What is the relation between $\angle 5$ and $\angle 6$?

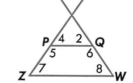

4. Construct isosceles $\triangle ABC$, having $AB = AC$. Through A construct XY parallel to BC.
   (a) What appears to be true of $\angle$ XAB and YAC?
   (b) Prove the conclusion reached in part (a).

5. Lines on a sheet of ruled paper are parallel. Prove that a line in their plane that is perpendicular to one of them must be perpendicular to each of them.

6. In the adjoining figure prove:
   (a) If $\angle 1 = \angle 8$, then $\angle 3 = \angle 7$.
   (b) If $\angle 4 = \angle 7$, then $\angle 6$ is a supplement of $\angle 8$.
   (c) If $\angle 1 = \angle 2$, then $\angle 3$ is a supplement of $\angle 5$.

7. Prove: If two parallel lines are cut by a transversal, alternate-exterior angles are equal.

8. Prove: If two parallels are cut by a transversal, exterior angles on the same side of the transversal are supplementary.

9. $\triangle DBE$ is isosceles, having $DE = BE$. Line BA is drawn parallel to DE. Extend DB through B to X. Prove that $\angle XBA$ and $\angle DBE$ are either equal or supplementary.

Note. Ex. 37 through 43, p. 390, can be done now.

102. (*a*) Notice the relation between §90, p. 93, and §97, p. 96. Both refer to plane figures.

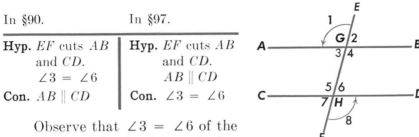

In §90.	In §97.
Hyp. *EF* cuts *AB* and *CD*. ∠3 = ∠6	**Hyp.** *EF* cuts *AB* and *CD*. *AB* ∥ *CD*
Con. *AB* ∥ *CD*	**Con.** ∠3 = ∠6

Observe that ∠3 = ∠6 of the hypothesis of §90 is the conclusion of §97, and that *A B* ∥ *C D*, the conclusion of §90, is the hypothesis of §97.

The theorem in §97 is a *converse* of that in §90.

(*b*) **A converse of a theorem** is obtained when an essential statement of the hypothesis of the theorem is interchanged with an essential statement of the conclusion.

If both the hypothesis and the conclusion consist of single statements, then *the* converse of the theorem is obtained when the hypothesis and the conclusion are interchanged.

(*c*) *A converse of a theorem is not necessarily true even if the theorem itself is true.*

Thus: *If two angles are right angles, the angles are equal.* The converse of this theorem is:

If two angles are equal, the angles are right angles.

Clearly this second theorem is not true.

What is the converse of each of the following statements? Is the original statement true? Is the converse true?

1. If a man lives in Chicago, he lives in Illinois.
2. If Mr. Smith owns a Buick, he owns an automobile.
3. Every horse is a four-legged animal.
4. If angles are vertical angles, they are equal.
5. If triangles are congruent, their corresponding sides are equal.
6. If triangles are congruent, their corresponding angles are equal.
Note. For more about converses, see pp. 383 and 384.

1. (*a*) Select and copy (1) the hypothesis and (2) the conclusion of §92, p. 93.
   (*b*) Write (1) the hypothesis and (2) the conclusion of the converse.
   (*c*) State this converse in the *if-then* form.
   (*d*) If this converse has been proved, in what section was it proved?

2. As in Ex. 1, write the corresponding answers:
   (*a*) For §93, p. 93.   (*b*) For §94, p. 94.

3. (*a*) Write in the *if, then* form the following theorem:
   Complements of equal angles are equal.
   (*b*) Write (1) the hypothesis and (2) the conclusion of the original theorem and of the converse theorem.
   (*c*) Has the converse been proved?

4. (*a*) What is the converse of §27(*a*), p. 27?
   (*b*) Is the converse true?

5. (*a*) What is the converse of §42, p. 40?
   (*b*) Is this converse true?

6. (*a*) Write (1) the hypothesis and (2) the conclusion of:
   If corresponding sides of two triangles are equal, then corresponding angles of the triangles are equal.
   (*b*) Is this theorem true?
   (*c*) Write as a theorem the converse of part (*a*).
   (*d*) Has this converse been proved?
   (*e*) Determine by drawings whether the converse appears to be true?

7. (*a*) Write the converse of §69, p. 72.
   (*b*) Determine by experiment whether or not this converse appears to be true.
   (*c*) Prove your conclusion about this converse.

8. (*a*) What is the converse of Postulate 10?
   (*b*) Is the converse true?
   (*c*) Prove your conclusion about the converse.

9. Is the converse of the following statement true?
   If a pupil is late in arriving at school, he is tardy.

10. Is the converse of the following statement true?
    If it is snowing, the temperature probably is near or below 32°.

11. *If an automobile has defective brakes, it is unsafe.*
    (*a*) What is the converse statement?
    (*b*) Is the converse statement true?

12. *Students who are on the stage crew are excused early.*
    (*a*) What is the converse statement?
    (*b*) Is the converse necessarily true?

1. State three theorems that prove triangles congruent.

2. (a) State the fundamental theorem for proving lines parallel.
   (b) State four other theorems for proving lines parallel.

3. (a) State the fundamental theorem about two parallels cut by a transversal.
   (b) State three other theorems about angles that are formed when a transversal cuts two parallels.

4. State two theorems for proving two angles supplementary.

5. State the theorem about an exterior angle of a triangle.

6. What is the postulate about parallels?

7. What are the two fundamental plans of demonstration?

8. (a) How is a converse of a theorem formed?
   (b) Is a converse necessarily true when the theorem is true?
   (c) Illustrate your answer.

9. What are the six fundamental constructions?

10. In the adjoining figure:
    (a) How large is each of the other angles if $AB \parallel CD$ and $\angle 1 = 100°$?
    (b) Are AB and CD parallel:
        (1) If $\angle 4$ and $\angle 5$ each equal $120°$?
        (2) If $\angle 2 = 70°$ and $\angle 8 = 110°$?

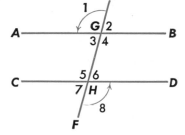

11. In $\triangle MNO$, let $\angle MNO = 90°$ and NP be perpendicular to MO.
    (a) If $\angle 6 + \angle 1 = 90°$, compare $\angle 6$ and $\angle 2$.
    (b) How does $\angle 1$ compare with $\angle 5$ if, also, $\angle 6$ is the complement of $\angle 5$?

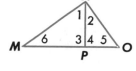

12. **Hyp.** At the right,
    $YX = YZ$,
    YW bisects $\angle XYZ$
    Con. (a) $\triangle XYW \cong \triangle ZYW$
    (b) $XW = ?$

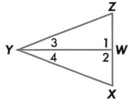

13. (a) Construct the equilateral triangle each of whose sides equals the segment s.

    _____ s _____

    (b) Construct the bisectors of the three angles. What do you discover about them?

PARALLEL LINES AND PLANES

103. The exercises on pages 102 and 103 suggest some conclusions about parallel lines and perpendicular lines in relation to parallel planes. No proofs are involved. On pages 103–105, the important definitions and theorems are summarized, are clarified by drawings, and either are assumed or are proved informally.

1. (a) Where in your room do you see two planes that cannot meet even if they are extended? What would you call such planes?
   (b) Where in your room do you see a line that you would consider parallel to a plane?

2. Look at a straight line on the floor of your room. Can such a line ever meet the ceiling? What theorem is suggested?

3. Place a pencil on the top of your desk. Hold another pencil above the desk parallel to the first one. In what relative positions are the desk top and the second pencil? What theorem is suggested?

4. Hold a pencil to represent a line AB that is parallel to the top of your desk. Place a card against the pencil, intersecting the top of your desk in line EF. What kind of lines do AB and EF appear to be? What conclusion is suggested?

5. Observe the intersections of the front wall of your room with the ceiling and the floor. What kind of lines are the intersections? What conclusion is suggested?

6. Hold two pencils, each perpendicular to the top of your desk. What theorem do they suggest?

7. Have one pupil hold a pencil stationary. Have another pupil hold two other pencils, each of them parallel to the stationary pencil. In what relative positions are the second and third pencils?

8. Hold two cards, each parallel to the top of your desk. What kind of planes is suggested by the two cards?

9. (a) Have one pupil hold two pencils in parallel positions. Have another pupil hold a card perpendicular to one pencil.
   (b) What are the relative positions of the second pencil and the card?

10. Have one pupil hold two cards to represent two parallel planes. Have another pupil hold a pencil perpendicular to one of the cards. What are the relative positions of the pencil and the second card?

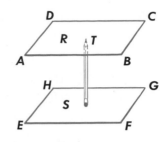

11. (a) Have one pupil hold a pencil stationary to represent a line. Have another pupil hold two cards to represent planes that are perpendicular to the pencil.
    (b) What kind of planes is suggested by the cards?

12. How are the conditions of Ex. 8 illustrated in a building with three or more stories?

13. Give an illustration of the conditions stated in Ex. 6.

14. Give an illustration of the conditions described in Ex. 7.

SG 22. Definitions. (a) Two **planes are parallel** if they do not meet when extended.

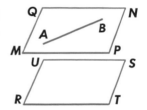

(b) A **line and a plane are parallel** if they do not meet when extended.

SG 23. *If two planes are parallel, a line in one of them is parallel to the other.* (See Ex. 2, p. 102, and the figure for SG 22.)

Thus: If $MPNQ \parallel RTSU$, AB in $MPNQ$ must be parallel to $RTSU$.

Informal proof. If AB were to meet $RTSU$ at a point O, then O would be in $MPNQ$ and $RTSU$. (SG 1, p. 46) This is impossible since $MPNQ \parallel RTSU$.

SG 24. *If a line outside a plane is parallel to a line in the plane, it is parallel to the plane.* (See Ex. 3, p. 102.)

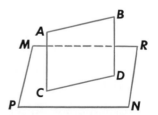

Thus: If $AB \parallel CD$ in $PNRM$, then $AB \parallel PNRM$.

Informal proof. AB and CD determine a plane $ACDB$ that intersects $PNRM$ in CD. (SG 7, p. 47) If AB meets $PNRM$ in a point O, then O is on CD. (SG 7, p. 47) But $AB \parallel CD$. $\therefore AB \parallel PNRM$.

SG 25. *If a line is parallel to a plane, the intersection of that plane with any plane that contains the line is parallel to the line.* (See Ex. 4, p. 102.)

Thus: In the figure for SG 24, if $AB \parallel PNRM$ and plane $ACDB$ intersects plane PR in CD, then $AB \parallel CD$.

Informal proof. If AB were to intersect CD at a point O, then O would be in $PNRM$. But $AB \parallel PNRM$. $\therefore AB \parallel CD$.

SG 26. *If two parallel planes are cut by a third plane, the intersections are parallel.* (See Ex. 5, p. 102.)

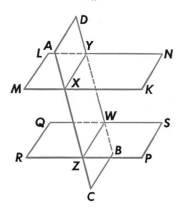

Thus: If plane $MN \parallel$ plane RS, and AB cuts MN in XY and RS in ZW, then $XY \parallel ZW$.

Informal proof. If XY were to intersect ZW at a point O, then O would be in plane MN and RS. (SG 1, p. 46) But $MN \parallel RS$. $\therefore XY \parallel ZW$.

SG 27. *Lines that are perpendicular to the same plane are parallel.* (See Ex. 6, p. 102.)

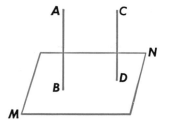

Thus: If $AB \perp$ plane MN and $CD \perp MN$, $AB \parallel CD$.

Accept this theorem without proof. It can be proved.

SG 28. *If one of two parallel lines is perpendicular to a plane, the other is also.* (See Ex. 9, p. 102.)

Thus: Above, if $AB \parallel CD$ and $AB \perp$ plane MN, then $CD \perp MN$.

Informal proof. In the figure for SG 27, if CD is not perpendicular to plane MN, assume a line $CE \perp MN$. Then $CE \parallel AB$ (SG 27). Then CE and CD would both be parallel to AB. But this is impossible, by Post. 23, p. 90. Therefore CD must be $\perp$ plane MN.

SG 29. *If two lines in space are parallel to a third line, they are parallel to each other.* (See Ex. 7, p. 102.)

Thus: If $AB \parallel CD$ and $EF \parallel CD$, then $AB \parallel EF$.

Informal proof. Assume a plane $MN \perp CD$. Then $AB \perp MN$ and $EF \perp M$. (SG 28)
Then $AB \parallel EF$. (Why?)

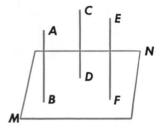

SG 30. *If a straight line is perpendicular to one of two parallel planes, it is perpendicular to the other also.* (See Ex. 10, p. 103.)

Thus: If plane $MN \parallel$ plane RS, and $AB \perp RS$, then $AB \perp MN$.

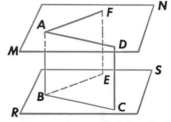

Informal proof. Let a plane $ABCD$ intersect plane RS in BC and plane MN in AD. Let plane $ABEF$ intersect RS in BE and MN in AF. Then $AD \parallel BC$ and $AF \parallel BE$. (Why?)
Since $AB \perp$ plane RS, then $AB \perp BC$ and $AB \perp BE$. (SG 8)
Therefore $AB \perp AD$ and $AB \perp AF$. (Why?)
Therefore $AB \perp$ plane MN. (SG 11, p. 84)

SG 31. *If two planes are perpendicular to the same line, they are parallel.* (See Ex. 11, p. 103.)

Thus: If plane $MN \perp AB$ and plane $RS \perp AB$, then plane $MN \parallel$ plane RS. Accept this theorem without proof.

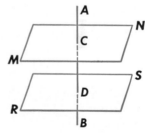

SG 32. *If two planes are parallel to a third plane, they are parallel.* (See Ex. 8, p. 102.)

Thus: If plane $MN \parallel$ plane XY and plane $RS \parallel XY$, then $MN \parallel RS$.

Informal proof. If line $ABC \perp XY$, then $ABC \perp MN$ and $ABC \perp RS$ (SG 30). ∴ $MN \parallel RS$. (Why?)

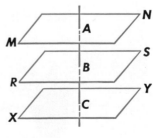

THEOREMS BASED ON PARALLELS

The theorems about parallel lines in Chapter 3 were based on a fundamental postulate, stated in §84. The equivalent of this postulate was assumed by Euclid, who about 300 B.C. assembled the knowledge of geometry of that time in books that have been the forerunners of all subsequent books on the subject. Euclid's development of geometry is called *Euclidean geometry*.

In later years, other mathematicians assumed different postulates about parallels and, as a consequence, obtained some different theorems. Their developments of geometry are called *non-Euclidean Geometry*.

The first theorem of Chapter 4 and the ones based on it are true in Euclidean Geometry but not in non-Euclidean Geometry.

In this chapter, you will study this important theorem, some consequences of it, and some other theorems based on parallel lines. Among these consequences are two more theorems for determining congruence of triangles.

Parallel lines and parallel planes are evident in these pictures—the interior of the San Gabriel High School in California, a home in Rhode Island, and a nest of modern tables.

TOP: ROPERT C. CLEVELAND, LOS ANGELES   CENTER: DAVE LAWLOR, BOSTON   BOTTOM: DUNBAR FURNITURE COMPANY

sum of the angles of a triangle is one straight angle.

ypothesis. $\triangle ABC$ is any tri-

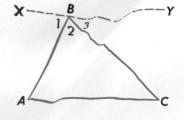

Conclusion.

$\angle A + \angle ABC + \angle C = 1$ st. $\angle$

Plan. Find angles that are equal to $\angle A$, $\angle ABC$, and $\angle C$, whose sum is one st. $\angle$.

Proof.

	Statements	Authorities
1.	Through B, construct $XY \parallel AC$.	1. §95
2.	Then $\angle A = \angle 1$	2. Why?
3.	$\angle C = \angle ?$	3. Why?
4.	$\angle ABC = \angle 2$	4. Why?
5.	$\therefore \quad \angle A + \angle ABC + \angle C = \angle 1 + \angle 2 + \angle 3$	5. Ax. 3, p. 32
6.	$\angle 1 + \angle 2 + \angle 3 = \angle XBY$	6. Ax. 7, p. 32
7.	$\angle XBY = 1$ st. $\angle$	7. Def.
8.	$\therefore \quad \angle 1 + \angle 2 + \angle 3 = 1$ st. $\angle$	8. Ax. 2, p. 32
9.	$\therefore \quad \angle A + \angle ABC + \angle C = 1$ st. $\angle$	9. Ax. 1, p. 32

1. If $\angle A$ of a triangle equals $75°$ and $\angle B$ equals $25°$, how large is $\angle C$?
2. How large is each angle of an equiangular triangle?
3. How large is each angle of an equilateral triangle?
4. Prove that the sum of the angles of any quadrilateral that lies in a plane is two straight angles.
5. One of the base angles of an isosceles triangle equals $50°$. How large is each of the other angles of the triangle?
6. Do Example 5 when the vertex angle equals $50°$.
7. Given $\angle A$ and $\angle B$ of a $\triangle ABC$. Construct the third angle of the triangle without measuring the angles.

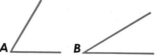

105. **Cor. 1.** *Only one angle of a triangle can be a right angle or an obtuse angle.*

106. **Cor. 2.** *Only one perpendicular can be drawn to a line from a point that is not on the line.*

104. *The sum of the angles of a triangle is one straight angle.*

Hypothesis. $\triangle ABC$ is any triangle.

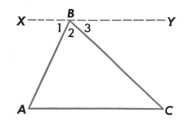

Conclusion.

$\angle A + \angle ABC + \angle C = 1$ st. $\angle$

Plan. Find angles that are equal to $\angle A$, $\angle ABC$, and $\angle C$, whose sum is one st. $\angle$.

Proof.

Statements	Authorities
1. Through B, construct $XY \parallel AC$.	1. §95
2. Then $\angle A = \angle 1$	2. Why?
3. $\angle C = \angle ?$	3. Why?
4. $\angle ABC = \angle 2$	4. Why?
5. $\therefore$ $\angle A + \angle ABC + \angle C = \angle 1 + \angle 2 + \angle 3$	5. Ax. 3, p. 32
6. $\angle 1 + \angle 2 + \angle 3 = \angle XBY$	6. Ax. 7, p. 32
7. $\angle XBY = 1$ st. $\angle$	7. Def.
8. $\therefore$ $\angle 1 + \angle 2 + \angle 3 = 1$ st. $\angle$	8. Ax. 2, p. 32
9. $\therefore$ $\angle A + \angle ABC + \angle C = 1$ st. $\angle$	9. Ax. 1, p. 32

1. If $\angle A$ of a triangle equals $75°$ and $\angle B$ equals $25°$, how large is $\angle C$?

2. How large is each angle of an equiangular triangle?

3. How large is each angle of an equilateral triangle?

4. Prove that the sum of the angles of any quadrilateral that lies in a plane is two straight angles.

5. One of the base angles of an isosceles triangle equals $50°$. How large is each of the other angles of the triangle?

6. Do Example 5 when the vertex angle equals $50°$.

7. Given $\angle A$ and $\angle B$ of a $\triangle ABC$. Construct the third angle of the triangle without measuring the angles.

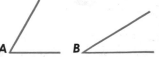

105. **Cor. 1.** *Only one angle of a triangle can be a right angle or an obtuse angle.*

106. **Cor. 2.** *Only one perpendicular can be drawn to a line from a point that is not on the line.*

THEOREMS BASED ON PARALLELS

The theorems about parallel lines in Chapter 3 were based on a fundamental postulate, stated in §84. The equivalent of this postulate was assumed by Euclid, who about 300 B.C. assembled the knowledge of geometry of that time in books that have been the forerunners of all subsequent books on the subject. Euclid's development of geometry is called *Euclidean geometry*.

In later years, other mathematicians assumed different postulates about parallels and, as a consequence, obtained some different theorems. Their developments of geometry are called *non-Euclidean Geometry*.

The first theorem of Chapter 4 and the ones based on it are true in Euclidean Geometry but not in non-Euclidean Geometry.

In this chapter, you will study this important theorem, some consequences of it, and some other theorems based on parallel lines. Among these consequences are two more theorems for determining congruence of triangles.

Parallel lines and parallel planes are evident in these pictures—the interior of the San Gabriel High School in California, a home in Rhode Island, and a nest of modern tables.

TOP: ROBERT C. CLEVELAND, LOS ANGELES CENTER: DAVE LAWLOR, BOSTON BOTTOM: DUNBAR FURNITURE COMPANY

107. (*a*) A **right triangle** is a triangle in which one angle is a right angle. The **hypotenuse** of the triangle is the side opposite the right angle; the **legs** are the two sides that form the right angle.

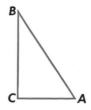

(*b*) An **isosceles right triangle** is a right triangle whose legs are equal.

108. Cor. 3. *The acute angles of a right triangle are complementary.*

Suggestion. What is the sum of the acute angles?

109. Cor. 4. *An exterior angle of a triangle equals the sum of the two nonadjacent interior angles.*

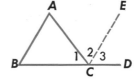

Prove. ∠*DCA* = ∠*A* + ∠*B*.
Plan. Draw *CE* ∥ *BA*.

110. Cor. 5. *If two angles of one triangle are equal respectively to two angles of another triangle, then the third angles are equal.*

111. Cor. 6. *If two triangles have a side, the opposite angle, and another angle of the one equal respectively to a side, the opposite angle, and another angle of the other, the triangles are congruent.* (The Fourth Congruence Theorem, s.a.a. = s.a.a.)

Hyp.   In △*MNO* and △*PQR*,
MN = *PQ*, ∠*O* = ∠*R*,
∠*N* = ∠*Q*

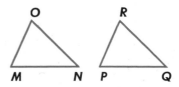

Con.   △*MNO* ≅ △*PQR*

Suggestion. Prove ∠*M* = *P*. Then prove △*MNO* ≅ △ *PQR*.

1. State each of the fundamental congruence theorems.

2. If △*ABC* and △*XYZ* have ∠*A* = ∠*X*, ∠*B* = ∠*Y*, and ∠*C* = ∠*Z*:
   (*a*) Must △*ABC* be congruent to △*XYZ*?
   (*b*) May △*ABC* be congruent to △*XYZ*? If it is, what other information must be true?

Note. Ex. 44 through Ex. 60, pp. 391 and 392, can be done now.

1. How many degrees are there in each angle of a triangle, if the second angle is twice the first, and the third is $\frac{3}{2}$ of the first?

2. How large is each angle of an isosceles right triangle?

3. Represent the second acute angle of a right triangle if the first acute angle contains $x°$.

4. (a) If $\angle 1$ of $\triangle ABC$ below equals $100°$ and $\angle ACB = 60°$, how large is each of the other interior angles of the triangle?

   (b) How large is the exterior angle at each of the other two vertices?

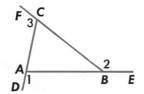
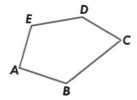

5. What is the sum of the interior angles of the above *pentagon?*

Suggestion. Draw all the diagonals from vertex A.

6. (a) Draw any triangle. Extend the sides to form an exterior angle at each vertex. What is the sum of the exterior angles?

   (b) Repeat part (a) with a quadrilateral and with a pentagon.

   (c) What conclusion is suggested by the three results?

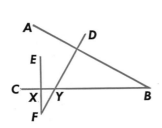
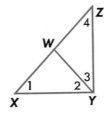
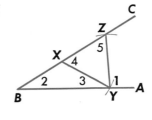

7. If the sides of $\angle DFE$ are perpendicular respectively to the corresponding sides of $\angle CBA$, prove that $\angle F = \angle B$.

8. If the median YW of a $\triangle XYZ$ equals half the side to which it is drawn, how large is $\angle XYZ?$

9. From any point X on side BC of $\angle ABC$, locate Y on AB so that $XY = XB$, and locate Z on BC so that $YZ = YX$. Prove that $\angle AYZ = 3\angle B$.

10. If GBE intersects two parallels AC and DF at B and E so that $\angle FEB = 70°$, and $GH \perp AC$, how large is each angle of $\triangle GBH?$

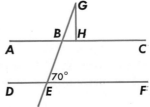

112. *If two right triangles have the hypotenuse and a leg of one equal respectively to the hypotenuse and a leg of the other, the triangles are congruent.*

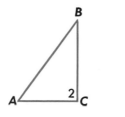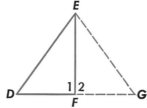

Hypothesis.   In $\triangle ABC$ and $\triangle DEF$,
$\angle C$ and $\angle DFE$ are rt. $\angle$,
$AB = DE$, $BC = EF$.

Conclusion. $\triangle ABC \cong \triangle DEF$

Plan.   Try to prove $\angle A = \angle D$; then use §111.

Proof.

Statements	Authorities
1. Place $\triangle ABC$ so that BC coincides with its equal EF, B on E, C on F, and A falls at G on DF extended through F.	1. Why possible?
2. $\angle 2 = $ rt. $\angle$, $\angle 1 = $ rt. $\angle$	2. Hypothesis.
3. $\therefore$ $\angle DFG$ is a st. $\angle$.	3. Why?
4. $\therefore$ DFG is a straight line.	4. Post. 18, p. 35
5. $\therefore$ $EDFG$ is a triangle.	5. §47, p. 51
6. EG is line AB.	6. Step 1.
7. $AB = DE$	7. Hypothesis.
8. $\therefore$ $EG = DE$	8. Ax. 2, p. 32
9. $\therefore$ $\angle G$ or $\angle A = \angle D$	9. §60, p. 64
10. In $\triangle ABC$ and $\triangle DEF$, $AB = DE$, $\angle 2 = \angle 1$, $\angle A = \angle D$	10. Hypothesis. Step 9.
11. $\therefore$ $\triangle ABC \cong \triangle DEF$	11. Why?

1. Two right triangles are congruent if a leg and an acute angle of one equal a leg and the corresponding angle of the other.
2. Two right triangles are congruent if the hypotenuse and an acute angle of one equal the corresponding parts of the other.

113. (a) *Any point in the perpendicular-bisector of a segment is equidistant from the ends of the segment.*

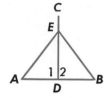

Hyp. $CD \perp AB$, $AD = DB$
             E is any pt. in CD.

Con. $EA = EB$

(b) *Any point that is equidistant from the ends of a segment lies in the perpendicular-bisector of the segment.*

Hyp. $PR = PS$

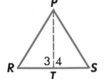

Con. P lies in the perpendicular-bisector of RS in plane PRS.

Plan. Let T bisect RS. Prove $PT \perp RS$.

114. (a) *Any point in the bisector of an angle is equidistant from the sides of the angle.*

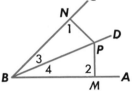

Hyp. BD bisects $\angle ABC$.
             P is in BD.
         $PM \perp AB$, $PN \perp BC$

Con. $PM = PN$

(b) *Any point equidistant from the sides of an angle lies in the bisector of the angle, if the point and angle are coplanar.*

Hyp. P lies inside $\angle XYZ$.
         $PR \perp YZ$, $PS \perp YX$
             $PR = PS$

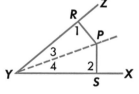

Con. P lies in the bisector of $\angle XYZ$.

Plan. Draw YP. Prove $\angle 3 = \angle 4$, using §112, p. 111.

1. The exterior angle of $\triangle ABC$ at vertex B is twice the nonadjacent interior angle at C. If the nonadjacent interior angle at A equals 80°, how large are angle C and the exterior angle at B?

2. (a) Let $\angle T$ of $\triangle RST$ equal 90° and ST equal half of RS. Extend ST to W so that TW equals ST. Draw RW.
   (b) What kind of triangle does $\triangle RSW$ appear to be?
   (c) Prove your tentative conclusion.

Note. Ex. 61 through Ex. 68, p. 392, can be done now.

115. Adopt the following general plan.

(1) Make certain that you understand each geometrical term in the theorem. If necessary, see the Index.

(2) Draw the figure as accurately as possible, making it general. For example, if it is to be *a* triangle, do not draw a right triangle, isosceles triangle, or equilateral triangle.

(3) Decide upon the hypothesis and conclusion.
   (*a*) If the theorem is stated in the *if-then* form, the hypothesis and conclusion are evident at once.
   (*b*) If the theorem is not in the *if-then* form, the subject of the sentence with its modifiers is the hypothesis, and the predicate is the conclusion.
   Thus: In the theorem
      The bisectors of the base angles of an isosceles triangle are equal
the hypothesis names an isosceles triangle and the bisectors of its base angles; the conclusion is the assertion that the bisectors (already named) are equal.
   (*c*) You will be guided to the correct figure, hypothesis, and conclusion if you draw a figure that contains all the special points and lines named in the theorem and if you describe at once, in the hypothesis, every point placed in a special position and every line drawn in special manner.
   Thus: For the theorem above, you should first draw an isosceles triangle. At once, name it in the hypothesis.
   Then you should bisect one base angle. At once, describe the bisector in the hypothesis; similarly, the second bisector.
   You are then prepared to write, as conclusion, the statement that the bisectors are equal.

(4) Prepare a plan for the proof.
   (*a*) Ask "What does the conclusion mean?" and next, "How can I prove it?"
   (*b*) After you have a plan, ask "What do I know about the figure that will help me?"
   The statements in the hypothesis and any statements about the figure derived from those in the hypothesis are ones on which you must depend for your proof.

ARMSTRONG CORK CO.

ISOSCELES AND EQUILATERAL TRIANGLES

116. *If two angles of a triangle are equal, the sides opposite them are equal and the triangle is isosceles.*

Hypothesis. In $\triangle ABC$, $\angle A = \angle B$.

Conclusion. $AC = BC$,
  or $\triangle ABC$ is isosceles.

Plan. Prove AC and BC corresponding sides of congruent triangles. A possible pair of such triangles is obtained if we bisect angle ACB.

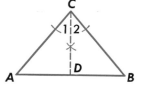

Proof.

	Statements	Authorities
1.	Construct CD bisecting $\angle ACB$ and meeting AB at D.	1. §73, p. 74
2.	$\triangle ACD \cong \triangle BCD$	2. Prove this.
3.	$\therefore \quad AC = ?$	3. Why?
4.	$\therefore \quad \triangle ABC$ is isosceles.	4. Why?

1. Prove an equiangular triangle is also equilateral.

Read §102, p. 99, again. If there are two or more statements in either or in both the hypothesis and conclusion of a theorem, then there are several converses of that theorem. The truth of each must be examined.

Example. If the vertex angle of an isosceles triangle is bisected, the bisector bisects and is perpendicular to the base.

Hyp. In $\triangle ACD$,
  (1) $AC = AD$
  (2) AB bisects $\angle CAD$.

Con. (3) $AB \perp CD$
  (4) $BC = BD$

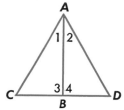

A converse is made by interchanging one (or more) statements of the hypothesis with statements of the conclusion. Preferably change one at a time. Thus:

Converse #1. **Hyp.** In $\triangle ACD$,   **Con.** (2) AB bisects
  (1) $AC = AD$ $\angle CAD$.
  (3) $AB \perp CD$ (4) $BC = BD$

Converse #2. **Hyp.** In $\triangle ACD$,   **Con.** (1) $AC = AD$
  (2) AB bisects   (4) $BC = BD$
      $\angle CAD$.
  (3) $AB \perp CD$

Converse #3. **Hyp.** In $\triangle ACD$,   **Con.** (2) AB bisects
  (1) $AC = AD$ $\angle CAD$.
  (4) $BC = BD$ (3) $AB \perp CD$

Converse #4. **Hyp.** In $\triangle ACD$,   **Con.** (1) $AC = AD$
  (2) AB bisects   (3) $AB \perp CD$
      $\angle CAD$.
  (4) $BC = BD$

Converse #5. **Hyp.** In $\triangle ACD$,   **Con.** (1) $AC = AD$
  (3) $AB \perp CD$ (2) AB bisects
  (4) $BC = BD$ $\angle CAD$.

1. (*a*) Try to prove each of these theorems.
  (*b*) State in *if-then* form, the converses you are able to prove.

2. If perpendiculars are drawn to the equal sides of an isosceles triangle from the opposite vertices of the triangle, these perpendiculars are equal. Write all possible converses of this statement.

117. *If one acute angle of a right triangle contains 30°, the side opposite it equals half the hypotenuse.*

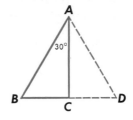

Hyp.   In $\triangle ABC$, $\angle BCA = 90°$,
$\qquad \angle BAC = 30°$.

Con. $BC = \frac{1}{2} BA$

Plan.   Extend BC to D, making
$CD = BC$.
Prove $\triangle BDA$ is equilateral.
Then BC must equal $\frac{1}{2} BA$.

1. What kind of triangle is $\triangle RST$ if $\angle R = 50°$ and $\angle S = 80°$?
2. One angle of an isosceles triangle equals 60°. Prove that the triangle is equilateral.
3. One acute angle of a right triangle measures 45°. What kind of right triangle is it?
4. In $\triangle ABC$, if $AB = AC$ and $DE \parallel BC$, then $AD = AE$.
5. (a) Write two converses of Ex. 4.
   (b) Try to prove each of them.
6. The bisectors of the base angles of an isosceles triangle form with the base another isosceles triangle. Prove this.
7. If perpendiculars are drawn from the midpoint of the base of an isosceles triangle to the equal sides of the triangle, they are equal. Prove this.
8. Write three converses of Ex. 7 and try to prove them.

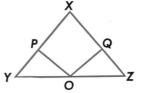

9. Prove that the three altitudes of an equilateral triangle are equal.
10. (a) If the altitudes drawn to two sides of a triangle from the ends of the third side are equal, then the triangle must be isosceles.
    (b) Of what previous exercise is part (a) a converse?
11. Prove that the bisector of the vertex angle of an isosceles triangle bisects the base and is perpendicular to it.
12. Prove that an altitude of an equilateral triangle is also a median, an angle-bisector, and the perpendicular-bisector of a side.
13. (a) If the hypotenuse of a right triangle is double one of the legs of the triangle, prove that the acute angles of the triangle measure 30° and 60° respectively.
    (b) Of what theorem is part (a) a converse?

In Exercises 1 through 4:

(a) *Prove the theorem whose hypothesis and conclusion are given.*

(b) *Write the hypothesis and conclusion for each possible converse of the original theorem.*

(c) *Try to prove each converse. If the converse is true, state it in if-then form.*

1. Hyp.   (1) $AB = AC$
         (2) $AD \parallel BC$

   Con.   (3) $\angle 1 = \angle 2$

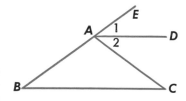

2. If AB and AC, equal sides of a $\triangle ABC$, are extended through B and C, respectively, the bisectors of the exterior angles form with the base an isosceles triangle.

3. Hyp.   (1) $AB = AC$, (2) $AS = SC$,
         (3) $AR = RB$

   Con.   (4) $BS = RC$

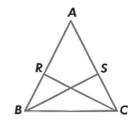

4. Hyp.   (1) $AB = AC$, (2) BS bisects $\angle CBA$,
         (3) RC bisects $\angle BCA$.

   Con.   (4) $BS = RC$

118. There may be more than one converse also for nonmathematical statements and, as above, one or more of these converses may or may not be true. For example:

   If a man breaks the law and is caught, he is arrested.

   Converse #1. If a man breaks the law and is arrested, he has been caught.

   Converse #2. If a man has been caught and is arrested, he has broken the law. This may not be true. He may be only suspected of having broken the law.

State all possible converses for Exercises 5, 6, and 7.

5. If soil is fertile, is properly prepared, and is properly seeded, and if the weather is favorable, there will be a good growth from the seeds planted.

6. If an automobile engine is in good mechanical condition, if it has a supply of gasoline, if its ignition system is in working order, then it will run when the starter is pressed.

7. If a camera is in fine condition, if a film is properly installed, and if the shutter is released, a good picture will result.

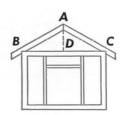

1. In the gable in the front of a garage, the two boards whose upper edges are AB and AC are of equal length and meet at a point A on a line AD that is perpendicular to BC.
   If $\angle ACD = 30°$, how large is:
   (a) $\angle ABD?$ (b) $\angle CAD?$ (c) $\angle BAD?$

2. (a) The first figure below shows how a draftsman draws a line through C parallel to AB. Why is his method correct?
   (b) The second figure below shows how a draftsman draws several parallel lines by use of his T-square. Why are the lines parallel?

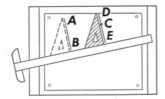

3. In the figure for Ex. 1, AD is called the *rise* of the roof, BD the *run*, and AB a *rafter*.
   How does the length of rafter from A to B compare with the rise AD when $\angle ABD = 30°$?

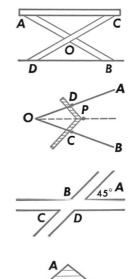

4. An ironing board is supported by legs as shown at the right. If $AO = OB$ and $DO = OC$, prove that AC must be parallel to DB, the floor line.

5. Books for carpenters tell how to bisect an angle by means of the "square" alone.
   (a) Take $OD = OC$. Place the square so that $DP = CP$. Then OP bisects $\angle BOA$. Prove it.
   (b) Is it necessary that $\angle DPC$ be a rt. $\angle$?

6. Two streets cross so that the angle formed at one corner is 45°. Since the opposite sides of each street are parallel, what angles are formed at the other corners?

7. Boards with parallel edges are to be fitted into a gable. A carpenter sets his *bevel gauge* to equal $\angle CBA$. Why can he use this angle to mark all the ends of boards that fit against AB and against AC?

Note. Ex. 69 through Ex. 78, pp. 392 and 393, can be done now.

SMITH, POWELL, MORGUDGE

PARALLELOGRAMS

119. (*a*) A **polygon** is a *closed, broken line* lying in a plane, as
polygon *ABCDE*, which has five *sides*.

A, B, C, D, and E are the **vertices** of
the polygon. *AB, BC, CD, DE, EA* are the
sides. Angles *A, B, C, D,* and *E* are the
angles. *AC* is a **diagonal**.

A **diagonal** of a polygon is the segment that joins two nonconsecutive vertices of the polygon.

A polygon is a *broken line* because it consists of consecutive connected segments of straight lines. It is a *simple
closed* line because you can travel from any point of it back
to that same point by moving along it without retracing any
part of the polygon, and without crossing any of its sides.

(*b*) **Post 24.** *A polygon like ABCDE encloses a part of the plane,*
called the **interior of the polygon.**

(*c*) A polygon is **equilateral** if all its sides are equal; it is **equiangular** if all its angles are equal.

120. A **quadrilateral** is a polygon that has four sides.

121. A **parallelogram** ($\square$) is a quadrilateral whose opposite sides are parallel. (Read §36 again.) This is sufficient as definition even though we shall prove and must remember other facts about a parallelogram.

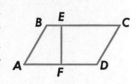

Any side of a parallelogram may be used as its **base,** as *A D.* The perpendicular to it from any point of the opposite side is the **altitude** to that base, as *EF.*

122. (a) *A diagonal of a parallelogram separates it into two congruent triangles.*

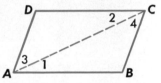

Hyp.   *ABCD* is a parallelogram, or
       A B ∥ *DC* and *BC* ∥ *A D.*

Con.   △*ABC* ≅ △ *ADC*
       (Proof left to you.)

(b) *Opposite sides of a parallelogram are equal.*

(c) *Opposite angles of a parallelogram are equal.*

(d) *Two consecutive angles of a parallelogram are supplementary.*

Suggestion. Prove ∠*BAD* the supplement of ∠*ADC.* (§99, p. 96)

123. *Segments of parallels between parallels are equal.*

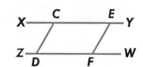

Hyp.   *XY* ∥ *ZW, CD* ∥ *EF*

Con.   *DC* = *EF*
       (Proof left to you.)

1. Guided by the adjoining figure construct a $\square$*ABCD* having *AB* 3 in. long, *AD* 2 in. long, and ∠*A* = 45°.
   Why is ∠1 constructed as indicated?
   Why is ∠2 constructed as indicated?
   Why is *ABCD* then a parallelogram?

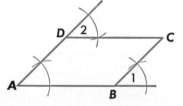

2. (*a*) In the figure for Ex. 1, from *X* on *DC* construct *XY* ⊥ *AB.*
   (*b*) Prove *XY* ⊥ *DC.*

3. In Ex. 1, how large is each of the other angles of $\square$*ABCD?*

124. If a segment between two parallel lines is perpendicular to one of them, it is perpendicular to the other also. (§100, p. 97) We define the **distance between two parallel lines** as the segment of a line between them that is perpendicular to them and cutting them.

125. *Two parallel lines are everywhere equidistant.*

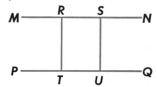

Thus: If $MN \parallel PQ$,
$RT \perp PQ$, $SU \perp PQ$,
then $RT = SU$.
(Proof left to the pupil.)

126. *The diagonals of a parallelogram bisect each other.*

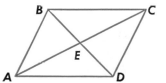

Hyp. $ABCD$ is a parallelogram. Diagonals AC and BD intersect at E.
Con. $AE = EC, BE = ED$
(Plan and proof left to the pupil.)

127. The **center of a parallelogram** is the point of intersection of the diagonals.

1. Prove that the sum of the angles of any parallelogram equals two straight angles, or 360°.

2. If one angle of a parallelogram is a right angle, then each of the angles must be a right angle.

3. If two adjacent sides of a parallelogram are equal, then all four sides must be equal.

4. From a point D in the base AB of an isosceles $\triangle ABC$, $DE \parallel BC$ and $DF \parallel AC$.
   (a) Prove that $DECF$ is a $\square$.
   (b) Prove that the perimeter of $\square DECF$ equals $CA + CB$.

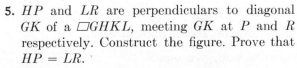

5. HP and LR are perpendiculars to diagonal GK of a $\square GHKL$, meeting GK at P and R respectively. Construct the figure. Prove that $HP = LR$.

6. If a line, XY, drawn through the center of a parallelogram, is terminated by two opposite sides, the line is bisected by the center of the parallelogram.

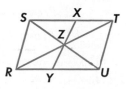

128. *If two sides of a quadrilateral are equal and parallel, the quadrilateral is a parallelogram.*

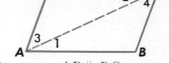

Hyp.   In $ADCB$,
          $BC \parallel AD$, $BC = AD$.

Con. $ADCB$ is a $\square$.

Analysis. 1. What is a $\square$?
          2. Since $BC \parallel AD$, try to prove $AB \parallel DC$.

Plan. Draw AC. Prove $\angle 1 = \angle 2$ by proving $\triangle ABC \cong \triangle ADC$.

(Proof left to the pupil.)

129. *If the opposite sides of a quadrilateral are equal, the quadrilateral is a parallelogram.*

Use the figure for §128 above.

Hyp. In $ADCB$, $AB = DC$, $BC = AD$.

Con. $ADCB$ is a $\square$.

Analysis. $ADCB$ is a $\square$ if $AB \parallel DC$ and $BC \parallel AD$.

Plan. Draw AC. To prove $AB \parallel DC$, prove $\angle 1 = \angle 2$ by proving $\triangle ABC \cong \triangle ADC$. Similarly prove $BC \parallel AD$.

(Proof left to the pupil.)

130. *If the diagonals of a quadrilateral bisect each other, the quadrilateral is a parallelogram.*

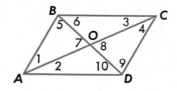

Hyp. In $ADCB$, $AO = OC$,
          $BO = OD$.

Con. $ADCB$ is a $\square$.

(Analysis, plan, and proof are left to the pupil.)

131. **Fundamental Plan 3.** *To prove a quadrilateral is a parallelogram:*

(a) *Prove its opposite sides are parallel.*

(b) *Prove one pair of sides equal and parallel.*

(c) *Prove its opposite sides are equal.*

(d) *Prove its diagonals bisect each other.*

1. §129 is a converse of what theorem?
2. §130 is a converse of what theorem?

132. *If a line bisects one side of a triangle and is parallel to a second side, it bisects the third side.*

Hyp. D is mid-point of side AB of $\triangle ABC$.

$$DE \parallel BC$$

Con. $AE = EC$

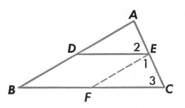

Plan. Draw $EF \parallel AB$. Prove $\triangle EFC \cong \triangle ADE$.

1. The line joining the mid-points of two opposite sides of a parallelogram is parallel to the other two sides of the parallelogram.
   Construct the figure. Prove the theorem.

2. Copy the figure for Exercise 1. Draw RX and SZ and prove that RX is equal and parallel to SZ.

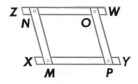

Suggestion. See Fundamental Plan 3.

3. In the adjoining figure *parallel rulers* are pictured. They are made so that $MN = PO$, and $NO = MP$. The figure is not rigid, so ZW can be brought close to XY or moved away from XY.
   Why is ZW always parallel to XY?

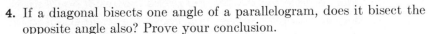

Note. M, N, O, P are the points at which the rulers are pivoted.

4. If a diagonal bisects one angle of a parallelogram, does it bisect the opposite angle also? Prove your conclusion.

5. Prove that the segments that join in order the mid-points of the sides of a parallelogram form another parallelogram.

6. Draw the diagonals of a large parallelogram. Bisect each of the halves of the diagonals. Join the bisection points in order around the figure. What kind of quadrilateral is formed? Why?

7. Draw a large $\square XYZW$, with diagonal XZ. Place R on XZ near X and S on XZ so that $SZ = XR$.
   Draw YR, YS, WR, and WS.
   (a) What kind of quadrilateral does $YRWS$ appear to be?
   (b) Try to prove the conclusion you reached in part (a).

8. Prove that the line joining the mid-points of two opposite sides of a parallelogram bisects each diagonal of the parallelogram.

133. *The segment that joins the mid-points of two sides of a tri-angle is parallel to the third side and equals half of it.*

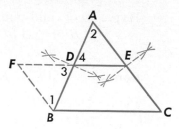

Hyp.   In $\triangle ABC$,
    $AD = DB,\ AE = EC.$
Con. $DE \parallel BC,\ DE = \frac{1}{2}BC$

Plan. Extend ED to F, making $EF = 2DE$. Prove $FE = BC$ and $FE \parallel BC$ by proving $BCEF$ is a $\square$.

Proof.

Statements	Authorities
1. Extend ED. Make $DF = ED$. Draw BF.	1. Why possible?
2. $\triangle FBD \cong \triangle DEA$	2. Give full proof.
3. $\therefore\ \ \angle 1 = \angle 2$	3. Why?
4. $\therefore\ \ BF \parallel AC$ or $BF \parallel EC$	4. Why?
5. $BF = AE$	5. Why?
6. $\therefore\ \ BF = EC$	6. Why?
7. $\therefore\ \ BCEF$ is a $\square$.	7. §128, p. 122
8. $\therefore\ \ FE$ or $DE \parallel BC$	8. Why?
9. $FE = BC$	9. Why?
10. $\therefore\ \ DE = \frac{1}{2}BC$	10. Why?

134. Fundamental Plan 4. *To prove that one segment is double another, double the shorter and prove the result equal to the longer, or halve the longer and prove the result equal to the shorter.*

The first of these plans is followed in the proof of §133.

135. *The mid-point of the hypotenuse of a right triangle is equi-distant from the vertices of the triangle.*

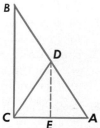

Hyp.   In $\triangle ACB$,
    $\angle C = 90°,\ AD = DB.$

Con. $DA = DB = DC$

Plan.   Draw $DE \parallel BC$. Prove $CE = EA$ (§132). Prove $DC = DA$. Prove $DB = DC$.

136. A **rectangle** is a parallelogram that has one right angle. It will be proved and it is important to remember that all the angles of a rectangle are right angles.

1. Are the opposite sides of a rectangle equal? Why?
2. Are the opposite angles of a rectangle equal? Why?
3. Do the diagonals of a rectangle bisect each other? Why?
4. Prove that each angle of a rectangle is a right angle.
5. Prove that the diagonals of a rectangle are equal.
6. Are the diagonals of every parallelogram equal?
7. Prove that a quadrilateral whose angles are all right angles is a rectangle.
8. (*a*) If the diagonals of a parallelogram are equal, then the parallelogram must be a rectangle.

   Plan. Prove $\angle BAD + \angle ADC = 1$ st. $\angle$
   and that $\angle BAD = \angle ADC$.

   (*b*) Of what theorem is part (*a*) the converse?

125

137. A **square** is a rectangle having two adjacent sides equal. It will be proved and it is important to remember that all the sides of a square are equal and all the angles are right angles.

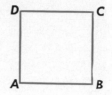

1. (*a*) Prove that the opposite sides of a square are equal.
   (*b*) Prove that all the sides of a square are equal.

2. Why are all the angles of a square right angles?

3. Prove that the diagonals of a square are perpendicular to and bisect each other.

4. Prove that each diagonal of a square bisects the angles through which it is drawn.

5. A quadrilateral is a square if its diagonals are equal and are perpendicular-bisectors of each other.

6. Construct a square whose diagonals are 2 in. long.

138. A **rhombus** is a parallelogram with oblique angles, that has two adjacent sides equal. It will be proved and it is important to remember that all the sides of a rhombus are equal.

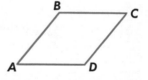

7. (*a*) Prove that the opposite sides of a rhombus are equal.
   (*b*) Prove that all the sides of a rhombus are equal.

8. Prove that the diagonals of a rhombus are perpendicular to and bisect each other.

9. Prove that a diagonal of a rhombus bisects the angles through which it is drawn.

10. Prove that a quadrilateral is a rhombus or a square if its diagonals are perpendicular to and bisect each other according as its diagonals are unequal or equal.

11. Construct a rhombus having diagonals that are 2 in. and 3 in. long.

12. If the obtuse angles of a rhombus contain 120°:
    (*a*) How large are the acute angles of the rhombus?
    (*b*) How large are the acute angles of the triangle that is formed when the diagonal of the rhombus is drawn through its acute angles?

13. Construct a rhombus whose sides are 3 in. long, and whose acute angles measure 60°.

139. (*a*) A **trapezoid** is a quadrilateral that has one and only one pair of parallel sides, as *ABCD* with *AB* ∥ *DC*. The other two sides are called its **nonparallel sides,** as *AD* and *CB*.

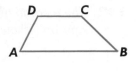

The parallel sides are the **bases.** The distance between the bases is the **altitude.**

(*b*) An **isosceles trapezoid** is a trapezoid whose nonparallel sides are equal.

140. *The base angles of an isosceles trapezoid are equal.*

> **Hyp.**   In *EFGH*, *HG* ∥ *EF*,
>   *EH* = *FG*.
>
> **Con.**   ∠*E* = ∠*F*

Plan. Draw *HX* ∥ *GF*. Prove *HX* = *GF*, *HX* = *HE*, ∠*E* and ∠*F* both equal ∠1.

1. (*a*) In the figure for §139, prove ∠*A* and ∠*D* are supplementary.
  (*b*) State the conclusion of part (*a*) as a theorem.

2. In the figure for §140, prove ∠*EHG* = ∠*FGH*.

Suggestion. Use the conclusions of §140 and Ex. 1.

3. Prove that the opposite angles of an isosceles trapezoid are supplementary.

4. Prove that the diagonals of an isosceles trapezoid are equal.

5. If a line bisects one of the nonparallel sides of a trapezoid and is parallel to the bases, it bisects the other nonparallel side.

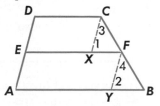

Suggestions. In *ABCD*, *AB* ∥ *DC*,
          DE = *EA*, *EF* ∥ *AB*.
          Prove *CF* = *FB*.

> **Plan.**   Draw   *CX* ∥ *DA*,   *FY* ∥ *DA*.
>   Prove   *CX* = *FY*, ∠3 = ∠4,
>   ∠1 = ∠2, △*YBF* ≅ △*XFC*.

141. The **median** of a trapezoid is the segment that joins the mid-points of the nonparallel sides.

6. Construct an isosceles trapezoid whose lower base measures 3 in., its lower base angles equal 60°, and whose nonparallel sides measure 2 in.

142. *The median of a trapezoid is parallel to the bases and equals one half their sum.*

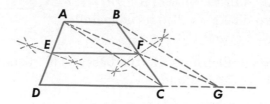

Hypothesis. $DCBA$ is a trapezoid.
E is the mid-point of AD, and F of BC.

Conclusion. $EF \parallel AB$ and DC
$EF = \frac{1}{2}(AB + DC)$

Plan. Construct a segment equal to $AB + DC$, and prove EF parallel to it and equal to one half of it.

Proof.

Statements	Authorities
1. Extend DC to G, making $CG = AB$. Draw AC, BG, AG.	1. Why possible?
2. $CGBA$ is a $\square$.	2. Why?
3. $\therefore$ AG passes through F and $AF = FG$.	3. §126
4. $AE = ED$	4. Why?
5. $\therefore$ $EF \parallel DG$ or $EF \parallel DC$	5. §133
6. $\therefore$ $EF \parallel AB$	6. Why?
7. Also $EF = \frac{1}{2}DG$	7. Why?
8. $\therefore$ $EF = \frac{1}{2}(AB + DC)$	8. Ax. 2, p 32

1. In trapezoid $ABCD$ above, if base AB is 12 in. and DC is 18 in., how long is the median?

2. $ABCD$ is a trapezoid whose parallel sides AD and BC are perpendicular to CD. If E is the mid-point of AB, prove $EC = ED$.

Suggestion. Draw EF parallel to AD.

3. Prove that the median of a trapezoid bisects each of the diagonals of the trapezoid.

143. *If three or more parallels intercept equal segments on one transversal, they intercept equal segments on any transversal.*

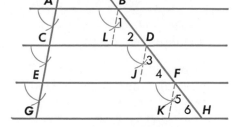

Hyp. On AG,
$$AC = CE = EG;$$
$$AB \parallel CD \parallel EF \parallel GH;$$
and the $\parallel$s cut BH in points B, D, F, and H.

Con. $BD = DF = FH$

Plan. Prove BD, DF, and FH corresponding sides of congruent triangles.

Proof.

Statements	Authorities
1. Construct BL, DJ, $FK \parallel AG$	1. §95, p. 95
2. $\therefore \quad BL \parallel DJ \parallel FK$	2. Why?
3. $\therefore \quad \angle 1 = \angle 3 = \angle 5$	3. Why?
4. $BL = AC$, $DJ = CE$, $FK = ?$	4. Why?
5. But $AC = ? = ?$	5. Why?
6. $\therefore \quad BL = ? = ?$	6. Why?

(Now prove $\triangle$ BDL, DFJ, and FHK are congruent and $BD = DF = FH$.)

144. *A segment can be divided into any number of equal segments.*

Note. A segment will be divided into five parts.

Given. Segment AB.

Required. To divide AB into five equal segments.

Construction.

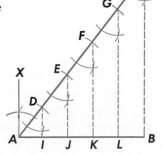

1. Draw AC to form acute $\angle BAC$. On AC locate D, E, F, G, and H so that $AD = DE = EF = FG = GH$.

2. Draw HB. Construct GL, FK, EJ, DI, and $XA \parallel HB$, cutting AB at L, K, J, and I.

Statement. $AI = IJ = JK = KL = LB$ (Why?)

145. *The medians of a triangle intersect at a point that is two thirds the distance from each vertex to the mid-point of the opposite side.*

Hyp. AD, BE, and CF are the medians of $\triangle ABC$.

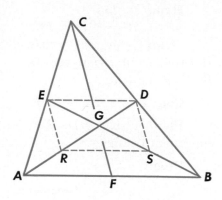

Con. AD, BE, and CF meet at a point G such that $AG = \frac{2}{3}AD$, $BG = \frac{2}{3}BE$, $CG = \frac{2}{3}CF$.

Plan. Let AD cut BE at point G. Let $AR = RG$, and $BS = SG$. Prove $RG = GD$ and $SG = GE$.

Informal Proof. 1. Draw ER, RS, SD, and ED. (Possible?)

2. In $\triangle ACB$, $ED = \frac{1}{2}AB$, and $ED \parallel AB$.   (Why?)

3. In $\triangle AGB$, $RS = ?$, and $RS \parallel ?$ (Why?)

4. ∴ $ED = RS$, and $ED \parallel RS$ (Why?)

5. ∴ $ERSD$ is a $\square$.   (Why?)

6. ∴ $RG = GD$, and $SG = GE$ (Why?)

7. ∴ $AR = RG = GD$, and $BS = SG = GE$ (Why?)

8. ∴ $AG = \frac{2}{3}AD$, and $BG = \frac{2}{3}BE$ (Why?)

9. Similarly CF would pass through the point on AD that is $\frac{2}{3}$ the distance from A to D, namely point G. ∴ $CG = \frac{2}{3}CF$

146. The **center of gravity** of a triangle or **centroid** of a triangle is the point of intersection of the medians of the triangle.

1. (*a*) Construct an equilateral triangle whose sides equal 3 in.
   (*b*) Construct the medians of the triangle.
   (*c*) Find as accurately as possible the length of each median and also the distance from each vertex to the center of gravity.
   (*d*) Do the results in part (*c*) verify the conclusions of §145?
2. Repeat all the parts of Exercise 1 when the sides of the triangle measure 2 inches, 3 inches, and 4 inches, respectively.

TEST A

1. The segments joining in order the mid-points of the sides of a triangle divide the triangle into four congruent triangles.

2. The segment that joins the mid-points of two sides of a triangle bisects any segment drawn to the third side from the opposite vertex.

3. The segments drawn from the mid-point of the base of an isosceles triangle to the mid-points of the sides of the triangle form a rhombus or a square with the upper halves of the sides of the triangle.

4. If D is any point in side AC of $\triangle ABC$ and E, F, G, and H are the mid-points of AD, CD, BC, and AB respectively, then $EFGH$ is a parallelogram.

Suggestion. Draw DB.

5. If E, F, G, and H are the mid-points of the sides AB, BC, CD, and AD respectively of quadrilateral $ABCD$, then $EFGH$ is a parallelogram.

6. In quadrilateral $ABCD$, if $\angle A = 50°$, $\angle D = 130°$, and $\angle C = 120°$, how large is $\angle B$ and what kind of lines are AB and CD?

TEST B

1. The perpendiculars to a side of a triangle from the mid-points of the other two sides are equal.

2. The segments joining the mid-points of opposite sides of a quadrilateral bisect each other.

3. A line that is perpendicular to a leg of a right triangle at its mid-point bisects the hypotenuse of the triangle.

4. If X and Y are the mid-points of UT and RS respectively of $\square RSTU$, prove that RX and YT trisect SU.

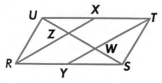

Suggestion. Prove $RX \parallel TY$.

5. If E and G are the mid-points of AB and CD respectively of quadrilateral $ABCD$ (with no parallel sides), and K and L are the mid-points of the diagonals AC and BD respectively, then $EKGL$ is a parallelogram.

6. Point X bisects AB, Y bisects BC, and Z bisects AC of $\triangle ABC$. If $AB = 14$ in., $BC = 16$ in., and $AC = 18$ in., what kind of figure is $XBYZ$, and what is the distance around it?

7. In $\triangle MNO$, $\angle N = 90°$, $\angle O = 60°$, and $NO = 8$ in. How long are MO and ZN if Z bisects MO?

1. If the segment joining the mid-points of the bases of a trapezoid is perpendicular to the bases, the trapezoid is isosceles.

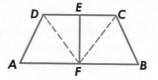

Suggestion.   Prove $FD = FC$,
$$\triangle AFD \cong \triangle BFC.$$

2. The mid-point of a base of an isosceles trapezoid is equidistant from the mid-points of the nonparallel sides.

3. $ABCF$ is a parallelogram with $BC > AB$ and $\angle A < 90°$. BE is drawn to E on AF so that $BE = AB$. CD is drawn to D on AF extended so that $\angle ABE$ equals $\angle FCD$. Prove $ABCD$ is an isosceles trapezoid.

4. Prove that the bisectors of two opposite angles of parallelogram $ABCD$ are parallel.

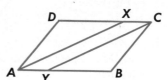

5. The bisectors of two consecutive angles of a parallelogram are perpendicular.

Suggestion. In the figure for Ex. 4, draw the bisector of $\angle ADC$ and prove it perpendicular to AX.

6. On the diagonal BD of square $ABCD$ a segment BE is taken equal to AB, EF is drawn perpendicular to BD, meeting AD at F. Prove that $AF = EF = ED$.

7. If perpendiculars AE, BF, CG, and DH be drawn from the vertices of parallelogram $ABCD$ to any line in its plane not intersecting its surface, prove that $AE + CG = BF + DH$.

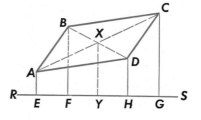

Suggestion. See adjoining figure. Prove that $EACG$ is a trapezoid in which $XY = \frac{1}{2}(AE + CG)$, by using §142. Similarly, study $BF + DH$.

8. $XYZW$ is a square. RS is perpendicular to XZ at O on XZ, meeting YZ at R and WZ at S. Prove that $\triangle RSZ$, ZSO, and ZRO are isosceles right triangles.

9. Prove that the bisectors of the angles of a rectangle that has unequal sides form a square.

10. In isosceles $\triangle ABC$, line AD is perpendicular to base BC at D. Point X is any point on BE which is perpendicular to BC. CX intersects AD, or AD extended, at Y. Prove that Y bisects CX.

Note. Ex. 79 through Ex. 86, pp. 393 and 394, can be done now.

POLYHEDRONS AND PRISMS

SG 33. First read again the definitions in §119. The corresponding figures of solid geometry are surfaces
that consist of parts of planes. The most
familiar is the rectangular solid. It consists
of parts of six planes that intersect in edges.
All of it lies on one side of one of its faces.
It encloses a part of space.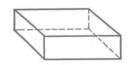

(*a*) In general a **polyhedron** is a (simple) closed surface that
consists of parts of planes (called its **faces**) which intersect
in lines (called its **edges**). It encloses a part of space (called
its **interior**) and lies wholly on one side of any face.

The following drawings represent common polyhedrons.

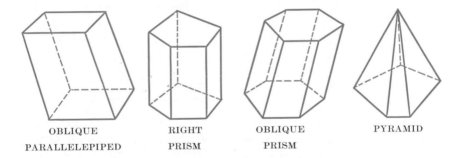

| OBLIQUE | RIGHT | OBLIQUE | PYRAMID |
| PARALLELEPIPED | PRISM | PRISM | |

(*b*) A **prism** is a polyhedron that has two parallel faces, called
its **bases,** and three or more **lateral faces** that intersect in
parallel lines, called its **lateral edges.** Its **altitude** is the
distance between its bases.

(*c*) A **right prism** is a prism whose **lateral edges** are perpendicular to one, and therefore to both bases. (SG 30, p. 105)

(*d*) A prism is **triangular, rectangular,** etc., according as its base
is enclosed by a triangle, rectangle, etc.

(*e*) A **parallelepiped** is a prism whose base is enclosed by a
parallelogram. It may be an oblique or a right parallelepiped.

(*f*) A **rectangular parallelepiped** or **rectangular solid** is a right
parallelepiped whose base is enclosed by a rectangle.

(*Continued on p. 134.*)

(g) A **pyramid** is a polyhedron that has one face, its base, enclosed by a polygon, and three or more lateral faces, enclosed by triangles, that meet at one point, called its **vertex.** The lateral faces intersect in lines, called the **lateral edges.** Its **altitude** is the perpendicular from its vertex to its base.

(h) A **regular pyramid** is a pyramid whose base is enclosed by a polygon that is both equilateral and equiangular, and whose vertex lies in the perpendicular to its base at the **center** of the base.

SG 34. *If two intersecting lines are each parallel to a given plane, their plane is parallel to the given plane.*

Hyp. $AB \parallel$ plane RS, $BC \parallel$ plane RS. AB and BC determine plane MN.

Con. $MN \parallel RS$

Suggestion. Refer to pages 104 and 105 for authorities.

Plan. Assume $BD \perp RS$. Plane ABD intersects RS in DE. Plane CBD intersects RS in DF.

Prove. (1) $BD \perp DE, BD \perp DF$ (2) $DE \parallel BA, DF \parallel BC$
(3) $BD \perp BA, BD \perp BC$ (4) $BD \perp$ plane MN
(5) Plane $MN \parallel$ plane RS.

SG 35. *If two angles in space have their corresponding sides parallel and extending in the same direction from their vertices, the angles are equal.*

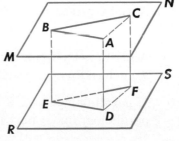

Hyp. $\angle ABC$ and $\angle DEF$, in different planes, have $BA \parallel ED$ and $BC \parallel EF$, extending in the same direction.

Con. $\angle ABC = \angle DEF$

Plan. Take $BA = ED$, and $BC = EF$. Draw $BE, AD, CF, AC,$ and DF.

Prove. (1) $AD \parallel BE, CF \parallel BE, AD \parallel CF$
(2) $\triangle ABC \cong \triangle DEF$ (3) $\angle ABC = \angle DEF$

1. Name one or more objects that have the shape of:
   (a) A right prism. (They have a prismatic shape.)
   (b) A rectangular parallelepiped. (They are generally called rectangular solids.)

2. Why must the lateral edges of a right prism be perpendicular to both bases?

3. Prove that any face of a prism intersects the bases of the prism in parallel lines.

4. What figure encloses each lateral face of a prism?

5. Prove that the lateral edges of a prism are equal.

6. Prove that the lateral faces of a right prism are enclosed by rectangles.

7. Obviously *two polygons are congruent* if the sides and angles of one are equal respectively to the corresponding sides and angles of the other. Prove that the bases of a prism are enclosed by congruent polygons.

8. Prove that opposite faces of a parallelepiped are enclosed by congruent parallelograms.

SG 36. A **section** of a solid by a plane is the intersection of the solid and the plane. It is a *line*. If the solid is a polyhedron, the section is a polygon.

9. Prove that the section of a prism made by a plane that passes through two nonconsecutive lateral edges is a parallelogram.

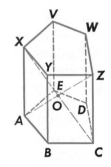

10. Prove that the diagonals *AZ* and *CX* in the prism of Ex. 9 bisect each other.

11. Prove that the section of a rectangular solid made by a plane that passes through two nonconsecutive lateral edges is a rectangle.

12. Prove that any two diagonals of a rectangular solid are equal and bisect each other.

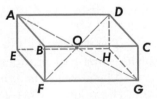

Suggestion. Prove *AG* equals and bisects *DF*.

13. Prove that the section of a rectangular solid made by a plane that is parallel to the base is enclosed by a rectangle.

SOME RELATED ANALYTIC GEOMETRY

147. Your study of graphs in algebra was an *introduction to analytic geometry*. Recall: On a plane, perpendiculars $X'OX$ and YOY', called **coordinate axes,** intersect at a point, called the **origin.** They separate the plane into **quadrants** numbered I, II, and III, and IV, counted around the origin in counterclockwise order. On $X'OX$, the origin is marked by O. It is associated with the number zero. At its right, a point is marked by $+1$. The segment from 0 to $+1$ is the **unit distance** on $X'OX$ and YOY'.

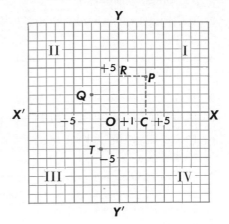

On OX, each point is marked by or associated with the positive real number that indicates its distance from O, measured by the unit distance. The points on OX', in like manner, are associated with the negative real numbers. Conversely, every positive and negative real number is associated with a point on the line $X'OX$, thereby forming a *scale* of the positive and negative real numbers. The same unit is used on the Y axis to associate points on OY with positive and those on OY' with negative real numbers that indicate their distances above or below the origin, respectively.

Each point of the plane, as point P, is located and named by its distances from the two axes, measured by the unit. The distance of P from the Y axis is called its **abscissa,** as $+3$. The distance of P from the X axis is called its **ordinate,** as $+4$. These distances are recognized easily because $RP = OC = +3$, and $CP = OR = +4$.

Together, the abscissa and ordinate of a point form an ordered pair of numbers called its **coordinates.**

The abscissa is named first so point P is the point $(+3,+4)$. Q is the point $(-3,+2)$. $T:(-2,-4)$ means the point T, *whose abscissa is -2 and whose ordinate is -4.*

1. Prepare axes on some coordinate paper, and locate points:
   (a) $M:(+5,-2)$ (b) $N:(-3,-5)$ (c) $A:(-4,+6)$ (d) $B:(+5,-8)$

2. (a) Locate $A:(+3,+5)$, $B:(+13,+5)$, $C:(+11,-1)$, and $D:(+1, -1)$.
   (b) Draw $ABCD$. What figure is it? Prove your inference.
   (c) What are the coordinates of the intersection of AC and BD?

3. (a) Locate $A:(2,5)$ and $B:(10,9)$. Draw AB.
   (b) Locate C, the mid-point of AB. Find the coordinates of C.
   (c) Try to find a relation between:
      (1) The abscissa of C and those of A and B.
      (2) The ordinate of C and those of A and B.

4. Let $P_1:(x_1,y_1)$ and $P_2:(x_2,y_2)$ be any two points with positive or zero coordinates. Draw P_1P_2. Locate $P:(x,y)$ the mid-point of P_1P_2.
   (a) Prove that $x = \frac{1}{2}(x_1 + x_2)$.
   (b) Prove that $y = \frac{1}{2}(y_1 + y_2)$.

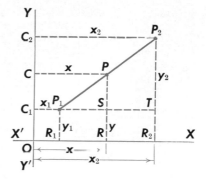

Suggestion. What kind of figure is $C_1P_1P_2C_2$? In it, what is the segment CP?

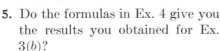

5. Do the formulas in Ex. 4 give you the results you obtained for Ex. 3(b)?

6. (a) Locate $A:(2,3)$, $B:(8,7)$, $C:(6,9)$. Draw AB, BC, and AC.
   (b) Using the formulas obtained in Ex. 4, find the coordinates of the mid-points of AB, BC, and AC.

7. (a) Locate $D:(4,2)$, $E:(10,2)$, $F:(10,12)$, and $G:(4,12)$.
   (b) What kind of figure is $DEFG$?
   (c) Find the coordinates of the mid-points of DF and EG.
   (d) What do the results in part (c) show about DF and EG?
   (e) What theorem is recalled by part (d)?

8. (a) Locate $P:(3,8)$, $Q:(8,2)$, $R:(10,7)$, and $S:(5,13)$. Draw $PQRS$.
   (b) Prove that $PQRS$ is a parallelogram by finding the coordinates of the mid-points of the diagonals, and using §131(d).

9. (a) Locate $P:(0,0)$, $Q:(10,0)$, $R:(15,6)$ and $S:(5,6)$. Draw $PQRS$.
   (b) Prove that $PRQS$ is a parallelogram.

10. (a) Locate $A:(3,0)$, $B:(12,0)$, and $C:(6,10)$. Draw $\triangle ABC$.
    (b) Locate $X:(4.5,5)$. How does it divide AC?
    (c) Draw $XY \parallel AB$, intersecting BC at Y. What are the coordinates of Y? How does Y divide BC?
    (d) What theorem is verified by part (c)?

Symmetry in architecture (Oneonta Congregational Church, South Pasadena, California), in modern furniture, and in nature (luna moth).
TOP: SUMMERBELL ROOF STRUCTURES, LOS ANGELES
CENTER: DUNBAR FURNITURE COMPANY
BOTTOM: L. F. VOGEL, NEEDHAM, MASSACHUSETTS

H. ARMSTRONG ROBERTS   H. ARMSTRONG ROBERTS   KEYSTONE VIEW

SYMMETRICAL POINTS

148. (a) Two points C and D are **symmetrical with respect to a third point** F if F bisects CD.

(b) Two points C and D are **symmetrical with respect to a line** AB if AB is the perpendicular-bisector of CD.

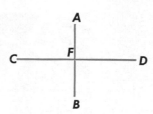

(c) A figure is **symmetrical with respect to a line,** called the **axis of symmetry,** if the figure consists of pairs of points that are symmetrical with respect to the line. $XCZRSWDY$ is symmetrical with respect to AB.

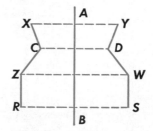

(d) A figure is **symmetrical with respect to a center of symmetry** if the figure consists of pairs of points symmetrical with respect to the center of symmetry, as the pairs of corresponding points of the adjoining ellipse.

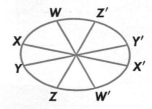

1. Does a circle have a center of symmetry?
2. Does a circle have an axis of symmetry? Many?
3. (a) Locate a point O and four points X, Y, Z, and W.
   (b) By constructions locate points X', Y', Z', and W' that are symmetrical to X, Y, Z, and W, respectively, with respect to O.
4. (a) Draw a line AB. Place points X, Y, Z, and W on one side of AB in random position.
   (b) By constructions locate X', Y', Z', and W' that are symmetrical to X, Y, Z, and W, respectively, with respect to AB.

CHAPTER 5

INEQUALITIES

In algebra and, so far, in geometry, we have been concerned chiefly with equalities of numbers, of angles, and of segments, and congruence of triangles.

It will interest you to learn that inequalities also have a place in mathematics. Although it may seem that there would not be much to say about unequals, actually several interesting and useful relations between the unequal parts of triangles, circles, and some figures of solid geometry can be demonstrated.

In this chapter we shall introduce some axioms about inequalities on which to base our reasoning. Then we shall explore the relations between unequal sides and angles in triangles, and, finally, introduce some related figures of solid geometry.

Designs for modern homes and bridges use scalene triangles as well as isosceles triangles. The basic forms of the wings of jet transports and of sails are polygons with unequal sides.

TOP: PHOTOGRAPH BY HAROLD M. LAMBERT, PHILADELPHIA   CENTER LEFT: H. ARMSTRONG ROBERTS, PHILADELPHIA   CENTER RIGHT: SARGENT, BOSTON   BOTTOM: DOUGLAS AIRCRAFT COMPANY, INC., SANTA MONICA, CALIFORNIA

149. (a) In §7, p. 16, you learned that a A———————B
segment AB is less than a segment CD
if B falls between C and D when AB is C————————D
placed on CD, with A on C. This means
that *one segment is less than another* when it equals a part of
the other. (§8(b), p. 17)

Recall that the symbol $<$ means *is less than* and that $>$
means *is greater than*. Above, $AB < CD$ and $CD > AB$. To
write *is not equal*, we use the symbol $\neq$, as $x \neq y$ to mean
x *is not equal to* y. If $x \neq y$, then $x < y$ or $x > y$. If $x \not< y$,
then $x = y$ or $x > y$. These possibilities are indicated by
$x \geq y$; similarly for $x \not> y$.

(b) *One angle is less than another*
when it equals a part of the
other; or $\angle AOB$ is less than
$\angle CDE$ if the terminal side OB
of $\angle AOB$ falls inside $\angle CDE$
when $\angle AOB$ is placed on $\angle CDE$ with the initial side OA of
$\angle AOB$ on the initial side CD of $\angle CDE$. (§11(b), p. 19)

150. **Two inequalities of the same order** are inequalities in
which the smaller quantity appears at the left of the inequality
sign in both, or at the right in both.

Thus: $4 < 9$ and $5 < 13$ are inequalities of the *same order*.
$4 > 2$ and $5 < 8$ are inequalities of *opposite order*.

1. Read the inequalities:
(a) $7 < 19$ (b) $5 \neq 20$ (c) $12 > 9$ (d) $AB \neq CD$
(e) $9 \neq 6$ (f) $12 \not> 15$ (g) $\angle AOB \neq \angle COD$ (h) $MN \not< RS$

2. Are the following inequalities of the same or opposite order?
(a) $x > y$ and $r < s$ (b) $m > n$ and $y > z$

3. (a) Write as an inequality the result of adding 4 to both sides of the
inequality $15 > 8$.
(b) Express as an axiom the conclusion suggested by (a).

4. (a) Multiply both sides of $4 < 9$ by 3, also by 5.
(b) Express as an axiom the conclusion suggested by part (a).

5. (a) Subtract 4 from both sides of $15 < 20$, also 8.
(b) Express as an axiom the conclusion suggested by part (a).

151. **Axioms for equalities and inequalities of positive quantities.** Eight axioms dealing principally with equalities appeared on page 32; five for dealing with inequalities follow.

Ax. 9. *If equals are added to unequals, the sums are unequal in the same order.*
Thus: $3 = 3, 5 < 7. \therefore 3 + 5 < 3 + 7$, or $8 < 10$.

Ax. 10. *If equals are subtracted from unequals, the differences are unequal in the same order.*
Thus: $8 < 10, 4 = 4. \therefore 8 - 4 < 10 - 4$, or $4 < 6$.

Ax. 11. *If $a > b$ and $b > c$, then $a > c$.*
Thus: $9 > 6$, and $6 > 2. \therefore 9 > 2$.

Ax. 12. *If unequals are added to unequals of the same order, the sums are unequal in the same order.*
Thus: $7 < 9$ and $12 < 20. \therefore 7 + 12 < 9 + 20$, or $19 < 29$.

Ax. 13. *If unequals are subtracted from equals or from unequals of opposite order, the differences are unequal and the order is opposite to that of the subtrahend.*
Thus: $3 < 4$, and $8 = 8. \therefore 8 - 3 > 8 - 4$, or $5 > 4$.
$3 < 4$, and $8 > 5. \therefore 8 - 3 > 5 - 4$, or $5 > 1$.

152. **Fundamental inequalities for segments.**

(a) *Any side of a triangle is less than the sum of the other two sides.*

$BC < AB + AC.$ (Post. 5, p. 34)

Since $AC < BC + AB$, if we subtract AB from both sides, $AC - AB < BC$ (Ax. 10). Therefore

(b) *Any side of a triangle is greater than the difference of the other two sides.*

1. If two sides of a triangle measure 5 in. and 8 in.:
  (*a*) Prove that the third side must be more than 3 in.
  (*b*) Prove that the third side must be less than 13 in.
2. Can a triangle be formed with sides that measure:
  (*a*) 2 in., 3 in., and 4 in. ? Construct it.
  (*b*) 3 in., 4 in., and 7 in. ?
3. In $\triangle XYW$, assume that $XZ = YZ$. Prove that YW is less than XW.

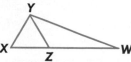

153. Recall that an exterior angle of a triangle is greater than either nonadjacent interior angle. (§89, p. 92)

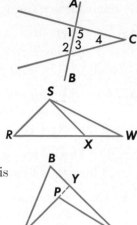

1. At the right:
  (a) Which angles are smaller than ∠1?
  (b) Is ∠5 smaller or larger than ∠2?

2. In △RSW at the right, if RS = SX, prove that ∠R is greater than ∠W.

3. Point P lies inside △ABC below. Prove that ∠APC is greater than ∠ABC.

4. In the figure for Ex. 3, prove that AP + PC is less than AB + BC.

Suggestions. AP + PY < AB + BY (Why?)
    PC < PY + YC (Why?)

Add these inequalities and simplify.

154. *If two sides of a triangle are unequal, the angle opposite the longer side is larger than the angle opposite the shorter side.*

Hypothesis. In △ABC, AC > AB

Conclusion.   ∠CBA > ∠C

Plan. Prove ∠CBA is greater than an angle that is known to be greater than ∠C.

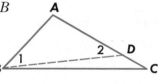

Proof.

	Statements	Authorities
1.	On AC, take AD = AB.	1. Why possible?
2.	Draw BD.	2. Why possible?
3.	∠1 = ∠2	3. Why?
4.	∠2 > ∠C	4. Why?
5.	∴ ∠1 > ∠C	5. Ax. 2, p. 32
6.	∠CBA > ∠1	6. Ax. 8, p. 32
7.	∴ ∠CBA > ∠C	7. Ax. 11, p. 143

155. *If two angles of a triangle are unequal, the side opposite the larger angle is longer than the side opposite the smaller angle.*

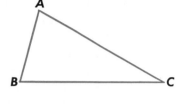

Hypothesis.   In $\triangle ABC$,
$\angle B > \angle C$.

Conclusion. $AC > AB$

Plan. Use the indirect method of proof. Assume that $AC \not> AB$, that is:
(*a*) Assume $AC = AB$.
(*b*) Assume $AC < AB$.

Proof.

Statements	Authorities
(*a*) 1. If $AC = AB$, $\angle B = \angle C$	1. Why?
2. But $\angle B > \angle C$	2. Why?
3. $\therefore$ $AC \neq AB$	3. Principle, §86, p. 91
(*b*) 1. If $AC < AB$, $\angle B\ ?\ \angle C$	1. §154, p. 144
2. But $\angle B\ ?\ \angle C$	2. Why?
3. $\therefore$ $AC \not< AB$	3. §86, p. 91
(*c*) 1. Since $AC \neq AB$	1. Step (*a*) 3
2. and $AC \not< AB$	2. Step (*b*) 3
3. $\therefore$ $AC > AB$	3. The remaining possibility.

Note. Observe in this proof that assuming the negative of the conclusion compels us to assume two other possibilities, listed as (*a*) and (*b*). Consideration of these possibilities leads us to a contradiction in each case.

156. Cor. 1. *The perpendicular segment to a line from a point not on the line is less than any other segment drawn to the line from the point.*

Suggestion. If $AB \perp DE$ and AC is any other segment from A to DE, prove AB is less than AC by using $\angle 2$ and $\angle 3$.

157. Cor. 2. *The hypotenuse of a right triangle is longer than either leg.*

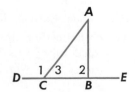

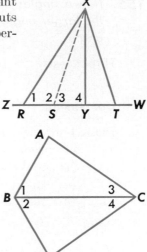

1. Of two segments drawn to a line from a point on a perpendicular to the line, the one that cuts off the longer segment from the foot of the perpendicular is the longer.

   Hyp. $XY \perp ZW$, $RY > YT$
   Con. $XR > XT$
   Plan. Take $SY = YT$. Prove $\angle 2 > \angle 1$ by comparing each with $\angle 3$.

2. In the adjoining figure, if $AB = BD$, $AC = CD$, and $AC > AB$ prove that $\angle ABD > \angle ACD$.

3. Prove that a diagonal of a rectangle with two unequal adjacent sides does not bisect the angles of the rectangle.

4. Prove that the sum of the lines drawn from any point within a triangle to the vertices is less than the sum of the three sides of the triangle.

   Suggestions. 1. Let O within a $\triangle ABC$ be joined to A, B, and C.
   2. $OA + OB < CA + CB$. (See Ex. 4, p. 144.)
   3. Similarly express $OB + OC$ and also $OC + OA$.
   4. Add these inequalities and divide by 2.

5. In $\triangle ABC$ assume $AB < AC$; take D on AC so that $AD = AB$. Prove that $BC > DC$.

   Suggestion. Compare $BC + AB$ with AC.

6. Prove that each of the equal sides of an isosceles triangle is greater than one half the base.

7. If O is any point within $\triangle ABC$, then $AO + BO + CO$ is greater than one half the perimeter of the triangle.

   Suggestion. Apply §152(a) to each side of the triangle.

8. Prove that any side of a triangle is less than one half the perimeter of the triangle.

9. Prove that the median to any side of a triangle is less than one half the perimeter of the triangle.

10. Prove that the median BD to side AC of triangle $\triangle ABC$ is less than half the sum of the other two sides of the triangle.

    Suggestion. Extend BD through D, its own length to E. Draw EC.

11. If the median drawn from any vertex of a triangle is greater than, equal to, or less than one half the opposite side, the angle at the vertex from which the median is drawn is acute, right, or obtuse, respectively. (Consider each possibility separately.)

INEQUALITIES IN TWO TRIANGLES

158. *If two triangles have two sides of one equal respectively to two sides of the other, and the included angle of the first larger than the included angle of the second, then the third side of the first is longer than the third side of the second.*

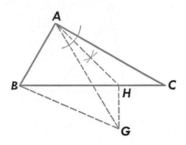 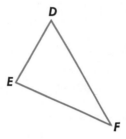

Hypothesis.   In $\triangle ABC$ and $\triangle DEF$,
$$AB = DE,\ AC = DF,\ \angle BAC > \angle EDF.$$

Conclusion. $BC > EF$

Proof.

Statements	Authorities
1. Place $\triangle DEF$ in the position ABG, DE coinciding with AB.	1. Post. 22, p. 52 §8(a), p. 17
2. DF falls on AG, inside $\angle BAC$.	2. §149(b), p. 142
3. Construct AH, bisecting $\angle CAG$, meeting BC at H. Draw GH.	3. §73, p. 74
4. $\triangle GAH \cong \triangle CAH$	4. Prove it.
5. $\therefore\ HG = HC$	5. Why?
6. In $\triangle BGH,\ BH + HG > BG.$	6. Why?
7. $\therefore\ BH + HC > BG$	7. Ax. 2, p. 32
8. $\therefore\ BC > EF$	8. Ax. 7, p. 32

1. Prove that the diagonals of a parallelogram are unequal if the angles of the parallelogram are not right angles.
2. In $\triangle TRS$, $RS = 8$ in., $ST = 10$ in., and $RT = 14$ in.
   (a) Which angle of the triangle is the largest?
   (b) Which angle of the triangle is the smallest?
3. In a parallelogram $ABCD$, if $BC > AB$, then BD does not bisect $\angle B$ or $\angle D$.

159. *If two triangles have two sides of the one equal respectively to two sides of the other, and the third side of the first longer than the third side of the second, then the angle opposite the third side of the first is larger than the angle opposite the third side of the second.*

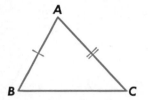 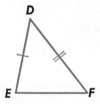

Hypothesis.   In $\triangle ABC$ and $\triangle DEF$,
$$AB = DE, \ AC = DF, \ BC > EF.$$

Conclusion. $\angle A > \angle D$

Plan. Use the indirect method of proof.

Proof.

	Statements	Authorities
1.	Assume $\angle A \not> \angle D$ that is: (*a*) Assume $\angle A = \angle D$ and (*b*) Assume $\angle A < \angle D$	1. Possible assumptions.
2.	If $\angle A = \angle D$, $\triangle ABC \cong \triangle$?.	2. Prove it.
3.	$\therefore$ $BC \ ? \ EF$	3. Why?
4.	But $BC \ ? \ EF$	4. Why?
5.	$\therefore$ $\angle A \neq \angle D$	5. §86
6.	If $\angle A < \angle D$, then $BC \ ? \ EF$.	6. §158
7.	But $BC \ ? \ EF$.	7. Why?
8.	$\therefore$ $\angle A \not< \angle D$	8. Why?
9.	$\therefore$ $\angle A > \angle D$	9. The remaining possibility.

1. Prove that the median to a side of a triangle is longer than the altitude to that side unless the side is the base of an isosceles triangle.

2. Prove that no two angles of a scalene triangle are equal.

3. By the indirect method, prove that two sides of a triangle are unequal if the median to the third side is not perpendicular to that side.

In each exercise give the answer, and be prepared to give the reason why your answer is correct.

1. *COD* and *BOA* are straight lines.
   (a) How large is ∠4 if ∠1 = 40°?
   (b) How large is ∠5 if ∠1 = 40°?
   (c) How large is ∠2 if ∠1 = 40° and
       ∠3 = 60°?

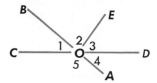

2. In a figure like that above, why must *COD* be a straight line if ∠5 equals 100° and ∠4 equals 80°?

3. In the adjoining figure:
   (a) What relation exists between △*FGH* and △*XYZ*?
   (b) How long is *YZ*?
   (c) How large is ∠*F*?

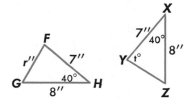

4. In the adjoining figure:
   (a) How long is *ST*?
   (b) How long is *AC*?
   (c) If the surface inside △*ABC* is *m* sq. in., what is the surface inside △*RST*?

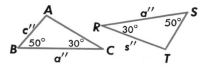

5. In the adjoining figure:
   (a) If *MO* = 10 in., ∠*O* = *x*°, and *MN* = 10 in., how large is ∠*N*?
   (b) If *MN* = *NO* = *MO*, how large is ∠*M*?

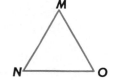

6. In the adjoining figure:
   (a) What kind of triangles are △*DCE* and △*XYZ*?
   (b) What angle does ∠*D* equal?
   (c) Does ∠*C* = ∠*X* or ∠*Z*?

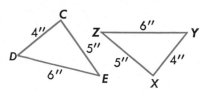

7. In the adjoining figure let ∠2 = 90°:
   (a) What kind of angle is ∠3?
   (b) What kind of angle is ∠1?
   (c) If ∠*R* = 30°, how large is ∠1?
   (d) If ∠*R* = 30°, how large is ∠3?
   (e) Can *RS* be ⊥ *XY* if *RT* ⊥ *XY*?

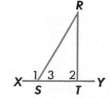

8. In this diagram, what is true:
   (*a*) If ∠3 = 80° and ∠6 = 80°?
   (*b*) If ∠1 = 120° and ∠5 = 120°?
   (*c*) If ∠4 = 100° and ∠6 = 80°?
   (*d*) If ∠1 = 110° and ∠8 = 110°?
   (*e*) If ∠2 = 115° and ∠8 = 65°?

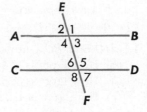

9. In the same figure, suppose
   AB ∥ *CD:*
   (*a*) How large is ∠4 if ∠8 = 110°?
   (*b*) How large is ∠2 if ∠7 = 75°?
   (*c*) How large is ∠3 if ∠5 = 105°?

10. In this figure:
    (*a*) What kind of triangles are
    △*HJK* and △*RST?*
    (*b*) How long is *RS?*
    (*c*) How much is *y?*

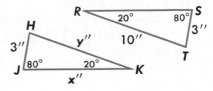

11. In this figure, *XZ* ⊥ *YW* and *YZ* = *ZW.*
    (*a*) If *XY* = 8 in., how long is *XW?*
    (*b*) If ∠1 = 40° and ∠*W* = 50°, how
    large are ∠2 and ∠*Y?*

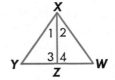

12. In the same figure, let ∠*Y* and ∠*W* each
    equal 60°.
    (*a*) If *XY* = 12 in., how long is *XW?*
    (*b*) If *XZ* bisects ∠*YXW*, how large is ∠2?
    (*c*) If *XZ* bisects ∠*YXW*, and *YZ* = 7 in., how long is *ZW?*

13. In this figure:
    (*a*) What can you prove about
    △*ABC* and △*HKT?*
    (*b*) If ∠*K* = *x*°, and ∠*T* = *y*°, how
    large is ∠*C?*

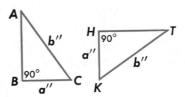

14. In this figure, *PS* ⊥ *ZX*, and *PR*
    ⊥*ZY*; ∠*XZP* = ∠*PZY.*
    (*a*) How long is *PR* if *PS* = *t* inches?
    (*b*) How long is *ZR* if *ZS* = 10 in.?
    (*c*) How large is ∠*SZP* if ∠*PZR* = *m*°?

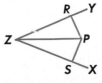

15. In a △*ABC*, **Hyp.** *AB* = *BC*
    Con. ∠*A* = ∠*C*
    (*a*) Write the hypothesis and conclusion of the converse theorem.
    (*b*) Is the converse theorem true?

16. In this figure, let $AB = 5$ in., $BC = 8$ in., $AB \parallel CD$, $CD = 5$ in., and $\angle ABC = x°$.
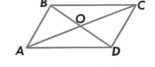
  (a) What kind of figure is $ABCD$?
  (b) How long is AD?
  (c) How large is $\angle ADC$?
  (d) How large is $\angle DAB$?

17. In the above figure, let AB and CD each be 6 in. long, and BC and AD each be 10 in. long.
  (a) What kind of figure is $ABCD$?
  (b) If $\angle ABC = 100°$, how large is $\angle ADC$?
  (c) How large is $\angle BCD$, when $\angle ABC = 100°$?
  (d) If $BO = x$ in., how long is OD?
  (e) If $CO = y$ in., how long is AC?

18. In this figure, let
$AX \parallel BY \parallel CZ \parallel DW$.
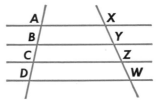
  (a) If $AB = BC = CD$, how long is XY when $XW = 15$ in.?
  (b) If $AB = BC = CD$, and YZ is 6 in., how long is XY? ZW?

19. In this figure, $HJ = HK$ and $\angle 3 = \angle 4$.
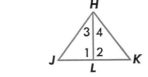
  (a) What must be true about JL?
  (b) What must be true about HL?

20. In this figure, $BA \parallel GH$ and $BC \parallel DF$.
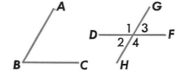
  (a) If $\angle B = 50°$, $\angle 3 = $?
  (b) If $\angle B = 60°$, $\angle 2 = $?
  (c) If $\angle B = 70°$, $\angle 1 = $?

21. In a figure of plane geometry:
  (a) If $RS \parallel XY$ and $CD \parallel XY$, what is true about RS and CD?
  (b) If $AB \perp MN$ and $CD \perp MN$, what is true about AB and CD?
  (c) If $FG \perp RS$ and $XY \parallel RS$, what is true about FG and XY?
  (d) If XY cuts ZW at O and $XY \parallel AB$, what is true about ZW and AB?

22. In the figure for Ex. 16, if $BO = 8$ in., $AO = 6$ in., $OC = 6$ in., and $OD = 8$ in., how long is CD if $AB = 5$ in.? Why?

23. If line $XY \perp$ side AB of $\angle ABC$, and $YZ \perp$ side BC, how large is $\angle Y$ if $\angle ABC = 65°$?

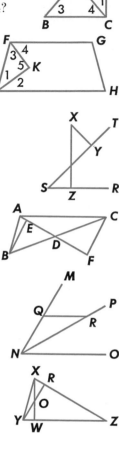

1. In $\triangle ABC$, $AB = AC$. BA is extended so that $AD = AB$. Prove that CD is perpendicular to BC.

Plan. Prove that $\angle 1 + \angle 4 = 90°$.

What do you know about $\angle 1$? $\angle 4$?

What do you know about $\angle 1 + \angle 2 + \angle 3 + \angle 4$?

2. If $EFGH$ is a trapezoid, EK bisects $\angle HEF$, and FK bisects $\angle EFG$, then $\angle EKF$ is a right angle.

Suggestion. Read §115(4), p. 113, again.

3. If perpendiculars are drawn to the sides of an acute angle from a point outside the angle and outside its vertical angle, they form an angle that is equal to the given angle.

4. If D is the mid-point of BC in $\triangle ABC$, and BE and CF are perpendicular to AD and AD extended, prove $BE = CF$.

5. If a line is drawn through a point in the bisector of an angle parallel to one side of the angle, then the bisector, the parallel, and the segment on the side of the angle form an isosceles triangle.

6. **Hyp.** $XW \perp YZ$, $YR \perp XZ$
    Con. (a) $\angle WXZ = \angle ZYR$
         (b) $\angle XOR = \angle Z$

Suggestion. Use §110, p. 109.

7. If lines are drawn through the vertices of a triangle parallel to the opposite sides of the triangle, they form a triangle whose sides are bisected by the vertices of the original triangle; also the new triangle is four times as large as the original triangle.

8. If lines are drawn through the vertices of a quadrilateral parallel to the diagonals of the quadrilateral, they form a parallelogram that is twice as large as the given quadrilateral.

9. If three angles of a quadrilateral are right angles, the quadrilateral is a rectangle.

TRIHEDRAL AND POLYHEDRAL ANGLES

160. **Trihedral angles** in solid geometry are like triangles in plane geometry in some respects but are different in others.

(*a*) Construct the following two patterns. Make them on stiff paper or light cardboard.

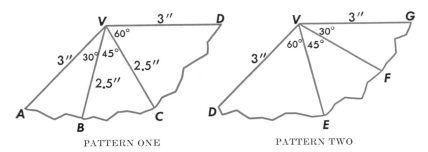

PATTERN ONE   PATTERN TWO

Note. The lengths of rays *VA*, *VB*, etc. are given for convenience.

(*b*) Cut both patterns along the outside lines.

(*c*) Taking Pattern One, bend part *AVB* down on ray *VB*. Bend part *CVD* down on ray *VC* until *VD* coincides with *VA*. Attach part *CVD* to *AVB* by means of Scotch Tape. You should now have trihedral ∠ *V–ABC*.

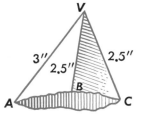

(*d*) Make trihedral ∠ *V–DEF*, using Pattern Two.

SG 37. (*a*) A **trihedral angle** is a surface that consists of parts of three planes, as *AVB*, *BVC*, and *CVA*, that intersect in **edges** that meet at one point.

(*b*) The **vertex** of a trihedral angle is the point of intersection of its three edges, as point *V*.

(*c*) The **faces** of a trihedral angle are the parts of the planes that intersect in its edges, as *VAB*, *VBC*, and *VCA*.

(*d*) The **face angles** of a trihedral angle are the angles on the respective faces, formed by the edges on the face, as ∠*AVB*.

(*e*) The **dihedral angles** of a trihedral angle are the angles formed by two adjoining faces, as ∠ *A–VB–C*.

161. Similarities and dissimilarities between triangles and trihedral angles. When you examine a triangle and a trihedral angle such as ∠ V–ABC that you made for p. 153, you observe the facts that are stated in the following table.

A TRIANGLE HAS	A TRIHEDRAL ANGLE HAS
Three vertices	Three edges
Three sides	Three faces
Three angles	Three dihedral angles
A side opposite each angle	A face opposite each dihedral angle

The following exercises suggest some conclusions about trihedral angles.

1. (a) Try to make your ∠V–ABC constructed for §160(c) coincide with the one made by a fellow pupil.
   (b) In what respects were these two trihedrals alike by construction?
   (c) What conclusion is suggested by parts (b) and (a)?
2. (a) Try to make your ∠V–ABC coincide with your ∠V–DEF.
   (b) In what respect were these trihedrals unlike by construction?
   (c) What conclusion is suggested by parts (b) and (a)?
3. (a) Give a definition of congruent trihedral angles.
   (b) What must be true of corresponding parts of them?
4. (a) Make a pattern for and try to make the model of a trihedral angle whose face angles are 50°, 60°, and 70°.
   (b) Repeat part (a) using angles of 50°, 70°, and 120°.
   (c) What conclusion is suggested by parts (a) and (b)?
5. (a) Compare the sum of any two face angles of your ∠V–ABC with the third angle of the same trihedral angle.
   (b) Repeat part (a), using your ∠V–DEF.
   (c) What conclusion is suggested by parts (a) and (b)?
6. (a) Construct a pattern for and make the model of a trihedral angle whose face angles measure 60°, 60°, and 40°. Try to compare the dihedral angles opposite the 60° face angles, using your trihedral angle and one made by a fellow pupil.
   (b) What conclusion is suggested?
   (c) To what theorem of plane geometry does this new theorem correspond?
7. (a) Construct ∠V-RST having ∠RVS = 60° and ∠SVT = 40°.
   (b) Using your ∠V-RST and one made by a fellow pupil, compare the dihedral angles opposite the given face angles.
   (c) What conclusion is suggested?

162. The following definitions and theorems correspond to the tentative conclusions that are suggested by the exercises on page 154.

SG 38. (*a*) Two trihedral angles are **congruent** if they can be made to coincide. Their corresponding face angles and dihedral angles are equal and are in the same orders around their vertices.

(*b*) Two trihedral angles are **symmetric** if their corresponding parts are equal but are arranged in opposite order around their vertices.

Note. They are like right-hand and left-hand gloves, which, though alike in all other respects, differ in the arrangement of the parts. Neither will fit the other hand.

SG 39. *Two trihedral angles are congruent if the face angles of the one are equal to the face angles of the other, and are arranged in the same order around their vertices. They are symmetric if the corresponding parts are arranged in opposite orders.*

Note. This theorem is suggested by Exercises 1 and 2, p. 154.

SG 40. *The sum of two face angles of a trihedral angle is greater than the third.* (See Ex. 4 and Ex. 5, p. 154.)

A proof of this theorem appears on page 156.

163. You can prove the first part of each of the following theorems by superposition.

SG 41. *If two trihedral angles have two face angles and the included dihedral angle of the one equal respectively to the corresponding parts of the other:*

(*a*) *They are congruent if the parts are in the same order.*

(*b*) *They are symmetric if the parts are in opposite orders.*

SG 42. *If two trihedral angles have two dihedral angles and the included face angle of the one equal respectively to the corresponding parts of the other:*

(*a*) *They are congruent if the parts are in the same order.*

(*b*) *They are symmetric if the parts are in opposite orders.*

SG 43. *If two face angles of a trihedral angle are equal, the opposite dihedral angles are equal.* (See Ex. 6, page 154.)

164. Proof of Theorem SG 40.

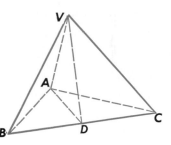

Hyp. In trihedral $\angle V$–ABC,
$\angle BVC$ is greater than
$\angle BVA$ or $\angle CVA$.

Con. $\angle BVA + \angle CVA > \angle BVC$

Informal proof.

1. On face BVC, make $\angle DVB = \angle AVB$ and $VD = VA$. Let plane ABD intersect the faces of the trihedral angle in $\triangle ABC$, and plane AVD in line AD.

2. $\qquad\qquad \triangle AVB \cong \triangle DVB$ $\qquad\qquad$ (Prove.)
3. $\qquad\qquad \therefore \quad AB = BD$ $\qquad\qquad\qquad$ (Why?)
4. In $\triangle ABC$, $AB + AC > BC$ $\qquad\qquad$ (Why?)
5. $\qquad\qquad \therefore \quad BD + AC > BD + DC$ $\qquad$ (Ax. 2, Ax. 7)
6. $\qquad\qquad \therefore \quad AC > DC$ $\qquad\qquad\qquad$ (Ax. 10)
7. In $\triangle AVC$ and $\triangle DVC$,
$\quad VA = VD$, $VC = VC$, $AC > DC$ $\qquad$ (Why?)
8. $\qquad\qquad \therefore \quad \angle AVC > \angle DVC$ $\qquad\qquad$ (§159, p. 148)
9. $\therefore \quad \angle AVB + \angle AVC > \angle AVB + \angle DVC$ (Why?)
10. $\therefore \quad \angle AVB + \angle AVC > \angle DVB + \angle DVC$ (Why?)
11. $\qquad\qquad \therefore \quad \angle AVB + \angle AVC > \angle BVC$ $\qquad$ (Ax. 7)

165. Proof of Theorem SG 43.

Hyp. $\quad$ In $\angle V$–YZW,
$\qquad \angle YVZ = \angle YVW$

Con. Dihedral $\angle Y$–VW–Z
$\qquad$ = dihedral $\angle Y$–VZ–W

Informal Proof.

1. Take $VY = VZ = VW$.
Let plane YVX bisect dihedral
$\angle Z$–VY–W.

2. $\qquad\qquad$ In $\angle V$–XYZ and $\angle V$–XYW,
$\qquad\qquad \angle YVZ = \angle YVW$, $\angle YVX = \angle YVX$
$\qquad\qquad\qquad \angle Z$–$VY$–$X = \angle W$–$VY$–$X$

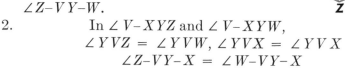

$\qquad\qquad$ The parts are in opposite orders.

3. $\therefore \quad \angle V$–$XYZ$ is symmetric to $\angle V$–XYW. $\qquad$ (SG 41(b))
4. $\qquad\qquad \therefore \quad \angle Y$–$VZ$–$X = \angle Y$–$VW$–$X$
$\qquad\qquad$ or $\quad \angle Y$–VZ–$W = \angle Y$–VW–Z. $\qquad\qquad$ (SG 38(b))

166. Just as there are similarities and dissimilarities between triangles and trihedral angles, so there are similarities and dissimilarities between polygons and polyhedral angles.

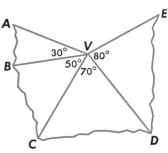

1. (*a*) On stiff paper construct the adjoining pattern, making the rays about 3 inches long for convenience. Cut it from the paper.

   (*b*) Fold the faces *AVB*, *BVC*, *CVD*, and *DVE* downward on rays *VB*, *VC*, and *VD* until *VE* coincides with *VA*. Attach *VE* to *VA*. The resulting surface is *polyhedral ∠ V–ABCD*.

SG 44. Def. A **polyhedral angle** is a surface that consists of the parts of three or more planes that intersect in edges which meet at a common vertex. It is such that the section of it by a plane that intersects all of its faces on one side of its vertex is a simple polygon.

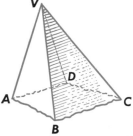

2. Draw a pattern for and form the polyhedral angle that has four 45° face angles.

3. In Exercises 1 and 2, what is the sum of the vertex angles?

4. (*a*) Try to construct a polyhedral angle whose four face angles each equal 90°.

   (*b*) Does part (*a*) suggest a theorem?

SG 45. *The sum of the face angles of any polyhedral angle is less than four right angles or 360°.*

5. (*a*) Construct the polyhedral ∠*V–ABCD* that has ∠*AVB* = 30°, ∠*BVC* = 40°, ∠*CVD* = 50°, and ∠*DVA* = 60°.

   (*b*) Construct the polyhedral ∠*W–EFGH* that has ∠*EWF* = 60°, ∠*FWG* = 50°, ∠*GWH* = 40°, and ∠*HWE* = 30°.

   (*c*) Is your ∠*V–ABCD* congruent to ∠*W–EFGH*?

   (*d*) Is your ∠*V–ABCD* congruent to the ∠*V–ABCD* made by other pupils of your class?

6. Give a definition of:

   (*a*) Congruent polyhedral angles.

   (*b*) Symmetric polyhedral angles.

CHAPTER 6

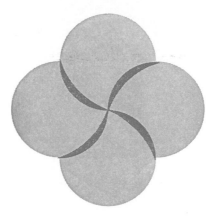

CIRCLES

People of early days must have been impressed by the outline of the full moon and of the rising and setting sun. They saw the same shape in the cross sections of some trees, and in the circular rings that indicated the annual growth of such trees.

Later, men found that a circle is a most useful curve. The first wheels probably were cross sections of trees. Circular parts in machinery stimulated industrial progress.

Men found that a circle can be drawn without having any very fine tool. They could draw it even with a bent stick. However, they reaped the full advantage of circles when they designed compasses with which to draw the circles, and learned the fundamental facts about circles.

You will learn these facts in Chapter 6.

Circles are evident in the design of a large transformer, in the rings of annual growth in the cross section of the trunk of a shortleaf pine, and in the shape of a portion of a Van Nuys California hospital.
TOP: GENERAL ELECTRIC COMPANY. CENTER: EWING GALLOWAY, NEW YORK. BOTTOM: STEED BROS.

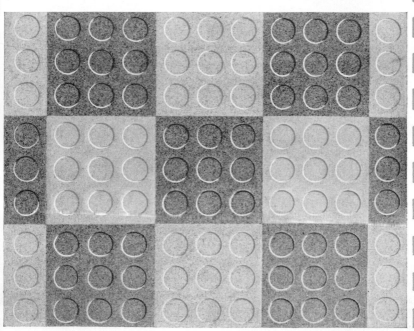

Circles form a prominent part in the patterns of these modern designs for floor coverings.

WHAT DO YOU KNOW?

1. Define and illustrate by a figure:
(*a*) Circle   (*b*) Radius   (*c*) Diameter
(*d*) Chord   (*e*) Arc   (*f*) Semicircle

2. When are two circles equal?

3. How do all radii and all diameters of the same circle or of equal circles compare?

4. In a plane, how many circles can be drawn from a point with a given segment as radius?

5. In a plane, draw a circle with 1-inch radius.
(*a*) Into how many parts does this circle separate the plane? What is the part inside the circle called?
(*b*) Where is a point if its distance from the center of this circle:
(1) Is $\frac{3}{4}$ in.?   (2) Is $1\frac{1}{4}$ in.?   (3) Is 1 in.?

6. (*a*) Draw a circle with radius of $1\frac{1}{2}$ inches.
(*b*) In it construct two perpendicular diameters.
(*c*) How do the diameters appear to divide the circle?
(*d*) How do the diameters appear to divide the interior of this circle?
(*e*) Satisfy yourself about the answers to questions (*c*) and (*d*) by cutting and using one of the parts of the figure you have after you draw the perpendicular diameters.

167. Summary. (*a*) *There is a circle with a given point as center and a given radius.* (Post. 11, p. 34)

(*b*) **Def.** The **interior of a circle** consists of, or is the set of, all points of the plane of the circle whose distances from the center of the circle are less than the radius.

(*c*) *A point is within, on, or outside a circle if its distance from the center of the circle is less than, equal to, or greater than the radius of the circle.*

(*d*) **Def. Equal circles** are circles which have equal radii. They can be made to coincide. (§17(*a*))

(*e*) *All radii and all diameters of the same circle or of equal circles are equal.* (Post. 13, p. 35)

This theorem is a consequence of §16(*a*) and §167(*d*).

(*f*) *A diameter of a circle bisects the circle and conversely, if a chord bisects a circle, it is a diameter of the circle.*

168. (a) *In a plane, a circle can be constructed that contains two given points.*

Given. Points A and B.

Construct. A circle that contains points A and B.

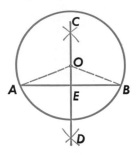

Construction. 1. Draw AB. Construct CD, the perpendicular-bisector of AB.

2. From O, any point on CD, as center, with radius OA, draw a circle.

Statement. The circle will contain points A and B.

Proof.

	Statement	Authorities
1.	Draw OA and OB.	1. Possible?
2.	$OA = OB$	2. Give proof.
3.	$\therefore$ A and B lie on the $\odot$.	3. §167(c)

(b) *In a plane, an infinite number of circles that will contain two given points can be constructed.*

Informal proof. Each point on CD can be used as center.

1. (*a*) Place points A and B about 2 in. apart.
  (*b*) Construct four circles that contain A and B.

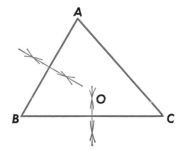

2. Draw any $\triangle ABC$. Construct a circle that contains points A, B, and C.

Suggestion. Construct the perpendicular-bisector of AB and that of BC. Let them intersect at point O. Use O as center of the circle.
  Prove $OA = OB = OC$.

169. A **circle circumscribes** a polygon if it contains all the vertices of the polygon, as the circle constructed in Ex. 2.
  The polygon is **inscribed in the circle.**

3. With any point O as center, draw three circles with radii equal to $\frac{3}{4}$ in., $1\frac{1}{4}$ in., and $1\frac{1}{2}$ in. These circles are *concentric*.

170. A **central angle** of a circle is an angle whose vertex is at the center of the circle, as $\angle COA$. The sides, extended if necessary, cut an **arc** from the circle, as arc CA (written $\overset{\frown}{CA}$).

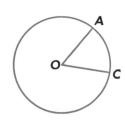

$\overset{\frown}{CA}$ is the arc of $\angle COA$. $\angle COA$ is the central angle of $\overset{\frown}{CA}$.

171. *In the same circle or equal circles:*

    (a) *If central angles are equal, their arcs are equal.*

    (b) *If arcs are equal, their central angles are equal.*

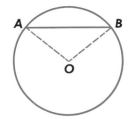 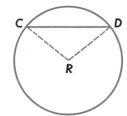

Informal proofs.

(a) Since $\odot O$ and R are equal, they can be made to coincide, with O on R. Since $\angle BOA = \angle DRC$, $\odot O$ can be turned around point R until OA falls on RC and OB on RD. Since the radii are equal, A will fall on C and B on D.

$$\therefore \quad \overset{\frown}{AB} = \overset{\frown}{CD}.$$

(b) Since $\odot O$ equals $\odot R$, they can be made to coincide, O falling on R. Since $\overset{\frown}{AB} = \overset{\frown}{CD}$, $\odot O$ can be turned around point R until $\overset{\frown}{AB}$ coincides with $\overset{\frown}{CD}$, A on C and B and D. Therefore $\angle BOA$ coincides with $\angle DRC$, or $\angle BOA = \angle DRC$.

172. *In the same circle or equal circles:*

    (a) *If central angles are unequal, their arcs are unequal, the greater angle having the greater arc.*

    (b) *If arcs are unequal, their central angles are unequal, the greater arc having the greater central angle.*

These theorems can be proved by the methods of §171.

1. What is the relation between the theorems in parts (a) and (b) of §171 and also those in §172?

173. The **chord** of an arc is the chord that joins the ends of the arc, as chord AB is the chord of arc ACB and also of arc ADB.

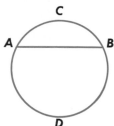

Unless AB is a diameter, a chord separates the circle into two unequal arcs. The smaller arc is called the **minor arc,** and the larger is called the **major arc** made by the chord.

The arc of a chord means the minor arc made by it, as minor $\overset{\frown}{ACB}$ of chord AB.

174. *In the same circle or in equal circles, if chords are equal, their arcs are equal.*

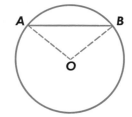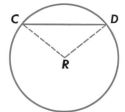

Hypothesis. $\odot O = \odot R,\ AB = CD$
Conclusion. $\overset{\frown}{AB} = \overset{\frown}{CD}$
Plan. 1. Draw $OA,\ OB,\ RC,\ RD$.
     2. Prove $\angle O = \angle R$ by congruent triangles.
        Apply §171(a).
         (Proof to be given by the pupil.)

175. *In the same circle or in equal circles, if arcs are equal, their chords are equal.*

Hypothesis. $\odot O = \odot R,\ \overset{\frown}{AB} = \overset{\frown}{CD}$ (Fig. §174)
Conclusion. $AB = CD$
Plan. Compare $\angle O$ and $\angle R$, using §171(b). Then prove $AB = CD$ by congruent triangles.
         (Proof to be given by the pupil.)

176. Fundamental Plan 5.
     To prove arcs are equal, prove their central angles are equal, or their chords are equal.
     To prove chords are equal, prove their arcs are equal.
     To prove central angles are equal, prove their arcs are equal.

1. What is the relation between the theorem in §174 and the theorem in §175?

2. If $\angle BOA = \angle DOC$, prove $\overarc{CA} = \overarc{DB}$.

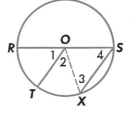

3. State and prove the converse of Ex. 2.

4. In the figure for Ex. 2, prove chord AC equals chord BD.

5. If chord BA = chord DC, prove $\overarc{CA} = \overarc{DB}$.

6. State and prove the converse of Ex. 5.

7. In the figure for Ex. 2, if chord CA = chord DB, then chord AB = chord CD.

8. Construct an equilateral triangle. Circumscribe a circle about it. Prove that the vertices of the triangle divide the circle into three equal parts. (See Ex. 2, p. 162.)

9. Draw chord RS of a circle. Let T bisect major arc RS and V bisect minor arc RS. Prove TV is the perpendicular-bisector of RS.
Suggestion. Draw chords RT, ST, RV, and SV.

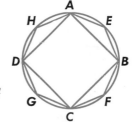

10. **Hyp.** $ABCD$ is a square. E, F, G, H are mid-points of $\overarc{AB}$, $\overarc{BC}$, $\overarc{CD}$, and $\overarc{AD}$.
Con. $AEBFCGDH$ is equilateral.

11. In Ex. 10, prove that angles H, E, F, and G are equal.

★12. If diameter COD of a circle O bisects central $\angle AOB$, it bisects minor arc AB and also bisects major arc AB.

13. **Hyp.** In $\odot O$, ROS is a diameter.
$$OT \parallel SX$$
Con. $\overarc{RT} = \overarc{TX}$

★14. **Hyp.** ROS is a diameter.
$$\overarc{RT} = \overarc{TX}$$
Con. $OT \parallel SX$
Suggestion. Compare $\angle ROX$ with $\angle 3 + \angle 4$.

★15. From the mid-point of an arc, perpendiculars are drawn to the radii that are drawn to the ends of the arc. Prove that these perpendiculars are equal.

Note. Ex. 87 through Ex. 97, pp. 394 and 395, can be done now.

177. *In the same circle or in equal circles, if two minor arcs are unequal, the greater minor arc has the longer chord.*

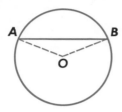
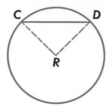

Hypothesis. $\odot O = \odot R$, $\overset{\frown}{BA} > \overset{\frown}{DC}$

Conclusion. $BA > DC$

Plan. Prove $\angle BOA > \angle DRC$, and use §158, p. 147.

Proof.

Statements	Authorities
1. Draw AO, BO, CR, and DR.	1. Why possible?
2. In $\triangle AOB$ and $\triangle CRD$, $AO = CR$, and $BO = DR$.	2. Why?
3. $\overset{\frown}{BA} > \overset{\frown}{DC}$	3. Why?
(Complete this proof.)	

178. *In the same circle or in equal circles, if two chords are unequal, the longer chord has the greater minor arc.*

Hypothesis. $\odot O = \odot R$, $BA > DC$ (Fig. §177)

Conclusion. $\overset{\frown}{BA} > \overset{\frown}{DC}$

Plan. Prove $\angle O > \angle R$, using §159, p. 148. Then use §172(a).

1. Construct $\triangle ABC$, having $AB = 2$ in., $BC = 3$ in., and $AC = 2.5$ in. Circumscribe $\odot O$ about $\triangle ABC$. Prove:
   (a) $\overset{\frown}{AB} < \overset{\frown}{AC} < \overset{\frown}{BC}$
   (b) $\angle AOB < \angle AOC < \angle BOC$

2. Locate points A, B, C, D, E, and F that divide a circle O into six equal arcs.
   (a) Prove that $ABCDEF$ is equilateral.
   (b) Prove that $\triangle BFD$ is equilateral.
   (c) Prove that $ABCDEF$ is equiangular.
   (d) Prove that $\triangle BFD$ is equiangular.

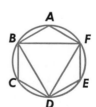

179. *If a diameter of a circle is perpendicular to a chord, it bisects the chord and its arcs.*

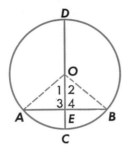

Hypothesis. In $\odot O$, diameter $CD \perp AB$ at E.

Conclusion. $AE = EB$, $\overset{\frown}{AC} = \overset{\frown}{CB}$, $\overset{\frown}{AD} = \overset{\frown}{DB}$

Plan. Prove AE and EB corres. parts of $\cong$ $\triangle$.

To prove $\overset{\frown}{AC} = \overset{\frown}{CB}$, prove $\angle 1 = \angle 2$.

Proof.

Statements	Authorities
1. Draw OA and OB.	1. Why?
2. $\triangle OAE \cong \triangle OEB$	2. Give full proof.
3. $\therefore$ $AE = ?$	3. Why?
4. $\angle 1 = \angle 2$	4. Why?
5. $\therefore$ $\overset{\frown}{AC} = ?$	5. Why?
6. $\overset{\frown}{CAD} = \overset{\frown}{CBD}$	6. Why?
7. $\therefore$ $AD = ?$	7. Ax. 4, p. 32

180. **Cor. 1.** *If any line through the center of a circle is perpendicular to a chord, it bisects the chord.*

181. **Cor. 2.** *The perpendicular-bisector of a chord passes through the center of the circle.*

Hyp. CD is $\perp$-bis. of AB, in $\odot O$.

Con. CD passes through O.

Plan. From O, draw $OE \perp AB$. Prove that OE must coincide with CD, by using §180, and §76.

1. A diameter of a circle is drawn perpendicular to chord AB, meeting the circle at X and Y. Prove that $\triangle AXY \cong \triangle BXY$.

1. If a radius bisects a chord, it is perpendicular to the chord and bisects the arc of the chord.

2. If a radius is perpendicular to a chord, it bisects the angle formed by joining the outer end of the radius to the ends of the chord.

3. Given an arc of a circle, bisect it.

4. If a line is drawn from the center of a circle to the mid-point of a chord, it is perpendicular to the chord, and, if it is extended, it bisects the arc of the chord.

5. If a radius is drawn to the mid-point of an arc, it is perpendicular to the chord of the arc.

6. If a line joins the mid-point of a chord and the mid-point of its arc, it is perpendicular to the chord.

7. (a) State two converses of Ex. 6.
   (b) Try to prove these converses.

★8. A square and an equilateral triangle are inscribed in the same circle. Prove that a side of the square is less than a side of the triangle.

★9. If a diameter bisects each of two or more chords, the chords are parallel.

★10. Two equal chords are drawn from one point on a circle. Prove that the radius drawn to the point bisects the angle between the chords.

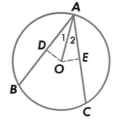

★11. State and prove converses of Ex. 10.

★12. (a) Draw a circle with radius 2 in. In it in-scribe any quadrilateral. Construct the perpendicular-bisectors of the sides of the quadrilateral.
   (b) Through what point do the perpendicular-bisectors pass?

★13. Given an arc of a circle of which the radius and the center are un-known. By proper constructions, determine the center of the circle.

★14. A straight line cuts two concentric circles (two circles with the same center) in points A, B, C, and D, in order, along the line. Prove AB = CD.

Suggestion. Draw a perpendicular to the line through the common center.

182. *In the same circle or in equal circles, if chords are equal, they are equidistant from the center.*

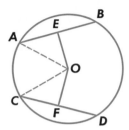

Hypothesis.   In $\odot O$,
$$AB = CD, OE \perp AB, OF \perp CD$$

Conclusion. $OE = OF$

Plan. Prove OE and OF corres. parts of congruent $\triangle$.

Proof.

Statements	Authorities
1. Draw OA and OC.	1. Why possible?
2. $\therefore$ $AE = \frac{1}{2}AB, CF = \frac{1}{2}CD$	2. Why?
3. But $AB = CD$.	3. Why?
4. $\therefore$ $AE = CF$.	4. Why?
(Complete the proof.)	

183. *In the same circle or in equal circles, if chords are equi-distant from the center, they are equal.*

Hypothesis.   In $\odot O$,
$$OE \perp AB, OF \perp CD, OE = OF$$

Conclusion. $AB = CD$

Plan. Prove $AE = CF$ by means of cong. $\triangle$; then prove $AB = CD$.

(Proof left to the pupil.)

1. Two equal chords intersect inside a circle. Prove that the radius drawn to the point of intersection bisects the angle between them.

Suggestion. From the center of the circle, draw a perpendicular to each chord. Use Fundamental Plan 1.

2. What is the relation between the theorems in §182 and §183?

184. A **secant** of a circle is a straight line that cuts the circle in two points, as lines ABE and DCE in Ex. 1, below.

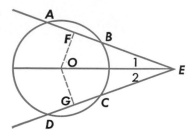

1. ABE and DCE are two secants. If $\angle 1 = \angle 2$, prove that chord AB equals chord DC.

2. Draw two equal circles. Construct a line parallel to the line through the centers of the circles, cutting each of the circles. Prove that the parts of this parallel that are chords of the two circles are equal.

3. Draw two concentric circles. Draw a diameter AB of the larger circle and a diameter XY of the smaller. Prove that $AXBY$ is a parallelogram.

4. Prove that a diameter of a circle that bisects one of two parallel chords of the circle must bisect the other also.

5. Construct two parallel chords AB and CD and the perpendicular-bisector of AB intersecting CD at X. How does CX compare with DX? Prove your conclusion.

6. XOY is a diameter of circle O. XZ and WY are parallel chords of the circle. Prove $XZ = WY$.

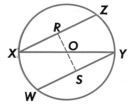

Suggestion. Draw $OR \perp XZ$ and $OS \perp WY$. Prove that $OR = OS$.

★7. In Ex. 6, prove that $XW = ZY$.

★8. Using the facts proved in Ex. 6 and Ex. 7, prove that WZ is a diameter of the circle.

★9. AB and CD are parallel and equal chords of a circle O. XY is drawn from X on AB through center O to Y on CD. Prove that $OX = OY$.

Suggestion. Draw $ROS \perp AB$, meeting CD at S.

10. Construct a circle with 2-inch radius. In it, construct a chord AB whose distance from the center of the circle is 1 inch. Find the length of this chord, correct to 16ths of an inch.

Suggestion. Use the following theorem learned in an earlier grade: *The square of the hypotenuse of a right triangle equals the sum of the squares of the other two sides.* It will be proved later.

185. *In the same circle or in equal circles, if two chords are unequal, the shorter of the chords is at the greater distance from the center of the circle.*

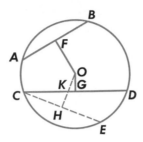

Hypothesis. $AB < CD$, $OF \perp AB$, $OG \perp CD$

Conclusion. $OF > OG$

Proof.

Statements	Authorities
1. $AB < CD$	1. Hyp.
2. $\therefore \ \ \overset{\frown}{AB} < \overset{\frown}{CD}$	2. Why?
3. On $\overset{\frown}{CD}$, take $\overset{\frown}{CE} = \overset{\frown}{AB}$.	3. Why possible?
4. $\therefore \ \ CE = AB$	4. Why?
5. Draw $OH \perp CE$, cutting CD at K.	5. §77*, p. 77
6. $OH > OK$	6. Why?
7. $OK > OG$	7. §157, p. 145
8. $\therefore \ \ OH > OG$	8. Ax. 11, p. 143
9. $OF = OH$	9. Why?
10. $\therefore \ \ OF > OG$	10. Why?

186. *In the same circle or in equal circles, if two chords are unequally distant from the center, the chord at the greater distance is the shorter.*

Hypothesis. $OF \perp AB$, $OG \perp CD$, $OF > OG$

Conclusion. $AB < CD$

Plan. Use the indirect method of proof.

Suggestions. Assume that $AB = CD$, and determine the consequences. Similarly assume that $AB > CD$.

* O and CE are on opposite sides of CD. $\therefore$ OH must cross CD at a point K.

187. Tangent line. (*a*) If secant AB turns about point A in the direction indicated by the arrow, point B moves toward A. When B finally coincides with A, secant AB takes the position of XY. XY is called a **tangent to the circle**.

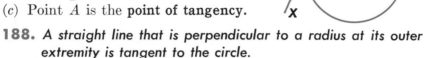

(*b*) *A tangent to a circle touches the circle at only one point.* The circle is said to be tangent to the line.

(*c*) Point A is the **point of tangency.**

188. *A straight line that is perpendicular to a radius at its outer extremity is tangent to the circle.*

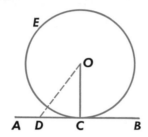

Hypothesis. OC is a radius of $\odot O$. $AB \perp OC$ at C.

Conclusion. AB is tangent to $\odot O$.

Plan. Prove all points of AB except C are outside $\odot O$.

Proof.

Statements	Authorities
1. From O, draw OD to D any point on AB except point C.	1. Why possible?
2. $OC \perp AB$	2. Why?
3. ∴ OD is not $\perp AB$.	3. §106, p. 108
4. ∴ $OD > OC$	4. Why?
5. ∴ D lies outside $\odot O$.	5. §167(c), p. 161
6. ∴ AB is tangent to $\odot O$.	6. §187(b)

189. *A tangent to a circle is perpendicular to the radius drawn to the point of tangency.*

In §188, since all points in AB except C lie outside the circle, OC is the shortest segment to AB from O. ∴$OC \perp AB$.

190. *A line perpendicular to a tangent at its point of tangency passes through the center of the circle.*

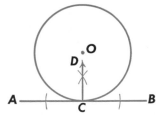

Let CD be $\perp AB$. By §189, the radius OC is $\perp AB$. Hence OC and DC coincide. (Why?) $\therefore$ CD passes through O.

191. *A line from the center of a circle perpendicular to a tangent passes through the point of tangency.*

$OC \perp AB$, by §189. A line from $O \perp AB$ must coincide with OC by §106, p. 108.

192. *The tangents to a circle from an outside point:*
(a) *Are equal.*
(b) *Make equal angles with the line that joins the point to the center of the circle.*

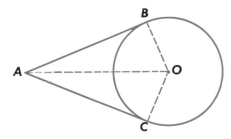

Hypothesis. AB and AC are tangents to $\odot O$ from A.

Conclusion. (*a*) $AB = AC$
(*b*) $\angle OAB = \angle OAC$

Plan. Draw AO, OB, and OC. Use §189.

193. Cor. *The bisector of the angle between two tangents to a circle from a point passes through the center of the circle.*

Plan. Let AX bisect $\angle CAB$. Draw AO. Prove that AX must coincide with AO by using §192(*b*) and Post. 7, p. 34.

194. **A polygon is circumscribed** about a circle when all its sides are tangent to the circle, as quadrilateral $EFGH$.

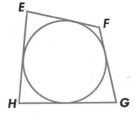

The circle is said to be **inscribed in the polygon.**

1. (*a*) Draw a circle and one of its diameters. At each end of the diameter construct a tangent to the circle. What kind of lines do the tangents appear to be?

   (*b*) Prove your tentative conclusion.

2. From a point draw two tangents to a circle, and then draw the chord joining their points of contact. Prove that the chord makes equal angles with the two tangents.

3. If *AB* and *AC* are tangents to circle *O*, prove that *OA* bisects ∠*COB*.

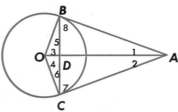

4. With the hypothesis of Ex. 3, prove also that *OA* is the perpendicular-bisector of *BC*.

5. Construct a chord *AB* of a circle *O*, a radius perpendicular to *AB*, meeting arc *AB* at *C*, and a tangent to the circle at *C*. Prove that *AB* is parallel to the tangent.

6. Draw any chord of a circle. Construct two tangents to the circle, each of which shall be parallel to the chord.

7. If the angle formed by two tangents to a circle from a point contains 60°, prove that the chord joining the points of tangency equals each of the tangents.

★8. If two circles are concentric, any chords of the greater that are tangents of the smaller are equal.

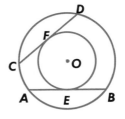

Suggestion. Draw *OF* and *OE*.

★9. Prove that all tangents drawn from the larger of two concentric circles to the smaller are equal.

Suggestion. In the figure for Ex. 8, prove *CF* = *AE*.

★10. Prove that the sum of two opposite sides of a circumscribed quadrilateral is equal to the sum of the other two opposite sides.

★11. The perpendicular to any side of a circumscribed polygon at its point of tangency passes through the center of the circle.

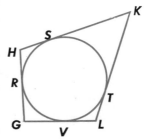

Note. Ex. 98 through Ex. 108, pp. 395 and 396, can be done now.

195. *Parallel lines intercept equal arcs on a circle.*

 Case. 1. When one line is a tangent and one a secant.

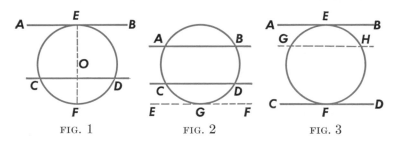

FIG. 1 FIG. 2 FIG. 3

Hypothesis. AB is tangent to $\odot O$ at E. (Fig. 1)
 Secant $CD \parallel AB$.

Conclusion. $\overset{\frown}{CE} = \overset{\frown}{ED}$

Plan. Prove diameter $EOF \perp CD$ and bisects $\overset{\frown}{CED}$.

Proof.

Statements	Authorities
1. Draw diameter EOF.	1. Why possible?
2. ∴ $EF \perp AB$	2. §189, p. 172
3. ∴ $EF \perp CD$	3. Why?
4. ∴ $\overset{\frown}{CE} = \overset{\frown}{ED}$	4. Why?

Case 2. When both lines are secants. (Fig. 2)

Hypothesis. AB and CD are parallel secants of the circle.

Conclusion. $\overset{\frown}{AC} = \overset{\frown}{BD}$

Plan. Assume EGF tangent to the circle at G, and parallel to CD. Compare $\overset{\frown}{ACG}$ and $\overset{\frown}{BDG}$, also $\overset{\frown}{CG}$ and $\overset{\frown}{DG}$.

Case 3. When both lines are tangents. (Fig. 3)

Hypothesis. AB and CD are tangent to circle O at E and F.

Conclusion. $\overset{\frown}{EGF} = \overset{\frown}{EHF}$

Plan. Draw $GH \parallel AB$. Compare $\overset{\frown}{GE}$ and $\overset{\frown}{EH}$, by Case 2; also compare $\overset{\frown}{GF}$ and $\overset{\frown}{FH}$. Add.

TEST A (Pages 161 to 175)

1. Prove that the chords that join in order the ends of two diameters of a circle form a parallelogram.

2. Point C bisects arc AB of a circle O. COD is the diameter from C to a point D of the circle. BO and AO are radii.
Prove: (*a*) $\angle DOA = \angle DOB$ (*b*) DC bisects $\angle ADB$.

3. Place points X, Y, Z, and W in order on a circle so that arc XY equals arc WZ. Draw quadrilateral $XYZW$.
(*a*) Prove that diagonals XZ and YW are equal.
(*b*) Prove $\angle XYZ$ equals $\angle WZY$.
(*c*) State and prove the converse of part (*a*).

4. Several chords of a circle are parallel. Prove that a diameter of the circle that is perpendicular to one of the chords bisects each of the chords.

5. If the angle between the two tangents to a circle from a point that is outside the circle measures 80°, how large is the angle formed by either tangent with the chord that joins the points of tangency?

6. Prove that the tangent to a circle at the mid-point of an arc of the circle is parallel to the chord of the arc.

TEST B (Cumulative Test)

1. On diagonal XZ of $\square XWZY$, place R near X and S near Z so that XR equals SZ. Draw YR, RW, WS, and SY.
Prove: (*a*) $YS \parallel RW$ (*b*) YW bisects RS.

2. Prove that the diagonals and the bases of an isosceles trapezoid form two isosceles triangles.

3. EF cuts parallels AB and CD at E and F respectively. EX bisects $\angle AEF$, meeting CD at X. EY bisects $\angle FEB$, meeting CD at Y.
Prove: (*a*) $XE \perp YE$ (*b*) $XF = FY$

4. Draw quadrilateral $ABDC$ so that $AB = BD$, $AC = CD$, and $AC > AB$. Prove that $\angle ABD > \angle ACD$.

5. In $\square XYZW$, $XY < YZ$. Prove that diagonal YW does not bisect either $\angle Y$ or $\angle W$.

6. If R and S bisect parallel sides BC and AD respectively of isosceles trapezoid $ADCB$, prove that RS is perpendicular to AD and to BC.

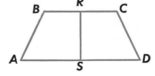

1. From point E on diagonal AC of square $ABCD$, EF is drawn perpendicular to AC, meeting AD at F. How many degrees are there in $\angle AFE$?

2. $\triangle RST$ is inscribed in circle O. $RS = RT$. Prove that the bisector of $\angle SRT$ passes through center O.

Suggestion. Prove that the bisector is $\perp ST$. Then use §113(b).

3. $MNPQ$ is an inscribed trapezoid having bases MN and QP. MX and NX are tangents of the circle, meeting at X. Prove that the bisector of $\angle MXN$ is the perpendicular-bisector of each of the bases of the trapezoid. (Use §193.)

4. If one of the diagonals of a rhombus equals each of the sides of the rhombus, how large are the angles of the rhombus?

5. If a parallelogram is inscribed in a circle, its diagonals are equal, and it is a rectangle.

6. BOD is a diameter of circle O. OA and OC are radii, such that $\angle AOB = \angle COD$. BA and DC, extended, meet at F. Prove that $\triangle BFD$ is isosceles.

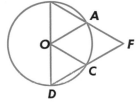

7. If XY and ZW are parallel chords of a circle, then $XW = YZ$, and $XZ = YW$.

8. If XY is one of the nonparallel sides of a trapezoid circumscribed about circle O, $\angle XOY$ is a right angle.

★9. In the figure for Ex. 8, prove that the median of the trapezoid equals one fourth of the perimeter of $XYZW$.

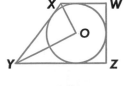

★10. $\triangle RST$ is an equilateral triangle circumscribed about circle O, with RS tangent at E, RT tangent at F, and ST tangent at G. Prove that the bisector of $\angle SRT$ passes through point G.

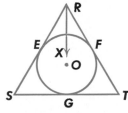

Suggestion. Use §193, p. 173. Prove RX, extended, is $\perp ST$. Use §191, p. 173.

★11. $ABCD$ is a rhombus. BX, DY, BW, and DZ are altitudes to the sides that they meet, intersecting at R and S, as in the adjoining figure.
Prove that $BSDR$ is a rhombus.

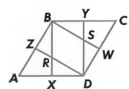

Suggestion. After proving $BSDR$ is a $\square$, prove
(1) $BW = DY$, and (2) $SW = SY$.

The rose window of the Cathedral of St. Nazaire in Carcasonne, France, illustrates how the circle can be used as the basis of a beautiful design.

196. **To measure a given quantity:**

(*a*) Select a unit of measure. This must be a quantity of the same kind as that being measured.

(*b*) Determine how many times the given quantity contains the unit of measure. This number is the measure of the given quantity in terms of the selected unit.

197. **Measuring angles and arcs.** The common unit for measuring angles is an **angle-degree.** (See §15, p. 21.)

If radii are drawn from center O of the circle so that 360 consecutive equal central angles are formed, then each of these angles is 1°. Let $\angle AOB$ *represent* 1°. ($\angle AOB$ is really larger.) These central angles divide the circle into 360 equal arcs. $\overset{\frown}{AB}$ represents one of these arcs. It is an **arc-degree.** (See §19, p. 23.)

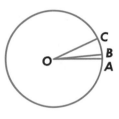

198. If $\angle AOC$ contains 25 angle-degrees, then $\overset{\frown}{AC}$ must contain 25 arc-degrees. Post. 14, p. 35 then becomes:

(*a*) *A central angle has the same measure as its arc* if the angle is measured by angle-degrees and parts thereof, and the arc is measured by arc-degrees and parts thereof.

(*b*) For the words *has the same measure as*, we shall write $\overset{m}{=}$, so that $\angle A \overset{m}{=} \overset{\frown}{BC}$ means $\angle A$ has the same measure as $\overset{\frown}{BC}$. Remember that this means that the number of angle-degrees in $\angle A$ equals the number of arc-degrees in $\overset{\frown}{BC}$.

Since the measures are numbers, the axioms on page 32 apply to them.

Thus: If $\angle A \overset{m}{=} \overset{\frown}{RS}$ and $\angle B \overset{m}{=} \overset{\frown}{ST}$,

then $\angle A + \angle B \overset{m}{=} (\overset{\frown}{RS} + \overset{\frown}{ST})$.

(*c*) A consequence of (*a*) is:

Central angles have the same ratio as their arcs.

Thus: If $\dfrac{\angle AOB}{\angle BOC} = \dfrac{1}{4}$, then $\dfrac{\overset{\frown}{AB}}{\overset{\frown}{BC}} = \dfrac{1}{4}$; or

if $\angle AOB = \frac{1}{4}\angle BOC$, then $\overset{\frown}{AB} = \frac{1}{4}\overset{\frown}{BC}$.

1. (a) What is an angle-degree? An angle-minute?
   (b) What geometric figure is an angle-degree?

2. (a) What is an arc-degree? An arc-minute?
   (b) What geometric figure is an arc-degree?

3. Are all angle-degrees of the same size?

4. Are all arc-degrees of the same size?

5. What is meant by: (a) $\overset{\frown}{XY} = 30°$? (b) $\angle M = 30°$?

6. By drawing two perpendicular diameters, locate points A, B, C, and D, in order, that separate circle O into four equal arcs. What kind of and how many degrees are there in $\overset{\frown}{AB}$ and in $\angle AOB$?

7. Suppose that circle O is separated into five equal arcs and that $\overset{\frown}{AB}$ is one of the arcs. How many degrees are there in $\overset{\frown}{AB}$? In $\angle AOB$?

8. In the adjoining figure, compare $\overset{\frown}{AB}$ and $\overset{\frown}{BC}$, also $\overset{\frown}{AB}$ and $\overset{\frown}{DC}$, also $\overset{\frown}{BC}$ and $\overset{\frown}{DC}$.

9. In a circle O, $\angle XOY$ is a right angle, and XOZ is a diameter.
   (a) What part of $\angle XOZ$ is $\angle XOY$?
   (b) What part of $\overset{\frown}{XYZ}$ is $\overset{\frown}{XY}$?

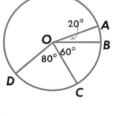

10. The total angle around a point is called a **perigon.**
    (a) What part of a perigon is a 60° angle?
    (b) What part of the circle is the arc whose central angle contains 60°?

11. If GH, any chord of a circle Q, is extended through H to K so that HK equals the radius of the circle, and KQ is drawn, cutting the circle at Z and E respectively, then $\overset{\frown}{GE} = 3\overset{\frown}{HZ}$.
    Suggestions. 1. Draw QG and QH. 2. Prove $\angle GQE = 3\angle HQZ$.

12. In a circle construct a central angle of 45°. How large is the arc of the angle?

199. An **inscribed angle** is the angle formed by two chords that meet at a point on the circle, as $\angle ABC$.

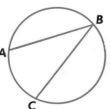

    $\angle ABC$ *intercepts* (or cuts out) $\overset{\frown}{AC}$.
$\overset{\frown}{AC}$ is *the arc of* $\angle ABC$.
    $\angle ABC$ is said to be **inscribed in the circle** or **in the arc** ABC.

200. *An inscribed angle has the same measure as half its arc.*

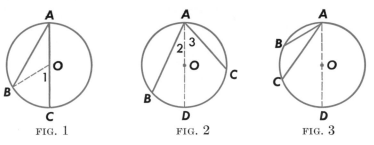

FIG. 1   FIG. 2   FIG. 3

Hypothesis. $\angle BAC$ is inscribed in $\odot O$.

Conclusion. $\angle BAC$ has the same measure as $\frac{1}{2}\widehat{BC}$.

(*a*) *Let the center of the circle lie on one side of the angle.*   (Fig. 1)

Proof.

Statements	Authorities
1.　　　Draw BO forming $\angle BOC$.	1. Why possible?
2.　　　　$\angle 1 = \angle A + \angle B$	2. Why?
3.　　$\therefore$　$\angle 1 = 2\angle A$, or $\angle A = \frac{1}{2}\angle 1$	3. Give full proof.
4.　　　　$\angle 1 \overset{m}{=} \widehat{BC}$	4. §198(*a*) *
5.　　$\therefore$　$\angle A \overset{m}{=} \frac{1}{2}\widehat{BC}$	5. Ax. 2, Ax. 6, p. 32

(*b*) *Let the center of the circle lie inside the angle.*   (Fig. 2)

Proof.

Statements	Authorities
1.　　　Draw diameter AOD.	1. Why possible?
2.　　　　$\angle 2 \overset{m}{=} \frac{1}{2}\widehat{BD}$	2. By part (*a*).
$\angle 3 \overset{m}{=} \frac{1}{2}\widehat{DC}$	
3.　　$\therefore$　$\angle 2 + \angle 3 \overset{m}{=} \frac{1}{2}(\widehat{BD} + \widehat{DC})$	3. Ax. 3
4.　　$\therefore$　$\angle BAC \overset{m}{=} \frac{1}{2}\widehat{BC}$	4. Ax. 7, Ax. 2

(*c*) *Let the center of the circle lie outside the angle.*   (Fig. 3)

Plan. Draw AOD. Measure $\angle BAD$ and $\angle CAD$. Subtract.

* Remember that " $\overset{m}{=} \widehat{BC}$" means that the number of angle-degrees in $\angle 1$ is the same as the number of arc-degrees in $\widehat{BC}$.

201. Cor. 1. *An angle inscribed in a semicircle is a right angle.*

Suggestion. At the right, what is the measure of ∠A?

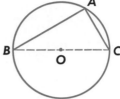

202. Cor. 2. *In the same circle or in equal circles, if inscribed angles have the same arc or equal arcs, they are equal.*

Suggestion. Draw two or more inscribed angles in a circle, all having the same arc. What is the measure of each?

203. Cor. 3. *In the same circle or in equal circles, if inscribed angles are equal, their arcs are equal.*

1. In §200, Fig. 1, how many degrees are there in ∠BAC:
   (a) If $\widehat{BC} = 50°$?   (b) If $\widehat{BC} = 70°$?   (c) If $\widehat{BC} = 85°$?

2. In §200, Fig. 2, how many degrees are there in ∠BAC:
   (a) If $\widehat{BDC} = 100°$?   (b) If $\widehat{AB} = 100°$ and $\widehat{DC} = 70°$?

3. In §200, Fig. 3, how many degrees are there in ∠BAC:
   (a) If $\widehat{BC} = 45°$?   (b) If $\widehat{AB} = 20°$ and $\widehat{CD} = 80°$?

4. What kind of angle is an inscribed angle whose arc is:
   (a) Less than a semicircle?
   (b) Greater than a semicircle?

5. In the drawing at the right, if $\widehat{BC} = \widehat{AD}$, prove $AC \parallel BD$.

6. Prove the converse of Ex. 5.

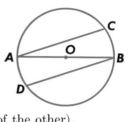

7. Chords XY and ZW intersect at E, inside a circle. Prove that $\triangle XZE$ and $\triangle YWE$ are mutually equiangular (the angles of one are equal respectively to the corresponding angles of the other).

8. Prove that the bisector of an inscribed angle, extended, bisects the arc of the angle.

9. Prove that the opposite angles of an inscribed quadrilateral are supplementary.

Suggestion. What is the measure of ∠D? Of ∠B? Therefore, ∠B + ∠D = ?

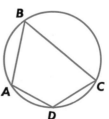

Note. Ex. 109 through Ex. 120, pp. 396 and 397, can be done now.

204. *The angle formed by a tangent and chord drawn to the point of tangency has the same measure as one half the intercepted arc.*

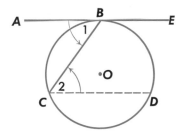

Hypothesis. AE is tangent to $\odot O$ at B. BC is a chord.

Conclusion. $\angle ABC$ has the same measure as $\frac{1}{2}\overset{\frown}{BC}$.

Proof.

	Statements	Authorities
1.	From C, draw $CD \parallel AE$.	1. Why possible?
2.	$\angle 1 = ?$	2. Why?
3.	$\angle 2 \overset{m}{=} ?$	3. §200
4.	$\therefore \quad \angle 1 \overset{m}{=} ?$	4. Ax. 2, p. 32
5.	But $\overset{\frown}{BC} = \overset{\frown}{BD}$.	5. §195, p. 175
6.	$\therefore \quad \angle 1 \overset{m}{=} ?$	6. Ax. 2

1. How many degrees are there in $\angle ABC$ and in $\angle EBC$:

   (a) If $\overset{\frown}{BC} = 80°$?   (b) If $\overset{\frown}{BDC} = 200°$?   (c) If $\overset{\frown}{CD} = 60°$?

2. Tangents are drawn to a circle at the ends of a chord. Prove that they make equal angles with the chord.

3. Two tangents drawn to a circle from a point P meet the circle at points X and Y. If minor arc $XY = 80°$, how large is each angle of $\triangle PXY$?

4. Prove that the tangent to a circle at the mid-point of an arc is parallel to the chord of the arc.

5. The bisector of the angle formed by a tangent and a chord drawn to the point of tangency bisects the arc of the chord.

6. How many arc-degrees are there in $\overset{\frown}{BC}$ and $\overset{\frown}{BDC}$ in §204:
   (a) When $\angle ABC = 45°$?   (b) When $\angle CBE = 140°$?

205. *The angle formed by two chords intersecting within a circle has the same measure as one half the sum of the arcs intercepted by it and its vertical angle.*

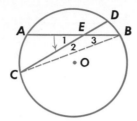

Hypothesis. Chords AB and CD intersect at E within $\odot O$.

Conclusion. $\angle AEC \overset{m}{=} \frac{1}{2}(\overset{\frown}{AC} + \overset{\frown}{BD})$.

Plan. Find two angles whose sum equals $\angle AEC$.

Proof.

Statements	Authorities
1. Draw CB, forming $\triangle CEB$.	1. Why possible?
2. Then $\angle 1 = \angle 2 + \angle 3$.	2. §109, p. 109
3. $\angle 2 \overset{m}{=} ?$	3. Why?
$\angle 3 \overset{m}{=} ?$	
4. $\therefore$ $\angle 1 \overset{m}{=} \frac{1}{2}(\overset{\frown}{AC} + \overset{\frown}{DB})$	4. Ax. 2, p. 32

1. How large is $\angle AEC$ if $\overset{\frown}{AC} = 60°$ and $\overset{\frown}{DB} = 40°$?

2. How large is $\overset{\frown}{AC}$ if $\angle AEC = 80°$ and $\overset{\frown}{DB} = 30°$?

3. How large is $\angle CEB$ if $\overset{\frown}{AC} = 45°$ and $\overset{\frown}{DB} = 25°$?

4. Two chords intersect at right angles. Prove that the sum of either pair of opposite arcs is a semicircle.

★**5.** If $\overset{\frown}{XA} - 30°$, $\overset{\frown}{YC} = 30°$, $\overset{\frown}{AC} = 80°$, and $\overset{\frown}{BX} = \overset{\frown}{BY}$, find the size of each of the angles of $\triangle MBN$.

★**6.** If $\overset{\frown}{AX} = \overset{\frown}{CY}$ and $\overset{\frown}{AB} = \overset{\frown}{CB}$, prove $\triangle MNB$ is an isosceles triangle.

★**7.** If a point lies inside a circle, the segments that join it to the ends of a diameter form an obtuse angle.

★**8.** Isosceles $\triangle ABC$, having $AB = AC$, is inscribed in a circle O. Prove that the bisectors of $\angle B$ and $\angle C$ are equidistant from O.

206. *The angle formed by two secants intersecting outside a circle has the same measure as one half the difference of the arcs cut from the circle by it.*

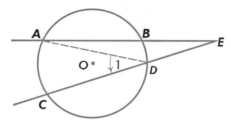

Hypothesis. AE and CE intersect at E outside $\odot O$.

Conclusion. $\angle E \overset{m}{=} \tfrac{1}{2}(\overset{\frown}{AC} - \overset{\frown}{DB})$

Plan. Express $\angle E$ as the difference of two ⧓ that can be measured.

Proof.

Statements	Authorities
1. Draw AD forming $\triangle ADE$.	1. Why possible?
2. $\therefore$ $\angle A + \angle E = \angle 1$	2. Why?
3. $\therefore$ $\angle E = \angle 1 - \angle A$	3. Why?
(Complete this proof.)	

207. **Cor. 1.** *The angle formed by a secant and a tangent has the same measure as one half the difference of its arcs.*
  Prove $\angle E \overset{m}{=} \tfrac{1}{2}(\overset{\frown}{BC} - \overset{\frown}{DB})$.

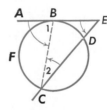

208. **Cor. 2.** *The angle formed by two tangents has the same measure as one half the difference of its arcs.*
  Prove $\angle E \overset{m}{=} \tfrac{1}{2}(\overset{\frown}{BFD} - \overset{\frown}{BGD})$.

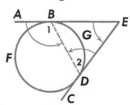

1. In §206, if $\overset{\frown}{AC} = 120°$ and $\overset{\frown}{BD} = 30°$, how large is $\angle E$?

2. In §206, if $\overset{\frown}{AC} = 100°$ and $\angle E = 30°$, how large is $\overset{\frown}{BD}$?

3. In §206, if $\overset{\frown}{AC} = 80°$ and $\angle A = 15°$, how large is $\angle E$?

Note. Ex. 121 through Ex. 136, pp. 397 and 398, can be done now.

209. *A tangent to a circle can be constructed:*
  (a) *At a point on the circle.*
  (b) *From a point not on the circle.*

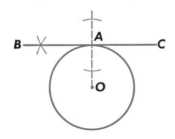

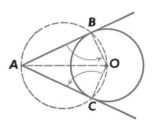

(*a*) **Given.** Point A on circle O.

  Required. To construct a tangent to $\odot O$ at A.
  (Construction suggested by figure (*a*). The description of the construction and the proof of its correctness are left to the pupil.)

(*b*) **Given.** Point A not on circle O.

  Required. To construct tangents to $\odot O$ from A.

Construction	Authorities
1. On OA as diameter, construct a $\odot$.	1. §74, p. 75; Post. 11, p. 34
2. The $\odot$ on OA cuts $\odot O$ at B and C.	2. Post. 21, p. 51
3. Draw AB and AC.	3. Why possible?

Statement. AB and AC are tangents to $\odot O$.

Plan. Prove AB and $AC \perp$ to the radii OB and OC.

1. (*a*) Draw a circle with radius 1 in. By constructing two perpendicular diameters, locate four points that divide the circle into four equal arcs. At each of the points, construct a tangent to the circle.
  (*b*) Prove that the four tangents form a square.

2. Draw a circle with radius 1 in. Locate a point that is 3 in. from the center of this circle. From this point, construct two tangents to the circle.

Top: Elevator cables are tangent to a cylinder.
Bottom: The problem of joining a clover-leaf and a road is essentially that of finding a tangent to a circle.
TOP: A. DEVANEY, INC., NEW YORK   BOTTOM: EWING GALLOWAY, NEW YORK

1. The radius of a circle is 2 in. Where is a point X if its distance from the center of the circle is:
   (*a*) 2.5 in.?   (*b*) 1.8 in.?   (*c*) 2 in.?

   In questions 2 through 11, are the statements true or false? Why?

2. Circle O passes through A, B, and C when C is a point in line AB.

3. Straight line RS cuts circle P at points X, Y, and Z.

4. In circle O, chord AB = chord XY; $\overset{\frown}{AB} = \overset{\frown}{XY}$.

5. Chord AB = chord CD; center O of the circle is 2 in. from AB and 2.1 in. from CD.

6. In equal circles O and R, $\angle AOB = 40°$ and $\angle XRY = 40°$. $\overset{\frown}{AB} = \overset{\frown}{XY}$.

7. From point P only one tangent can be drawn to circle X.

8. $XY \perp$ radius OR of circle O at its end R; XY touches the circle also at a point S.

9. The arc of inscribed $\angle CPB$ measures 40°; $\angle CPB = 80°$.

10. The opposite arcs intercepted between two chords contain 30° and 50°. The angle between the chords contains 80°.

11. Chords RS and XY are each 3 in. from the centers of their circles. RS is a chord of a circle of radius 2 in. and XY of a circle of radius 4 in.; $RS = XY$.

12. In circle P, central $\angle$s 1, 2, and 3 are equal. The arc of $\angle 1 = 27°$. How large are the arcs of $\angle 2$ and $\angle 3$?

13. On circle T there are four equal arcs; each arc has a central angle. One of these central angles contains 18°. How large is each of the other central angles?

14. In Ex. 13 the chords of the arcs are drawn. One of these chords is .8 in. long. How long is each of the other chords?

15. In circle O radius $ODC \perp AB$ at D. $AD = 1.5$ in. and $\overset{\frown}{AC} = 32°$.
    (*a*) How long is DB?
    (*b*) How long is AB?
    (*c*) How large is $\overset{\frown}{ACB}$?
    (*d*) How large is $\angle COB$?
    (*e*) How large is $\angle AOB$?

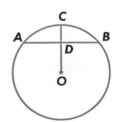

16. If $AE = EB$ and $\overset{\frown}{AC} = \overset{\frown}{CB}$:
   (a) Is $CE \perp AB$? Why?
   (b) Through what point will CE pass if it is extended downward?

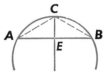

17. In circle O, $AB = CD$. $\overset{\frown}{ACB}$ contains 168°. How large is $\overset{\frown}{CBD}$?

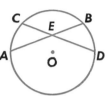

18. In circle O, $AB = CD$. AB is 2 in. from O. How far from O is CD?

19. In circle O, if $AB = 6$ in. and CD equals 5 in., which chord is nearer to O?

20. In circle O, if $\overset{\frown}{CA} = 40°$ and $\overset{\frown}{DB} = 60°$, $\angle CEA = ?$

21. $XY \perp$ radius RS at S. What is XY?

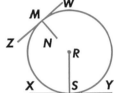

22. If $MN \perp ZW$ at M, and ZW is tangent to $\odot R$ at M, through what point will MN pass if it is extended?

23. $\angle OAB$ and $\angle OCB$ are right angles.
   (a) How long is BC if $AB = 10$ in.?
   (b) $\angle OBC = 20°$. How large is $\angle ABC$?

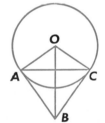

24. If $\angle AOC = 100°$, how large is $\overset{\frown}{AC}$?

25. If $\overset{\frown}{AC} = 160°$, how large is $\angle ABC$?

26. If $\overset{\frown}{AC} = 160°$, how large is $\angle ACB$?

27. (a) If $EF \parallel HG$ and $\overset{\frown}{EH} = 140°$, how large is $\overset{\frown}{FG}$?

   (b) If also $EH \parallel FG$, how large are $\overset{\frown}{EF}$ and $\overset{\frown}{GH}$?

28. If $EH = 1.2$ in., in Ex. 27(a), how long is FG?

29. At the right, $\overset{\frown}{MR} = 120°$, and $\overset{\frown}{NS} = 60°$, how large is $\angle MTR$?

30. O is the center of the circle.
   (a) If MN equals RS and $\angle 1 = 15°$, how large is $\angle MTR$?

   (b) If $OX \perp MT$ and $OY \perp RT$, and $OX = OY = 5$ in., how long is RS if $MN = 4$ in.?

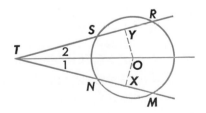

THEOREMS ABOUT TWO CIRCLES

210. (*a*) The **line of centers** of two circles is the straight line joining their centers, as *OR*.

(*b*) A **common tangent** of two circles is tangent to each of them. It may be a **common internal tangent** like *CD* or a **common external tangent** like *AB*. There are generally two of each kind.

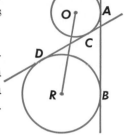

(*c*) The **length of a common tangent** is the length of it between its points of tangency, as *AB* or *CD*.

BELTS AROUND PULLEYS   CHAIN AROUND WHEELS

1. Prove that the common external tangents of two equal circles are parallel to their line of centers and equal.

2. Prove that either common internal tangent of two equal circles bisects their line of centers.

3. Prove that the common internal tangents of any two circles are equal. That is, prove that *AB* = *CD*.

4. Prove that the common external tangents of any two circles are equal.

Suggestion. Extend *XY* and *ZW* to a point *K*.

5. In Ex. 3, prove that *OR* passes through *E*.

Suggestion. Draw *OE* and *ER*. Prove *OER* is a straight line.

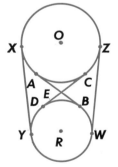

211. **Circles are tangent** to each other when they are both tangent to the same line at the same point. They are **tangent internally** if they are on the same side of their common tangent, as circles *A* and *B*. They are **tangent externally** if they are on opposite sides of their common tangent, as circles *C* and *D*.

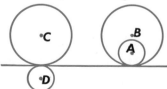

212. *If two circles are tangent externally, their line of centers passes through the point of tangency.*

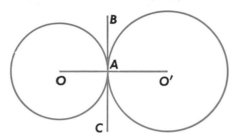

Hypothesis. ⊙O and O' are both tangent to CB at A.

OO' is the line of centers.

Conclusion. Line OO' passes through A.

Plan. Prove that OA and $O'A$ form a straight line that coincides with OO'.

Proof.

Statements	Authorities
1. Draw radii OA and $O'A$.	1. Why possible?
2. ∴ $OA \perp AB$ and $O'A \perp AB$.	2. §189, p. 172
3. ∴ $\angle O'AB + \angle BAO = 1$ st. $\angle$	3. Give the proof.
4. ∴ $O'AO$ is a st. line.	4. Post. 18, p. 35
5. ∴ $O'AO$ and $O'O$ coincide.	5. Post. 1, p. 34
6. ∴ OO' passes through A.	6. Since $O'AO$ does.

213. (a) *If two circles are tangent internally, their line of centers passes through their point of tangency.*

(b) *If the distance between the centers of two circles equals the sum of their radii, the circles are tangent externally.*

A point X can be taken on OO' so that OX is one radius and $O'X$ is the other. A perpendicular to OO' at X will then be tangent to each of the circles. Hence the circles are tangent. (§211)

(c) *If the distance between the centers of two circles equals the difference of their radii, the circles are tangent internally.*

1. Construct circles with radii 3 in., 4 in., and 5 in., each of which shall be tangent to each of the other two.

1. If a straight line through the point of tangency of two externally tangent circles terminates in the circles, tangents to the circles at its ends are parallel. (Prove $AC \parallel DE$.)

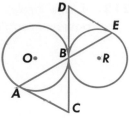

Suggestion. Draw DBC, the common internal tangent. Using $\triangle DBE$ and ACB, prove that $\angle DEB = \angle CAB$.

2. In the figure for Ex. 1, prove radii OA and RE are parallel.

3. Prove Ex. 1 when the circles are tangent internally.

4. Prove Ex. 2 when the circles are tangent internally.

5. If two circles are tangent externally at point A, the common internal tangent through A bisects the two common external tangents.

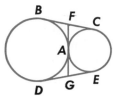

6. Two circles are tangent to each other externally at point A. Prove that the tangents to them from any point in their common tangent through A are equal.

7. Prove Ex. 6 when the circles are tangent internally.

8. Two circles are tangent externally at P. In one circle, $\triangle HKP$ is inscribed. HP and KP are extended, meeting the other circle at L and M respectively. Prove $LM \parallel HK$.

Suggestion. Draw the common tangent through point P.

9. Prove Ex. 8 when the two circles are tangent internally.

10. In the figure for Ex. 5, prove $BA \perp CA$.

11. Euclid's construction for the tangent to a circle with center M from a point A outside it was as follows:
    (1) Draw the circle with center M and radius MA.
    (2) Draw MA intersecting the given circle at B.
    (3) Draw $BC \perp MA$ at B, meeting the larger circle at C.
    (4) Draw MC intersecting the given circle at D.

    Statement. AD is tangent to the given circle. Make the construction and give the proof.

12. (*a*) Construct circles with radii 1 in. and 2 in. respectively, that are tangent externally at a point P.
    (*b*) Select point R on the common internal tangent so that PR equals 2 in. Construct the other tangent from R to each circle. Measure these tangents.

214. *If two circles intersect, their line of centers is the perpendicular-bisector of their common chord.*

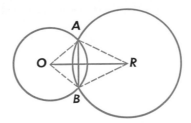

Hypothesis. Circles O and R intersect at A and B.

Conclusion. OR is the $\perp$-bisector of AB.

Plan. Draw OA, OB, RA, and RB.
(Proof left to the pupil.)

1. Prove the theorem of §214 for two circles like the ones adjoining.

2. If two circles O and R intersect at points M and N, and if OR extended intersects $\odot O$ at X and $\odot R$ at Y, then X and Y are each equidistant from M and N.

3. Two circles intersect at B and E. Secants ABC and DEF are drawn. Prove that AD is parallel to CF.

Suggestion. Try to prove that $\angle A$ plus $\angle C$ is one st. $\angle$, by comparing them with $\angle 1$ and $\angle 2$ respectively. Recall Ex. 9, p. 182.

4. Investigate the consequences of Ex. 3 when ABC and DEF are parallel.

5. If two circles intersect, their line of centers extended passes through the point of intersection of their common external tangents.

Suggestion. Draw OP and RP. Prove that each bisects $\angle APC$.

6. In the figure for Ex. 5, prove that AC, EF, and BD are parallel.

Suggestion. Prove $ORP \perp$ to AC, EF, and BD.

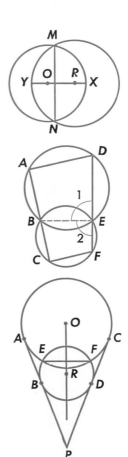

REMARKABLE POINTS AND CIRCLES

215. *The perpendicular-bisectors of the sides of a triangle meet at a point that is equidistant from the vertices of the triangle.*

Hypothesis. *FJ*, *DG*, and *EH* are the perpendicular-bisectors of the sides of $\triangle ABC$.

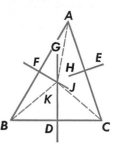

Conclusion. *FJ*, *DG*, and *EH* meet at a point that is equidistant from *A*, *B*, and *C*.

Plan. Prove *FJ* and *DG* intersect at a point that must lie on *EH*.

Informal Proof.

1.	*FJ* and *DG* meet at *K*.	See note.
2.	Then $KB = KA$ and $KB = KC$.	§113(a), p. 112
3.	∴ $KA = ?$	Why?
4.	Then *K* must lie on *EH*.	§113(b), p. 112

Note. If *FJ* ∥ *DG*, *AB* ∥ *BC* or coincides with *BC*. Why?

Therefore, *FJ* must intersect *DG*.

216. Cor. *One and only one circle can be drawn that will contain the vertices of a triangle, or circumscribe the triangle.*

Thus: Above, the circle with center *K* and radius *KA* will contain points *A*, *B*, and *C* (§167(c), p. 161). It is the only such circle because *FJ* and *DG* can intersect in only one point.

217. The **circumcenter of a triangle** is the point of intersection of the perpendicular-bisectors of the sides of the triangle.

1. (a) Construct an equilateral triangle whose sides are 3 inches in length.
   (b) Construct the circle that circumscribes it.

2. Construct an isosceles triangle whose base equals 3 inches, and whose equal sides are 2 inches. Circumscribe this triangle.

3. Construct a triangle whose three sides equal 2 inches, $2\frac{1}{2}$ inches, and 3 inches respectively. Construct the circle that circumscribes this triangle.

4. (a) Try to construct a triangle whose sides measure 2 inches, 2 inches, and 4 inches respectively.
   (b) What must be true of the lengths of the sides of a triangle?

218. *The bisectors of the angles of a triangle meet at a point that is equidistant from the sides of the triangle.*

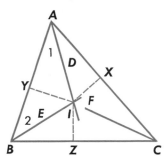

Hyp. AD, BE, and CF bisect the angles of $\triangle ABC$.

Con. AD, BE, and CF meet at a point, equidistant from the sides of $\triangle ABC$.

Plan. Prove AD and BE intersect at a point that must lie in CF.

Informal Proof.

1.   Let AD intersect BE at I.   See Note.
2. Draw $IX \perp AC$, $IY \perp AB$, and $IZ \perp BC$.   Possible.
3. $\therefore\ IX = IY,\ IZ = IY$ §114(*a*), p. 112
4. $\therefore\ IX = IY = IZ$ Why?
5. $\therefore\ I$ lies in CF.   §114(*b*), p. 112

Note. If $AD \parallel BE$, $\angle 1 + \angle 2 = 180°$. Impossible. Why?

219. Cor. *One and only one circle can be drawn that will be tangent to the sides of a triangle, or be inscribed in the triangle.*

Thus: Above, the circle with center I and radius IZ will be tangent to AB, AC, and BC. (§188, p. 172)

220. The **incenter of a triangle** is the point of intersection of the bisectors of the angles of the triangle.

221. By a proof like that above, *the bisectors of interior $\angle C$ and exterior angles at A and B intersect in a point O that is equidistant from the sides of* $\triangle ABC$. The circle with center O and radius OS will be tangent to CG, CH, and AB as in the

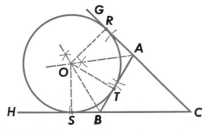

drawing. This circle is an **escribed circle** of $\triangle ABC$.

222. An **excenter of a triangle** is the center of an escribed circle.

1. Construct $\triangle ABC$ having $AC = 3$ in., $BC = 2$ in. and $AB = 2.5$ in. Construct the inscribed circle and *all* three escribed circles of $\triangle ABC$.

223. *The altitudes of a triangle meet at a point.*

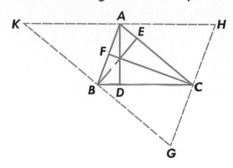

Hypothesis. AD, BE, and CF are the altitudes of $\triangle ABC$.

Conclusion. AD, BE, and CF meet at a point.

Plan. Form a second triangle in which AD, BE, and CF are the perpendicular-bisectors of the sides.

Proof.

Statements	Authorities
1. Through A, draw $KH \parallel BC$; through B, draw $KG \parallel AC$; and through C, draw $GH \parallel AB$, forming $\triangle GHK$.	1. Why possible?
2. Since $AD \perp BC$, then $AD \perp HK$.	2. Why?
3. $KACB$ is a parallelogram.	3. Why?
4. $\therefore$ $KA = BC$ Similarly $AH = BC$.	4. Why?
5. $\therefore$ $KA = AH$	5. Why?
6. $\therefore$ AD is the $\perp$-bisector of KH. Similarly BE is the $\perp$-bisector of GK, and CF is the $\perp$-bisector of GH.	6. Def.
7. $\therefore$ AD, BE, and CF meet at a point.	7. Why?

224. The **orthocenter of a triangle** is the point of intersection of the three altitudes of the triangle.

1. (*a*) Construct a $\triangle ABC$ having $AB = 2$ in., $BC = 3$ in. and $AC = 2$ in.
   (*b*) Find the orthocenter of $\triangle ABC$.
2. Prove that the *orthocenter*, *incenter*, and *circumcenter* of an equilateral triangle coincide.

1. If two opposite angles of a quadrilateral are supplementary, a circle can be drawn through the
vertices; that is, the vertices are *concyclic*.

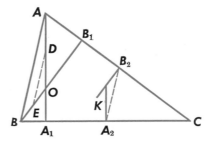

Hyp.   In $ABCD$, $\angle B + \angle ADC =$ one st. $\angle$.

Con. A, B, C, and D are concyclic.

Plan. A, B, and C lie on a circle ABC. Using the
hypothesis and Ex. 9, p. 182, prove by the indirect method:

(1) D cannot lie inside $\odot ABC$.

(2) D cannot lie outside $\odot ABC$.

2. If O is the orthocenter and K is
the circumcenter of $\triangle ABC$, then
$AO = 2KA_2$ and $BO = 2KB_2$,
where A_2 and B_2 are the mid-
points of BC and AC.

Plan. Let D bisect AO and E bisect BO.

Draw DE and A_2B_2.

Prove $\triangle ODE \cong \triangle KA_2B_2$.

3. The line that joins the orthocenter, O, and the circumcenter, K, of
$\triangle ABC$ passes through the center of gravity of $\triangle ABC$.

Plan. In the figure for Ex. 2, draw OK intersecting AA_2 at X.
Prove $AX = 2XA_2$. To do so, let Y bisect AX, and prove
$\triangle ADY \cong \triangle A_2KX$. Recall §146.

4. *An interesting conclusion suggested by inductive reasoning.*

(*a*) 1. Draw a large scalene
$\triangle ABC$. Let A_2, B_2, and C_2
be the mid-points of BC,
AC, and AB respectively.
Draw the altitudes AA_1,
BB_1, and CC_1 intersecting
at O. Let A_3, B_3, and C_3
bisect AO, BO, and CO respectively. Let N bisect
A_3A_2.

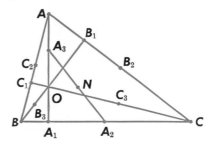

2. Draw the circle with center N and radius NA_2. Through what
points does the circle appear to pass?

(*b*) Repeat part (*a*) for a second triangle.

(*c*) What conclusion is suggested by parts (*a*) and (*b*)?

Note. A plan for proving this theorem appears in the *Teacher's Manual*.

SOME GEOMETRY OF THE SPHERE

225. A sphere in solid geometry corresponds to a circle in plane geometry.

SG 46. A **sphere** consists of, or is the set of, all points in space that are the same distance from a given point, called its **center.** The distance of the points from the center is the **radius** of the sphere. In the drawing, O is the center; OA, a radius; and AOD, a diameter. A sphere is a simple closed surface. If the surface of an object is a sphere, the object is **spherical.**

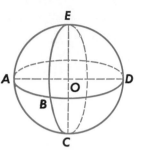

1. What is true of all radii and all diameters of a sphere?
2. When is a point within, on, or outside a given sphere?
3. Name two or more spherical objects that:
   (a) Are solid.   (b) Are relatively hollow.
4. (a) Try to cut through some spherical object, such as an orange, to illustrate the result of intersecting the object by a plane, as suggested by the adjoining drawing.
   (b) What kind of line is your intersection?

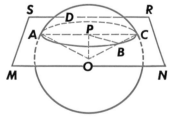

5. (a) Repeat Ex. 4, making the cut through the center of the sphere as on curve $ABCD$.
   (b) What conclusion is suggested by Exercises 4 and 5(a)?

SG 47. *The intersection of a sphere and a plane is a circle.*

> **Hyp.** Curve $ABCD$ is the intersection of sphere O and plane $MNRS$.
>
> **Con.** $ABCD$ is a circle.

Informal proof. 1. Draw $OP \perp$ plane MR, meeting the plane at P. Let A and B be any two points of $ABCD$. Draw OA, OB, PA, and PB.

2. Then $\triangle OAP \cong \triangle OBP$.   (Proof left to the pupil.)
3. Then $PA = PB$ and $ABCD$ is a circle. (Why?)

SG 48. A **great circle** of a sphere is the intersection of the sphere by a plane through the center of the sphere.

SG 49. A **small circle** of a sphere is the intersection of the sphere and a plane that does not pass through the center of the sphere.

1. Compare the radius of a great circle with the radius of the sphere.

2. Compare all great circles of the same sphere.

3. (a) If X and Y are two points of a sphere, not the ends of a diameter, how many planes can pass through X, Y, and center O of the sphere? How many great circles, then, are there through two such points X and Y?

   (b) If XW and RZ are diameters of the sphere, how many planes can pass through X, Z, W, and R? Why?

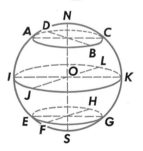

4. (a) If E and F are two points of a sphere, not the ends of a diameter, how many planes can pass through them?

   (b) What is the intersection of each such plane and the sphere?

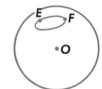

5. Let NOS be a diameter of a sphere. Let $ABCD$, $EFGH$, and $IJKL$ be the intersections of the sphere made by planes that are perpendicular to NOS.

   (a) What are the intersections $ABCD$ and $EFGH$?

   (b) If $IJKL$ is made by a plane that contains center O, what is $IJKL$?

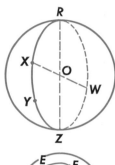

6. In Ex. 5, if the sphere represents the earth:
   (a) What is the circle $IJKL$ called?
   (b) What are the points N and S called?
   (c) What are circles like $ABCD$?

7. Let NOS be perpendicular to the plane of the equator WDE, and planes through NOS intersect the surface of the earth in curves NDS, NGS, NHS, etc.

   What are the intersections NDS, NGS, NHS on the earth called?

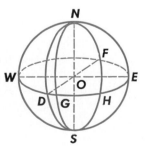

SG 50. *Through two points of a sphere that are not the ends of a diameter of the sphere:*
(a) One and only one great circle passes. (Ex. 3, p. 199)
(b) An infinite number of small circles pass. (Ex. 4, p. 199)

SG 51. *Through two points of a sphere that are the ends of a diameter of the sphere, an infinite number of great circles pass.* (Ex. 7, p. 199)

SG 52. Def. In a sphere the ends of the diameter that is perpendicular to the plane of a circle of the sphere are the **poles** of that circle, as N and S in Ex. 5, p. 199.

Therefore all circles made by parallel planes have the same poles. (SG 30, p. 105)

Strictly speaking, the "North and South Poles of the earth" are the "North and South Poles of the equator and of the circles of latitude of the earth."

SG 53. In an advanced course in mathematics, it is proved that *the shortest distance on a sphere between two points of the sphere is the minor arc of the great circle between those points.*

1. What two similarities are there between the straight line segment determined by two points of a plane and the great circle determined by two points of a sphere?

2. Let PAR and PBR be two great circles between P and R. Let $MABN$ be the great circle of which P and R are poles, so that $POR \perp$ plane $MABN$. Draw OA, OB, $PC \perp POR$ in plane $PORA$ and $PD \perp POR$ in plane $PORB$.

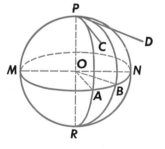

   (a) What kind of angle is formed by planes $PORA$ and $PORB$?
   (b) At what angle do OA and OB meet POR?
   (c) What relation has $\angle AOB$ to the angle between planes PRA and PRB?
   (d) How does $\angle CPD$ compare with $\angle AOB$? Why? (SG 35 p. 134)
   (e) What relation to $\odot PAR$ has CP? To $\odot PBR$ has DP?
   (f) What angle then can be used as measure of the angle between great circles PAR and PBR?

SG 54. Def. A **spherical angle** consists of arcs of two great circles that intersect at a point, as ∠RPB, in Ex. 2, page 200.

SG 55. *A spherical angle has the same measure as the plane angle formed by the tangents to the sides of the spherical angle at their point of intersection, and also as the dihedral angle formed by the planes of the sides of the spherical angle.*

In the figure on p. 200, P is the pole of ⊙ $MABN$. Assume that arc $AB = 1$ arc-degree, and that ∠$AOB = 1$ angular degree. Then we agree that spherical angle APB contains one degree of spherical angle.

If ∠CPD, which equals ∠AOB, contains 40 angular degrees, then spherical ∠APB contains 40 degrees. We may then say briefly that ∠$APB = 40°$ if ∠$CPD = 40°$.

SG 56. Def. A **spherical triangle** is a closed line of a sphere, consisting of the arcs of three great circles, as △ACB.

If the three vertices of △ACB are joined to the center O of the sphere, trihedral angle $O–ACB$ corresponds to △ACB.

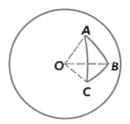

1. What is the relation between:
   (a) ∠AOC and $\overset{\frown}{AC}$? (b) ∠AOB and $\overset{\frown}{AB}$? (c) ∠COB and $\overset{\frown}{CB}$?
2. Using the conclusions of Ex. 1, what must be true of the sum of two sides of a spherical triangle? (SG 40, p. 155)
3. What is the relation between:
   (a) Dihedral ∠$A–OC–B$ and spherical ∠ACB?
   (b) Dihedral ∠$A–OB–C$ and spherical ∠ABC?
4. If the sides $\overset{\frown}{AC}$ and $\overset{\frown}{AB}$ of △ACB are equal, what is true of the opposite angles of △ACB? (SG 43, p. 155)
5. (a) What is true of the sum of the face angles of $O–ABC$? (SG 45)
   (b) What then must be true of the sides of △ACB?
6. Recall SG 41, p. 155. What theorem about two spherical triangles is obviously true?
7. What theorem is suggested by SG 42, p. 155?
8. Prove by superposition the conclusion
   (a) of Ex. 6.   (b) of Ex. 7.

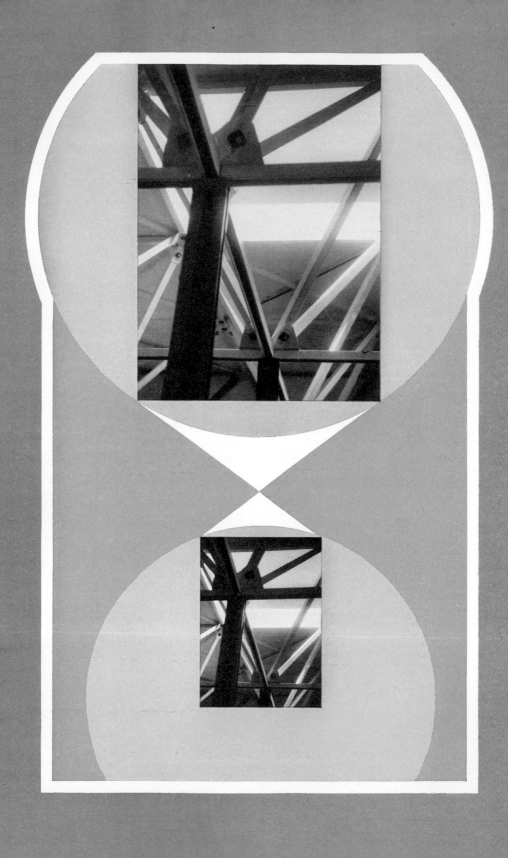

CHAPTER 7

SIMILARITY

You have seen snapshots and their enlargements. You may have noticed that the shape of every detail in the smaller picture on the opposite page resembles the corresponding part of the larger; but that every linear measurement in the larger is twice that in the smaller.

Mathematically speaking, we say that two figures are similar when they have the same shape. In the pictures opposite, the ratio of corresponding segments is two to one.

In Chapter 7, you will learn when figures are similar and you will study some of the consequences of similarity with some of their applications. You will prove one of the most important theorems in geometry—the Pythagorean Theorem, and you will make good use of the algebra that you have studied!

 Detail of a truss in an experimental building at the University of Michigan.

MICHEL BRAWNE, LONDON, ENGLAND

226. (a) The ratio of one number to another is the quotient of the first divided by the second. We assume that the numbers are positive, nonzero, real numbers. The ratio of 2 to 3 is $2 \div 3$, or $\frac{2}{3}$. Generally write ratios in fractional form.

(b) The ratio of a to b often is written $a:b$. Therefore, $2:5$ means $\frac{2}{5}$. This method is convenient in a printed book.

(c) The two numbers of a ratio are called its **terms**. Since a ratio is a fraction, ratios are added, subtracted, multiplied, and divided like any other fractions. In particular:

Both terms of a ratio may be divided or may be multiplied by the same number without changing the value of the ratio.

227. Angles, segments, and other quantities are compared only with quantities of the same kind.

The ratio of two quantities of the same kind is the ratio of their measures in terms of the same unit of measure.

Thus: The ratio of 350 lb. to 1 ton is $\dfrac{350}{2000}$, or $\dfrac{7}{40}$. The ratio of $\dfrac{2}{3}$ rt. angle to $\dfrac{3}{5}$ st. angle is found by changing each of these quantities to degrees, or to right angles.

$\dfrac{2}{3}$ rt. $\angle = 60°$; $\dfrac{3}{5}$ st. $\angle = 108°$. $\therefore$ the ratio is $\dfrac{60}{108} = \dfrac{5}{9}$.

1. Express the following ratios in their simplest form:

(a) 3 to 9   (b) 12 to 2   (c) $5x$ to $2x$

(d) $\dfrac{25}{375}$ (e) $\dfrac{2}{15}$ to $\dfrac{1}{3}$ (f) $6a^2:15a^3$

2. What is the ratio:
   (a) Of a right angle to a straight angle?
   (b) Of one angle of an equilateral triangle to the sum of all the angles of the triangle?

3. What is the ratio of $x + y$ to $x^2 - y^2$?

4. What is the ratio:
   (a) Of a side of a square to the perimeter of the square?
   (b) Of the perimeter of a square to the side of the square?

5. If a segment RS is separated by point T into two segments that have the ratio 2 to 3, how long is RT if RS equals 30 in.?

228. A **proportion** is a statement that two ratios are equal, as $\frac{1}{3} = \frac{5}{15}$ or $2 : 8 = 3 : 12$ or $\frac{a}{b} = \frac{c}{d}$.

$\frac{1}{3} = \frac{5}{15}$ is read *1 is to 3 as 5 is to 15.* It means that 1 has the same *multiplication* or *division relation* to 3 that 5 has to 15. Observe that 1 is $\frac{1}{3}$ of 3 and 5 is $\frac{1}{3}$ of 15.

The first and fourth terms of a proportion are its **extremes.** The second and third terms are its **means.** In $\frac{a}{b} = \frac{c}{d}$, the extremes are a and d. The means are b and c.

The first and third terms of a proportion are its numerators, or **antecedents.** The second and fourth are its denominators, or **consequents.**

1. Select four numbers that form a proportion like those in §228.

2. (*a*) Is $\frac{3}{4} = \frac{9}{12}$ a proportion? Read it as a proportion.

(*b*) Similarly examine and read: $\frac{2}{4} = \frac{10}{20}$; $\frac{3}{5} = \frac{6}{10}$; $\frac{2}{4} = \frac{4}{16}$

3. If $\frac{x}{t} = \frac{y}{r}$ and $x = 5t$, what does y equal?

4. If $\frac{a}{b} = \frac{c}{d}$ and $c = \frac{2}{3}d$, what does a equal?

229. **Changes in a proportion** can be made by ordinary algebraic processes. However, some changes become necessary so frequently that certain short-cuts are advantageous.

In a proportion, the product of the extremes equals the product of the means.

Proof.   If $\frac{a}{b} = \frac{c}{d}$, then $\overset{1}{\cancel{b}}d \times \frac{a}{\underset{1}{\cancel{b}}} = b\cancel{d} \times \frac{c}{\underset{1}{\cancel{d}}}$. $\therefore$ $ad = bc$

Thus: Since $\frac{2}{3} = \frac{6}{9}$, 2×9 should equal 3×6. Does it?

5. Use §229 to find what value x must have to make each of the following a proportion.

(*a*) $\frac{x}{4} = \frac{10}{8}$ (*b*) $\frac{x}{9} = \frac{2}{3}$ (*c*) $\frac{6}{x} = \frac{3}{4}$

(*d*) $\frac{a}{x} = \frac{b}{2}$ (*e*) $\frac{3}{x} = \frac{a}{b}$ (*f*) $\frac{cd}{x} = \frac{d}{e}$

230. Converse of §229. *If the product of two numbers equals the product of two other numbers, either pair may be made the means of a proportion of which the other pair are the extremes.* (None of the numbers is equal to zero.)

Proof. If $mn = xy$, then $\dfrac{mn}{xn} = \dfrac{xy}{xn}$. Ax. 6, p. 32

Simplify each fraction: then $\dfrac{m}{x} = \dfrac{y}{n}$.

Example. $3 \times 8 = 4 \times 6$ since each product is 24.

Therefore $\dfrac{3}{4} = \dfrac{6}{8}$.

3 and 8 have been used as extremes, 4 and 6 as means. To write the proportion, first write $\dfrac{3}{-} = \dfrac{-}{8}$. Then use 4 and 6 as means, writing either $\dfrac{3}{4} = \dfrac{6}{8}$ or $\dfrac{3}{6} = \dfrac{4}{8}$.

Check. $\dfrac{3 \times \overset{1}{\cancel{8}}}{\underset{4}{\cancel{32}}} = \dfrac{\overset{1}{\cancel{4}} \times 6}{\underset{8}{\cancel{32}}}$ or $\dfrac{3}{4} = \dfrac{6}{8}$.

231. *If the numerators of a proportion are equal, then the denominators are equal; if the denominators are equal, then the numerators are equal.*

Proof. If $\dfrac{a}{x} = \dfrac{a}{y}$, then $ay = ax$. §229

Therefore $y = x$. Why?

232. *If three terms of one proportion are equal respectively to the three corresponding terms of another proportion, then the fourth terms also are equal.*

Proof. If $\dfrac{a}{x} = \dfrac{c}{d}$ and $\dfrac{a}{x} = \dfrac{c}{y}$, then $\dfrac{c}{d} = \dfrac{c}{y}$. Why?

Therefore $cd = cy$, and $d = y$. Why?

233. *The terms of a proportion are in proportion by alternation; that is, the first is to the third as the second is to the fourth.*

Proof. If $\dfrac{a}{b} = \dfrac{c}{d}$, then $ad = bc$. Why?

Therefore $\dfrac{ad}{cd} = \dfrac{bc}{cd}$, or $\dfrac{a}{c} = \dfrac{b}{d}$. Why?

234. *The terms of a proportion are in proportion by inversion; that is, the second is to the first as the fourth is to the third.*

Proof. If $\dfrac{a}{b} = \dfrac{c}{d}$, then $bc = ad$. Why?

Then $\dfrac{b\!\!\!/c}{a\!\!\!/c} = \dfrac{a\!\!\!/d}{a\!\!\!/c}$ or $\dfrac{b}{a} = \dfrac{d}{c}$. Why?

Example. $\dfrac{3}{4} = \dfrac{6}{8}$. Then $\dfrac{4}{3}$ should equal $\dfrac{8}{6}$. Does it?

235. *The terms of a proportion are in proportion by addition; that is, the sum of the first and second is to the second as the sum of the third and fourth is to the fourth.*

Proof. If $\dfrac{a}{b} = \dfrac{c}{d}$, then $\dfrac{a}{b} + 1 = \dfrac{c}{d} + 1$. Why?

Therefore $\dfrac{a + b}{b} = \dfrac{c + d}{d}$.

Example. $\dfrac{2}{3} = \dfrac{8}{12}$. Then $\dfrac{2 + 3}{3}$ should equal $\dfrac{8 + 12}{12}$. Does it?

236. *The terms of a proportion are in proportion by subtraction; that is, the first minus the second is to the second as the third minus the fourth is to the fourth.*

Proof. If $\dfrac{a}{b} = \dfrac{c}{d}$, then $\dfrac{a}{b} - 1 = \dfrac{c}{d} - 1$. Why?

Therefore $\dfrac{a - b}{b} = \dfrac{c - d}{d}$.

Example. $\dfrac{6}{5} = \dfrac{12}{10}$. Then $\dfrac{6 - 5}{5}$ should equal $\dfrac{12 - 10}{10}$. Does it?

1. Since $\dfrac{4}{5} = \dfrac{12}{15}$, does 4×15 equal 5×12?

2. If $\dfrac{7}{a} = \dfrac{b}{8}$, how much is ab?

3. $4 \times 3 = 6 \times 2$. Guided by §230, write four proportions using the numbers 2, 3, 4, and 6.

4. Change each of the following proportions (1) by inversion, (2) by addition, (3) by alternation:

(a) $\dfrac{3}{4} = \dfrac{9}{12}$ (b) $\dfrac{1}{2} = \dfrac{x}{3}$ (c) $\dfrac{x}{y} = \dfrac{a}{2}$ (d) $\dfrac{AB}{CD} = \dfrac{MN}{XY}$

1. (a) Does $\dfrac{3}{5} = \dfrac{9}{15}$? Why?

(b) In (a), what are the terms of the proportion?
(c) If (a) is true, what should 3×15 equal? Does it?
(d) If (a) is true, write the proportion changed:
   (1) By inversion   (2) By alternation   (3) By addition

2. (a) Does $7 \times 4 = 2 \times 14$?
(b) If (a) is true, write two proportions using the numbers 7, 4, 2, and 14 in which 7 and 4 appear:
   (1) As extremes   (2) As means

3. If $\dfrac{7}{x} = \dfrac{3}{6}$, what is the value of x?

4. If $\dfrac{r}{s} = \dfrac{a}{b}$ and $\dfrac{r}{s} = \dfrac{a}{c}$, what does b equal?

5. Suppose that $ab = cy$. Write two proportions:
(a) In which y is the first term.
(b) In which y is the fourth term or *fourth proportional*.

6. Assume that $mx = ab \neq 0$. Write two proportions:
(a) In which x is the first term.
(b) In which x is the fourth term.

7. Given the proportion $\dfrac{4}{5} = \dfrac{8}{10}$:
(a) Does the product of the means equal the product of the extremes?
(b) Write this proportion:
   (1) By inversion   (2) By alternation   (3) By addition
(c) Is each proportion in (b) true?

8. Write four proportions that involve the numbers m, n, r, and t if $mn = rt \neq 0$.

9. (a) Write a proportion in which 3, 8, 16, and 6 appear as terms.
(b) Write other proportions which are derived from the proportion in (a) by §233 through §236.

10. If $(x - 2)$ is to $(x + 3)$ as 2 is to 3, what is the value of x?

11. If $x = \dfrac{mr}{s}$, write two proportions in which m, r, s and x are terms with x as the first term.

12. (a) What is the ratio of 9 in. to 1 yd.?
(b) What is the ratio of 1 sq. ft. to 1 sq. yd.?

237. Proportions of geometric quantities. The theorems on pages 206 and 207 and their proofs all refer to numbers. When we are concerned with ratios and proportions of geometric quantities, such as angles and segments, we agree that the geometric quantities are replaced by their measures. Since these measures are numbers, we can use the theorems about proportions taught in §229 to §236.

Thus: If AB, CD, EF, and GH are segments, it may happen that $\dfrac{AB}{CD} = \dfrac{EF}{GH}$. Then $AB \times GH = CD \times EF$.

This last equation means that the product of the measures of AB and GH equals the product of the measures of CD and EF.

238. Segments divided proportionally.

If $AE = EB$ and $CF = FD$, then $\dfrac{AE}{EB} = \dfrac{CF}{FD}$ because each ratio equals 1. *E and F divide AB and CD proportionally.* If G bisects AE and H bisects CF, then $\dfrac{AG}{GB} = \dfrac{1}{3}$ and also $\dfrac{CH}{HD} = \dfrac{1}{3}$. $\therefore \dfrac{AG}{GB} = \dfrac{CH}{HD}$. G and H also divide AB and CD proportionally.

Two segments are divided proportionally when two parts of the one have the same ratio as the corresponding parts of the other.

1. (a) Construct $\triangle ABC$ having AB equal to 2 in., AC equal to 3 in., and BC equal to 4 in.

   (b) Let D bisect AC. Construct $DE \parallel BC$ meeting AB at E. Measure AE and EB.

   (c) Write the value of the ratio $\dfrac{AD}{DC}$, also of the ratio $\dfrac{AE}{EB}$. How do they compare?

   (d) Write a proportion formed by AD, DC, AE, and EB?

2. Repeat Ex. 1, starting with D so that $\dfrac{AD}{DC} = \dfrac{1}{2}$.

3. What conclusion is suggested by Ex. 1 and Ex. 2?

239. *A parallel to one side of a triangle, intersecting the other two sides, divides the other two sides proportionally.*

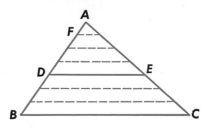

Hypothesis. $DE \parallel BC$, cuts AB at D and AC at E.

Conclusion.
$$\frac{AD}{DB} = \frac{AE}{EC}$$

(Let AD contain AF 4 times and DB contain AF 3 times. The method of proof would be unchanged if $AD = r$ times AF and $DB = s$ times AF, where r and s are any two whole numbers.)

Proof.

	Statements	Authorities
1.	$AD = 4\ AF,\ DB = 3\ AF$	1. By agreement.
2.	$\therefore \dfrac{AD}{DB} = \dfrac{4}{3}$	2. §237, p. 209
3.	$\parallel$s to BC from the division points on AB divide AE into 4 and EC into 3 equal parts.	3. §143, p. 129
4.	$\therefore \dfrac{AE}{EC} = \dfrac{4}{3}$	4. §237
5.	$\therefore \dfrac{AD}{DB} = \dfrac{AE}{EC}$	5. Ax. 1, p. 32

240. Segments like AD and DB that contain the same measure a whole number of times are said to be *commensurable*. A proof when the segments are not commensurable is not given usually in elementary geometry.

1. If $AD = \dfrac{6}{5}DB$, how does AE compare with EC?

2. If $AD = 1.25\ DB$, what does AE equal?

3. If $\dfrac{AD}{DB} = \dfrac{5}{8}$, what does $\dfrac{AE}{EC}$ equal?

241. By proofs like that in §239, you see that:

(a) $\dfrac{AB}{DB} = \dfrac{AC}{EC}$ because, in the figure, each ratio $= \dfrac{7}{3}$.

That is, *one side of the triangle is to its lower segment as the other side is to its lower segment.*

(b) $\dfrac{AB}{AD} = \dfrac{AC}{AE}$ because, in the figure, each ratio $= \dfrac{7}{4}$.

That is, *one side of the triangle is to its upper segment as the other side is to its upper segment.*

(c) $\dfrac{DB}{AD} = \dfrac{EC}{AE}$ because, in the figure, each ratio $= \dfrac{3}{4}$.

(d) $\dfrac{DB}{AB} = \dfrac{EC}{AC}$ because each ratio $= \dfrac{3}{7}$.

(e) $\dfrac{AD}{AB} = \dfrac{AE}{AC}$ because each ratio $= \dfrac{4}{7}$.

(f) From $\dfrac{AD}{DB} = \dfrac{AE}{EC}$ we get $\dfrac{AD}{AE} = \dfrac{DB}{EC}$ by using §233.

This new proportion cannot be obtained directly from the figure by the method used to obtain the other proportions since AD and AE are not divided by the same unit of measure. This shows the importance of §233.

The proportions in parts (a) to (e) also can be obtained from the conclusion of §239 by using one or more of the theorems in §229, and §233 through §236.

242. For convenience §239 may be given as the reason or authority for any of the proportions stated in §239 and §241.

Solve each of the following exercises by writing a proportion involving the segments as they appear in the figure for §239.

1. If $AD = 8$ in., $DB = 3$ in., and $EC = 6$ in., find AE.

Suggestion. Let $AE = x$. Write the proportion. Solve for x.

2. If $DB = 6$ in., $AE = 12$ in., and $EC = 8$ in., find AD.

3. If $AD = 8$ in., $AE = 16$ in., and $EC = 10$ in., find DB.

4. If $AB = 24$ in., $AC = 20$ in., and $AE = 5$ in., find AD.

5. If $AB = 15$ in., $AD = 6$ in., and $AE = 4$ in., find AC.

6. If $AB = 20$ in., $AE = 6$ in., $EC = 9$ in., find AD.

243. *A line that divides two sides of a triangle proportionally is parallel to the third side.* *

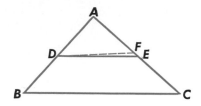

Hypothesis. In $\triangle ABC$, DE intersects AB and AC so that
$$\frac{AB}{AD} = \frac{AC}{AE}.$$

Conclusion. $DE \parallel BC$

Plan. Prove DE coincides with a line that is $\parallel BC$.

Proof.

Statements	Authorities
1. Assume $DF \parallel BC$, meeting AC at F.	1. §84, p. 90
2. $\therefore \dfrac{AB}{AD} = \dfrac{AC}{AF}$	2. §239. (See §242.)
3. But $\dfrac{AB}{AD} = \dfrac{AC}{AE}.$	3. Why?
4. $\therefore \quad AF = AE$	4. §232, p. 206
5. $\therefore \quad E$ coincides with F.	5. Why?
6. $\therefore \quad DE$ coincides with DF.	6. Why?
7. $\therefore \quad DE \parallel BC$	7. Steps 6 and 1.

   1. If $AD = 4$ in., $AB = 12$ in., $AC = 9$ in., $AE = 3$ in., is $DE \parallel BC$? Why?

   2. If $AD = 4$ in., $BD = 8$ in., $AE = 5$ in., $EC = 15$ in., is $DE \parallel BC$?

   3. What is the relation between §243 and §239?

★**4.** Give the proof of §243, starting with the assumption that $AD : DB = AE : EC$.

Suggestion. First use §235, p. 207.

   * By *divides two sides of a triangle proportionally* we mean that the segments of one side have the same ratio as the corresponding segments (with reference to the vertex) of the other side.

1. (*a*) Construct $\triangle ABC$, if $AB = 2$ in., $\angle A = 50°$, and $\angle B = 80°$; also construct $\triangle XYZ$, if $XY = 4$ in., $\angle X = 50°$, and $\angle Y = 80°$.

(*b*) Are the triangles congruent? Do they appear to have the same shape?

(*c*) Measure AC, BC, XZ, and YZ.

(*d*) Find the values of the ratios $\dfrac{AB}{XY}$, $\dfrac{AC}{XZ}$, and $\dfrac{BC}{YZ}$.

(*e*) How do the ratios in part (*d*) compare?

244. The triangles in Ex. 1 have the same shape but not the same size. They are *similar triangles*.

(*a*) **Two polygons are similar** ($\backsim$) if their corresponding angles are equal and their corresponding sides are proportional.

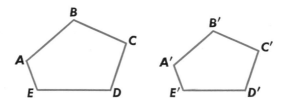

Thus. $ABCDE \backsim A'B'C'D'E'$ if:

(1) $\angle A = \angle A'$, $\angle B = \angle B'$, $\angle C = \angle C'$, etc.; and

(2) $\dfrac{AB}{A'B'} = \dfrac{BC}{B'C'} = \dfrac{CD}{C'D'} = \dfrac{DE}{D'E'} = \dfrac{EA}{E'A'}$

Note. A' is read *A-prime*; $A'B'$, *A-prime B-prime*.

(*b*) Conversely, **if two polygons are similar,** their corresponding angles are equal, and their corresponding sides are proportional.

(*c*) The **ratio of similitude** of similar polygons is the ratio of any two corresponding sides.

2. (*a*) Are similar triangles necessarily congruent?

(*b*) Can similar triangles be congruent?

3. Are congruent triangles necessarily similar?

4. Are squares necessarily similar? Why?

5. Are equilateral triangles necessarily similar? Why?

6. Are rectangles necessarily similar? Why?

7. Are two rhombuses necessarily similar? Why?

245. *Two triangles are similar if two angles of one are equal respectively to two angles of the other.*

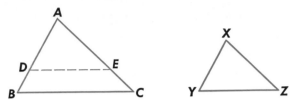

Hypothesis.   In $\triangle ABC$ and $\triangle XYZ$,
$$\angle A = \angle X \text{ and } \angle B = \angle Y.$$

Conclusion. $\triangle ABC \backsim \triangle XYZ$

Plan. Prove $\angle C = \angle Z$ and the corresponding sides are proportional.

Proof.

Statements	Authorities
1. Since $\angle A = \angle X$ and $\angle B = \angle Y$, then $\angle C = \angle Z$.	1. Why?
2. Place $\triangle XYZ$ in the position ADE, $\angle X$ coinciding with $\angle A$.	2. Post. 22, p. 52 §11(a), p. 19
3. $\angle ADE$ or $\angle Y = \angle ABC$	3. Why?
4. $\therefore \ \ DE \parallel BC$	4. Why?
5. $\therefore \dfrac{AB}{AD} = \dfrac{AC}{AE}$, or $\dfrac{AB}{XY} = \dfrac{AC}{XZ}$.	5. Why?
6. It can be proved by steps like 3, 4, and 5 that $\dfrac{AB}{XY} = \dfrac{BC}{YZ}$ by placing $\triangle XYZ$ on $\triangle ABC$ so that $\angle Y$ coincides with its equal $\angle B$.	
7. $\therefore \dfrac{AB}{XY} = \dfrac{AC}{XZ} = \dfrac{BC}{YZ}$	7. Why?
8. $\therefore \ \triangle XYZ \backsim \triangle ABC$	8. §244(a)

246. Cor. *Two triangles are similar if they are mutually equiangular;* that is, if the angles of the one equal respectively the angles of the other.

Note. Do not think that mutually equiangular polygons are similar just because mutually equiangular triangles are similar. Two rectangles are mutually equiangular but they are not necessarily similar. (§244(b))

1. Draw any $\triangle RST$ and a segment XY, 3 in. long. On XY construct $\triangle XYZ$ similar to $\triangle RST$.

2. (a) $DE \parallel BC$ in $\triangle ABC$. Prove $\triangle ADE$ similar to $\triangle ABC$.
   (b) State part (a) as a theorem.

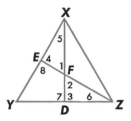

3. Do Ex. 2 if $DE \parallel BC$ but cuts BA and CA extended through A.

4. In $\triangle XYZ$, XD and ZE are altitudes. Prove that $\triangle XEF$ is similar to $\triangle DFZ$.

5. In the figure for Ex. 4, using XD and ZE as altitudes, prove that $\triangle XEF$ is similar to $\triangle XYD$.

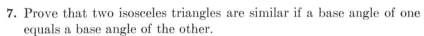

6. Again, using the figure and hypothesis of Ex. 4, prove that $\triangle XEF$ is similar to $\triangle YEZ$.

7. Prove that two isosceles triangles are similar if a base angle of one equals a base angle of the other.

8. Prove that two isosceles triangles are similar if the vertex angle of one equals the vertex angle of the other.

9. $ABCD$ is a trapezoid, having $BC \parallel AD$.
   (a) Prove $\triangle BOC \backsim \triangle AOD$.
   (b) Are triangles ABO and DCO similar?

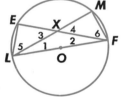

10. In circle O, chords EF and LM intersect at X. LF is a diameter.
    (a) Are $\triangle ELX$ and MFX similar?
    (b) If $\angle 1 = \angle 2$, prove that $\triangle ELF$ must be similar to $\triangle MLF$.

11. In a circle R, ARB is a diameter. AX is any other chord. Take any point Z on AX. Draw ZY perpendicular to AB, meeting AB at Y. Draw chord XB. Are triangles AZY and AXB similar? Prove your statement.

12. $\triangle HKL$ has a right angle at H. HM is the altitude to KL, meeting KL at M. Prove that $\triangle HKM$ is similar to $\triangle HKL$.

13. $\triangle ABC$ is inscribed in a circle with center O. No side of $\triangle ABC$ is a diameter. BD is perpendicular to AC. CE is a diameter. Prove $\triangle ABD \backsim \triangle BEC$.

Note. Ex. 137 through Ex. 149, pp. 398 and 399, can be done now.

247. **Fundamental Plan 6.** *To prove four segments proportional, prove them corresponding sides of similar triangles.*

A device that aids in use of this plan is illustrated by the proof of the following exercise.

Hyp. $AE \perp BC$, $BD \perp AC$

Con. $\dfrac{AC}{BC} = \dfrac{AE}{BD}$

Plan. AC and AE are in $\triangle AEC$;
  BC and BD are in $\triangle BDC$.

∴ Prove $\triangle AEC \backsim \triangle BDC$. (See 1 below.)

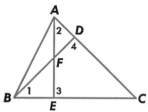

Proof.

	Statements	Authorities
	In $\triangle AEC$ and $\triangle BDC$,	
1.	$AC \mid \angle 3 = \angle 4 \mid BC$	1. Why? (See 2 below.)
2.	$AE \mid \angle C = \angle C \mid BD$	2. Why?
3.	$EC \mid \angle 2 = \angle 1 \mid DC$	3. §110
4.	∴ $\triangle AEC \backsim \triangle BDC$	4. §246
5.	∴ $\dfrac{AC}{BC} = \dfrac{AE}{BD}$	5. §244(b). (See 3 below.)

Observe:

1. If the numerators do not suggest one of the triangles, rewrite the proportion of the conclusion by *alternation*. Then, if the conclusion can be secured at once from two similar triangles, the numerators will suggest one of the triangles and the denominators the other.

2. The vertical lines and the names of the segments at the left and right of them are not written until after Step 4.

3. After you have Step 4, draw the vertical lines. At the left of each angle of $\triangle AEC$, write the side that is opposite it in $\triangle AEC$; at the right of each angle of $\triangle BDC$, write the side that is opposite it in $\triangle BDC$.

Then the two segments named in each line are corresponding segments. Thus, AC corresponds to BC, because they lie opposite equal angles.

1. In the adjoining figure, $XW \perp BA$ and $YZ \perp BA$.

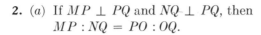

Prove $\dfrac{XW}{YZ} = \dfrac{BW}{BZ} = \dfrac{BX}{BY}$.

2. (a) If $MP \perp PQ$ and $NQ \perp PQ$, then $MP : NQ = PO : OQ$.

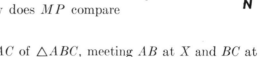

Suggestion. See §226(b).

   (b) If $PO = \frac{1}{4}OQ$, how does MP compare with NQ?

3. (a) XY is parallel to AC of $\triangle ABC$, meeting AB at X and BC at Y. Prove that $XY : AC = BX : BA$.
   (b) If $BX = \frac{2}{3}BA$ and $AC = 27$ in., how long is XY?

4. At the right, $XD \perp YZ$, and $ZE \perp XY$.

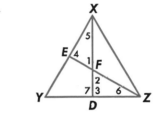

   (a) Prove $\dfrac{XF}{ZF} = \dfrac{EF}{DF}$.
   (b) Prove $XF : XY = XE : XD$.
   (c) Prove $FD : DZ = YD : XD$.

Suggestion. Read observation 1, p. 216.

5. If trapezoid $ABCD$ has $AB \parallel DC$, prove that diagonals AC and BD intersect in a point E that divides the diagonals proportionally.

6. If chords AB and CD of a circle intersect outside the circle at E, prove that AE and CE have the same ratio as ED and BE.

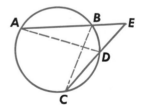

★7. In $\triangle GHK$, $\angle GHK = 90°$ and $HW \perp GK$ at W.
   (a) Prove that $HW : HK = GH : GK$.
   (b) Prove that $GW : GH = GH : GK$.

8. From X, Y, and Z on side OB of $\angle AOB$, perpendiculars are drawn to OA, meeting OA at R, S, and T respectively.

   (a) Prove that $\dfrac{XR}{OX} = \dfrac{YS}{OY} = \dfrac{ZT}{OZ}$.
   (b) Prove that $\dfrac{XR}{OR} = \dfrac{YS}{OS} = \dfrac{ZT}{OT}$.

Note. Ex. 150 through Ex. 158, pp. 399 and 400, can be done now.

248. *Two triangles are similar if an angle of one equals an angle of the other and the sides including these angles are proportional.*

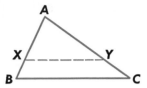 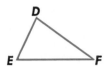

Hypothesis.   In $\triangle ABC$ and $\triangle DEF$,

$$\angle A = \angle D \text{ and } \frac{AB}{DE} = \frac{AC}{DF}.$$

Conclusion. $\triangle ABC \backsim \triangle DEF$

Plan. Prove two $\angle$ of one $\triangle$ = two $\angle$ of the other.

Proof.

Statements	Authorities
1. Place $\triangle DEF$ on $\triangle ABC$, so that $\angle D$ coincides with its equal $\angle A$, E falling at X and F at Y.	1. Why possible?
2. $\therefore \quad AX = DE,\ AY = DF$	2. Step 1.
3. $\dfrac{AB}{DE} = \dfrac{AC}{DF}$	3. Why?
4. $\therefore \quad \dfrac{AB}{AX} = \dfrac{AC}{AY}$	4. Ax. 2, p. 32
5. $\therefore \quad XY \parallel BC$	5. Why?
6. $\therefore \quad \angle AXY = \angle ABC,$ or $\angle DEF = \angle ABC$	6. Give the proof.
7. $\therefore \quad \triangle DEF \backsim \triangle ABC$	7. Give the proof.

1. On side AB of $\triangle ABC$, point X is located so that $AX = \frac{1}{3}AB$. On side AC, point Y is located so that $AY = \frac{1}{3}AC$. Prove:

(a) $\triangle ABC \backsim \triangle AXY$ (b) $XY = \frac{1}{3}BC$ (c) $XY \parallel BC$

2. On a straight line XY, lay off segments AB and DE so that $DE = 2AB$. Above XY, construct $BC \perp XY$ and $EF \perp XY$, so that $EF = 2BC$. Prove $DF = 2AC$, and $\angle A = \angle D$.

3. Two segments AOB and COD intersect so that $AO = 3OB$, and $CO = 3OD$. Prove $\triangle AOC \backsim \triangle BOD$, and $AC = 3BD$.

1. In any triangle, the product of one altitude and the side to which it is drawn equals the product of any other altitude and the side to which it is drawn.

2. $\angle B$ of $\triangle ABC$ is a right angle. $BD \perp AC$ at D. Prove that $AB \times BC = AC \times BD$.

3. XY is parallel to base KL of $\triangle HKL$, intersecting HK at X and HL at Y. Prove:
   (a) $HY \times HK = HX \times HL$
   (b) $HX \times LY = HY \times KX$

4. $ABCD$ is a parallelogram. BG intersects AC at E, AD at F, and CD extended at G. Prove:
   (a) $BE \cdot EC = EG \cdot EA$
   (b) $BF \cdot FD = AF \cdot FG$
   (c) $BE \cdot AE = EF \cdot EC$

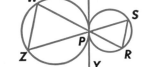

5. In the adjoining figure, the circles are tangent to XY at P, and therefore are tangent to each other.
   Prove: $WP \cdot PS = ZP \cdot PR$

Suggestion. Recall §204, p. 183.

6. Do Ex. 5 when both circles are on the same side of XY.

7. RT is a chord and RS is a diameter of a circle. From V, any point on RT, VW is drawn perpendicular to RS meeting it at W. Prove $RT \cdot RV = RS \cdot RW$.

8. XC is tangent to $\odot O$ at the end point B of diameter AOB. Secant AC cuts the circle at D. Prove that $AB \times BC = AC \times BD$.

★9. $\triangle ABC$ is inscribed in a circle O. Line MS is tangent to it at point A. From any point X of AB, a line XY is drawn parallel to MS, meeting AC at Y. Prove that $AX \times AB = AY \times AC$.

★10. Point C bisects $\overset{\frown}{AB}$ of a circle. Chord CY cuts chord AB at X, and chord CW cuts AB at Z. Prove that $CX \times CY = CZ \times CW$.

★11. A point P is 3 in. from the center of the circle having diameter of length 18 in. What is the product of the segments of any chord that is drawn through P?

★12. $\triangle ABC$ is inscribed in circle O. BOE is a diameter of the circle. $BD \perp AC$ at D. Prove that $AB \times BC = BD \times BE$.

258. *If the altitude is drawn to the hypotenuse of a right triangle:*
   (a) The altitude is the mean proportional between the seg-ments of the hypotenuse.
   (b) Each leg is the mean proportional between the whole hypotenuse and the adjacent segment.

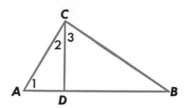

Hypothesis. In $\triangle ABC$, $\angle C$ is a rt. $\angle$ and $CD \perp AB$.

Conclusion. $\qquad (a) \dfrac{AD}{CD} = \dfrac{CD}{DB}$

Plan. Prove $\triangle ACD$ and $\triangle CBD$ are similar $\triangle$.

Proof.

	Statements	Authorities
1.	$\angle 1$ is a complement of $\angle 2$.	1. Why?
2.	$\angle 3$ is a complement of $\angle 2$.	2. Why?
3.	$\therefore \quad \angle 1 = \angle 3$	3. Why?
4.	$\triangle ADC \backsim \triangle CDB$	4. Give full proof.
5.	$\therefore \quad AD : CD = CD : DB$	5. Why?

Conclusions. (*b*) 1. $AD : AC = AC : AB$
   2. $BD : BC = BC : AB$
   (Proofs left to the pupil.)

Suggestions. To prove (*b*)1, prove $\triangle ADC \backsim \triangle ABC$.
   To prove (*b*)2, prove $\triangle BDC \backsim \triangle ABC$.

1. In §258: (*a*) Prove $\overline{CD}^2 = AD \cdot DB$.
   (*b*) Prove $\overline{AC}^2 = AD \cdot AB$.
   (*c*) Prove $\overline{BC}^2 = DB \cdot AB$.

2. The segments of the hypotenuse of a right triangle made by the altitude to it are 2 in. and 8 in. How long is the altitude? Each leg?

Suggestion. Obtain irrational results correct to tenths.

1. Find the length of the altitude and of each leg of a right triangle when the segments of the hypotenuse made by the altitude to the hypotenuse are:
   (*a*) 3 in. and 9 in.   (*b*) 4 in. and 12 in.

2. From a point X on a circle O, draw XY perpendicular to diameter AOB meeting it at Y. Prove that BX is the mean proportional between AB and YB.

3. C is the mid-point of $\overset{\frown}{GH}$ of a circle. Diameter CE cuts GH at D.
   (*a*) Prove GC the mean proportional between CD and CE.
   (*b*) Prove DH the mean proportional between CD and DE.

4. RS is a diameter of a circle. ST is tangent to the circle at S. RT cuts the circle at X. Prove:
   (*a*) RS is the mean proportional between RX and RT.
   (*b*) SX is the mean proportional between RX and XT.

5. AC is the hypotenuse of a right $\triangle ABC$. AD, perpendicular to AC at A, meets CB extended at D. CE, perpendicular to AC at C, meets AB extended at E. Prove that AC is the mean proportional between AD and CE.

6. M is the mid-point of major arc AB of a circle and Y is any point on minor arc AB. MY cuts AB at X. Prove that AM is the mean proportional between MX and MY.

7. In a $\triangle RST$, $RS = RT$. V is located on RT so that $SV = ST$. Prove that ST is the mean proportional between RT and TV.

★8. $\triangle RST$, having $RS = ST$, is inscribed in a circle. Y is on RT. SY extended meets arc RT at X. Prove that RS is the mean proportional between SY and SX.

★9. In $\triangle ABC$, $\angle A = 2\angle C$. AD bisects $\angle A$, meeting BC at D. Prove that AB is the mean proportional between BC and BD.

★10. Point K bisects minor arc HL of a circle. KMP is any chord meeting HL at M and major arc HL at P. Prove that HK is the mean proportional between KP and KM.

★11. $\triangle ABC$ has $AB = BC$. Line BX is drawn to side AC so that $\angle ABX = \angle A$. Prove that AB is the mean proportional between AC and AX.

★12. In a trapezoid $MBSR$, $RS \parallel MB$ and MS and RB intersect at T. $TX \parallel RS$, intersecting BS at X. Prove $RS \times XB = MB \times SX$.

Note. Ex. 179 through 189, p. 402, can be done now.

259. *The square of the hypotenuse of a right triangle equals the sum of the squares of the legs.*

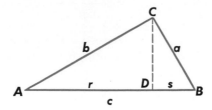

Hypothesis. In $\triangle ABC$, $\angle C$ is a right angle.

Conclusion. $c^2 = a^2 + b^2$

Plan. Find a^2 and b^2 and add the results.

Proof.

Statements	Authorities
1. Draw $CD \perp AB$.	1. Why possible?
2. $\therefore \quad \dfrac{c}{a} = \dfrac{a}{s}$, or $a^2 = cs$. Also $\dfrac{c}{b} = \dfrac{b}{r}$, or $b^2 = cr$.	2. §258(b) §229
3. $\therefore \quad a^2 + b^2 = cs + cr$	3. Ax. 3, p. 32
4. $\therefore \quad a^2 + b^2 = c(s + r)$	4. Factoring.
5. $\therefore \quad a^2 + b^2 = c \cdot c$	5. Ax. 7, Ax. 2
6. $\therefore \quad a^2 + b^2 = c^2$	6. Why?

This is one of the most important theorems in mathematics. It is called the Pythagorean Theorem or the Theorem of Pythagoras, who is given credit for proving it first. The theorem must have been known to the Egyptians, however.

The proof above is attributed to Hindu mathematicians. On p. 298, you will study a purely geometric proof.

If you have not read about Pythagoras previously, now would be a good time to do so. Your teacher will give you references.

260. Cor. *The square of either leg of a right triangle equals the square of the hypotenuse minus the square of the other leg.*

1. A baseball diamond is a square whose sides are 90 ft. long. What is the distance from "first" to "third"?

2. A second baseman caught a ball midway on the line between first and second. How far was he from third? How far from "home"?

3. A piece of silk 27 in. wide is folded on the bias along AB. How long is AB?

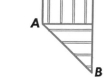

4. How long must a tent rope be to reach from the top of a 12 ft. pole to a point that is 16 ft. from the foot of the pole?

5. How long is the altitude of the isosceles triangle whose equal sides are 15 in. long and whose base is 18 in.?

6. (a) How long is a rafter from A to B if the total width of the building is 30 ft. and the height BD of the ridge above the plate AC is 8 ft.?

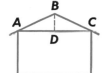

(b) In Ex. 6(a), the ratio of BD to AC is called the pitch of the roof. What is the pitch in (a)?

(c) Find AB when the width of the building is 24 ft. and the pitch is $\frac{1}{3}$.

7. How long is the base of an isosceles triangle if its equal sides are 12 in. long and its altitude is 8 in.?

8. How long is the altitude of the equilateral triangle whose sides are 12 in. long?

9. How long is the diagonal of a square whose sides are 10 in. long?

10. How far is it from one corner to the opposite corner of a rectangular lot that is 6 rods wide and 8 rods long?

11. The diagonals of a rhombus are 8 in. and 12 in., respectively. How long are the sides of the rhombus?

12. The equal sides of an isosceles trapezoid measure 6 in. The upper base is 8 in. and the lower base is 14 in. How long is the altitude of the trapezoid?

13. A rectangular field is 9 rods wide and 12 rods long. How much shorter is the distance from one corner to the opposite one along a diagonal, than along the two sides between these corners?

14. If the two legs of a right triangle measure 8 in. and 12 in. respectively, what must the length of the third side be?

Note. Ex. 190 through Ex. 216, pp. 402–404, can be done now.

1. Define and illustrate:
   (a) Ratio   (b) Proportion   (c) Means
   (d) Extremes   (e) Antecedents   (f) Consequents
   (g) Similar polygons   (h) Ratio of similitude

2. (a) Read $2 : 8 = 3 : 12$ as a proportion.
   (b) Write $2 : 8 = 3 : 12$ in another way.
   (c) What equal products follow from (a)?

3. (a) Does $4 \times 5 = 2 \times 10$?
   (b) Write three proportions using the terms 2, 4, 5, and 10.

4. If $x : a = y : a$, what is true about x?

5. If $\dfrac{a}{b} = \dfrac{c}{x}$ and $\dfrac{a}{b} = \dfrac{c}{y}$, what is the relation between x and y?

6. State three theorems by which two triangles can be proved similar. Be prepared to prove each of them.

7. Are mutually equiangular polygons necessarily similar? Illustrate your answer.

8. Are mutually equilateral polygons necessarily similar? Illustrate your answer.

9. Answer the questions of Exercises 7 and 8 when the polygons are triangles.

10. If $RS \parallel XZ$, $YR = 9$, $RX = 3$, and $YS = 12$, how long is SZ?

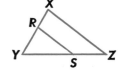

11. If $YR = 6$, $RX = 3$, $YS = 10$, and $SZ = 5$, what is true about RS? Why?

12. (a) In Exercise 10, is $\triangle YRS \backsim \triangle XYZ$? Why?
    (b) What is the ratio of RS and XZ in Exercise 10?

13. Sketch $\triangle ABC$ having $\angle A = 45°$, $\angle B = 60°$; also $\triangle XYZ$ having $\angle Z = 60°$, $\angle Y = 45°$, and $YZ = \dfrac{1}{2}AB$.
    (a) How are triangles ABC and XYZ related? Why?
    (b) If $AC = 6$ in., how long should XY be?

14. Sketch $\triangle CDE$ having $\angle C$ a rt. angle, $\angle D = 30°$; also $\triangle RTS$ having $\angle R$ a right angle, and $\angle T = 30°$.
    (a) How are triangles CDE and RTS related?
    (b) If $DE = 8$ in., how long is CD if $RT = .866\ ST$?

15. $\triangle ABC$ has $AB = 15$ in., $BC = 5$ in. $\triangle XYZ$ has $\angle X = \angle B$, $XY = 12$ in., and $XZ = 4$ in.

(a) How are triangles ABC and XYZ related? Why?

(b) How large is $\angle Y$ if $\angle A = 15°$?

16. **Hyp.** $AD \perp BC$
$CE \perp AB$

Con. (a) $\dfrac{AF}{FC} = \dfrac{EF}{FD}$

(b) Find a triangle that is similar to $\triangle CBE$. Prove them similar.

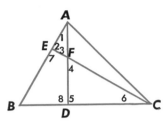

17. **Hyp.** In the adjoining figure, $FGH \parallel JKL$.

Con. $\dfrac{FG}{JK} = \dfrac{GH}{KL}$

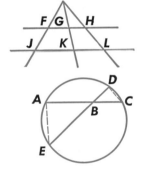

18. **Hyp.** Chord AC intersects chord DE at point B.

Con. $\dfrac{AB}{EB} = \dfrac{DB}{CB}$

19. **Hyp.** In $\triangle XYZ$,
$\angle YXZ$ is a right angle.
$XW \perp YZ$

Con. (a) $\triangle XYW \backsim \triangle XWZ$

(b) $\dfrac{XW}{YW} = \dfrac{WZ}{XW}$

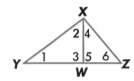

20. In the figure for Ex. 19:

(a) How long is XW if $ZW = 3$ and $WY = 12$?

(b) How long is XY if $YW = 2$ and $YZ = 8$?

(c) How long is YZ if $XY = 6$ and $XZ = 8$?

(d) How long is XZ if $YZ = 15$ and $WZ = 12$?

21. In the adjoining figure, SR is tangent to the circle.

(a) $XT = 4$, $TY = 6$, and $ZT = 3$. How long is TW?

(b) If $RS = 8$ and $RW = 4$, how long is RZ?

(c) Find RY if $RZ = 10$, $RW = 3$, and $RU = 6$.

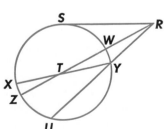

PYRAMIDS AND SIMILAR POLYHEDRONS

261. The adjoining drawing represents a pyramid that has a quadrilateral base. It is called a *quadrangular pyramid*.

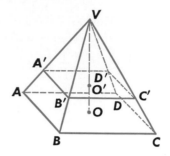

The lateral faces of the pyramid are cut by a plane that is parallel to the base $ABCD$. The altitude VO of the pyramid is intersected by this plane in the point O'.

Prove the answers that you give for the following exercises.

1. Since $VO \perp$ plane $ABCD$, how does VO intersect plane $A'B'C'D'$?

2. What kind of lines are:
 (*a*) $A'B'$ and AB?   (*b*) $B'C'$ and BC?   (*c*) $A'O'$ and AO?

3. What similar triangles do you find in the drawing?

4. What appears to be true about:
 (*a*) $\angle A'B'C'$ and $\angle ABC$?   (*b*) $\angle B'C'D'$ and $\angle BCD$?

5. (*a*) Prove $\dfrac{VA'}{VA} = \dfrac{VB'}{VB} = \dfrac{VC'}{VC} = \dfrac{VD'}{VD} = \dfrac{VO'}{VO}$.

★(*b*) State the conclusions of part (*a*) as a theorem.

6. Prove that $\dfrac{A'B'}{AB} = \dfrac{B'C'}{BC} = \dfrac{C'D'}{CD} = \dfrac{D'A'}{DA}$.

7. Recall the definition of similar polygons and of the ratio of similitude of similar polygons. (§244, p. 213)
 (*a*) Prove $A'B'C'D' \backsim ABCD$.
 (*b*) State part (*a*) as a theorem.

8. (*a*) If $A'B'C'D'$ bisects altitude VO, what is the ratio of VO' to VO? Of VA' to VA? Of $A'B'$ to AB?
 (*b*) What is the ratio of similitude for each pair of corresponding segments in the figure?

9. Repeat all the parts of Ex. 8 if VA' is $\dfrac{1}{3}$ of VA.

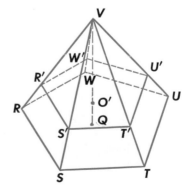

10. A *pentagonal pyramid* is represented at the right. If $R'S'T'U'W'$ is parallel to the base through a point that is $\dfrac{2}{3}$ the distance from V to the base, what is the ratio of similitude?

262. The exercises on page 232 teach the following facts.

SG 57. (a) *A plane that is parallel to the base of a pyramid divides the altitude of the pyramid and the lateral edges into segments that have the same ratio.* This ratio is the ratio of similitude for the resulting figure.

(b) *The **section** of the lateral faces made by the plane that is parallel to the base is a polygon that is similar to the polygon that encloses the base, and the ratio of similitude of the two polygons equals that of the division of the altitude.*

1. Suppose that a plane that is parallel to the base of a hexagonal (six lateral faces) pyramid divides the altitude of the pyramid so that the upper segment of it is $\frac{2}{3}$ of the altitude.
   (a) What is the ratio of similitude for all corresponding segments?
   (b) What part of each lateral edge is the upper segment of that edge?
   (c) For the section that is parallel to the base, what is the ratio of each side to the corresponding side of the base?

2. If all the edges of the base of an octagonal pyramid (eight lateral faces) equal 15 inches and the altitude of the pyramid is 25 inches, how long are the sides of the parallel section made by a plane that is parallel to the base if that plane cuts off the upper 5 inches of the altitude?

263. Just as there are similar polygons in plane geometry there are *similar polyhedrons* in solid geometry (SG 33, p. 133). In the drawing at the top of page 232, the pyramid that is above the plane $A'B'C'D'$ is similar to the original pyramid $ABCD$. From the drawing, or from a model like it that you can make, it is easy to see that the pyramid $V–A'B'C'D'$ has the same shape as $V–ABCD$; that corresponding face angles are equal (such as $\measuredangle A'VB'$ and AVB); that corresponding dihedral angles (such as $\measuredangle A–VB–C$ and $A'–VB'–C'$), and corresponding trihedral angles are equal; and that corresponding edges are proportional.

From the theorem stated as SG 57, it is clear that the ratio of similitude of the two similar polyhedrons is the ratio of any two corresponding segments, such as VO' and VO or $A'B'$ and AB.

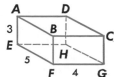

3. Let the adjoining figure represent a rectangular solid with the dimensions shown.
   (a) What kind of solid would be similar to it?
   (b) What dimensions would it have if its altitude is 4 in.?

SOME ANALYTIC GEOMETRY

264. The **XY-plane** is an abbreviated reference to a plane whose points are represented by coordinates that indicate distances from two perpendicular X and Y axes, as below.

The distance between two points in the XY-plane can be expressed by a formula called the **distance formula.**

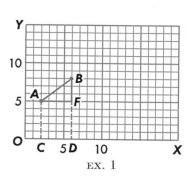

EX. 1

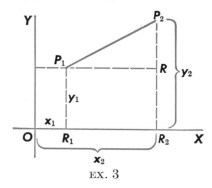

EX. 3

1. In the figure for Exercise 1, observe the points $A:(2, 5)$ and $B:(6, 8)$. $CA \perp OX$, $DB \perp OX$, and $AF \parallel OX$.
(a) How long is: (1) AF? (2) FB?
(b) How long is AB? (§259, p. 228)

2. As in Exercise 1, locate and then find the distance between:
(a) $(3, 4)$ and $(9, 12)$ (b) $(2, 8)$ and $(14, 3)$
(c) $(1, 7)$ and $(9, 13)$ (d) $(16, 6)$ and $(4, 11)$
(e) $(5, 12)$ and $(9, 13)$ (f) $(-5, 8)$ and $(8, -5)$

3. In the figure for Exercise 3, above, observe $P_1: (x_1, y_1)$, $P_2: (x_2, y_2)$, $R_1P_1 \perp OX$, $R_2P_2 \perp OX$, and $P_1R \parallel OX$.
(a) How long is: (1) P_1R? (2) RP_2?
(b) Using §259, express P_1P_2 as a formula.
This is the formula for the distance between (x_1, y_1) *and* (x_2, y_2).

4. (a) Locate $P:(2, 7), Q:(8, 11)$ and $R:(5, 12)$.
(b) Find the perimeter of $\triangle PQR$.

5. (a) Locate $A:(2, 3), B:(9, 4), C:(8, 8)$ and $D:(1, 7)$.
(b) Prove that $ABCD$ must be a parallelogram by proving that its opposite sides are equal.

6. (a) Locate $P:(0, 0), Q:(a, 0), R:(a, b)$, and $S:(0, b)$, where a and b are two convenient short segments that you select. Draw $PQRS$.
(b) What kind of figure does $PQRS$ *appear* to be?
(c) Prove that $PQRS$ is the kind of figure you name in part (b).
(d) Use the distance formula to find PR and QS.
(e) What fact about a figure like $PQRS$ does part (d) prove?

7. (a) Locate P:(0, 0), Q:(a, 0), and R:(0, b) after selecting some convenient short segments for a and b. Draw PQR.

   (b) What kind of triangle is $\triangle PQR$?

   (c) Use the formulas for the mid-point of a segment to determine the coordinates of the mid-point, S, of QR. (See Ex. 4, p. 137.)

   (d) Use the distance formula to find the lengths of SP, SQ, and SR.

   (e) What theorem is proved by the results of part (d)?

8. (a) Locate the points A:(2, 1), B:(8, 9), C:(6, 11), and D:(4, 11). Draw $ABCD$, and, freehand, locate the mid-points L, M, N, and P of AB, BC, CD, and DA, respectively.

   (b) By the mid-point formulas determine the coordinates of L, M, N, and P.

   (c) Prove that $LMNP$ is a parallelogram.

9. (a) Locate P:(7, 2), Q:(5, 8), and R:(3, 1). Draw PQR. Then, freehand, locate the mid-points, S and T, of PQ and QR, and draw ST.

   (b) By the distance formula find the length of ST.

   (c) Compare the lengths of ST and PR.

   (d) What theorem is verified by the result of part (c)?

10. (a) Locate A:(0, 0), B:(6, 0), C:(5, 4), and D:(3, 4). Draw $ABCD$.

    (b) What kind of polygon does $ABCD$ appear to be?

    (c) Prove that $ABCD$ is the polygon that you name in part (b).

    (d) Find the coordinates of the mid-point E of AD and F of BC.

    (e) By the distance formula find the length of EF.

    (f) Compare the result of part (e) with the sum of AB and CD.

    (g) What theorem is verified by this exercise?

11. Prove that the circle with center (4, 4) and radius of length 5 must pass through the points (1, 0), (7, 0), and (4, 9).

12. (a) Locate A:(0, 0), B:(2a, 0), and C:(a, b), after selecting for a and b, convenient short segments. Draw $\triangle ABC$.

    (b) What kind of triangle does ABC appear to be? Prove.

    (c) Freehand locate D, the mid-point of AB and draw DC. Find the length of DC.

    (d) Freehand locate E, the mid-point of BC, and F, the mid-point of AC. Draw AE and BF. Find the coordinates of E and F.

    (e) Find the lengths of AE and BF by the distance formula.

    (f) What theorem is verified by the foregoing parts of Ex. 12?

THEOREMS ABOUT SIMILAR POLYGONS

265. *Two polygons are similar if they consist of the same number of triangles, similar each to each, and similarly placed.*

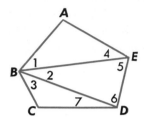 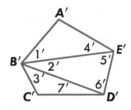

Hypothesis. $\triangle AEB \backsim \triangle A'E'B'$
$\triangle EBD \backsim \triangle E'B'D'$
$\triangle BCD \backsim \triangle B'C'D'$
The triangles are similarly placed.

Conclusion. Polygon $ABCDE \backsim$ polygon $A'B'C'D'E'$.

Plan. Prove corresponding $\angle$ equal and corresponding sides proportional.

Proof.

	Statements	Authorities
1.	$\angle A = \angle A'$, $\angle C = \angle C'$	1. Why?
2.	$\angle 1 = \angle 1'$, $\angle 2 = \angle 2'$, $\angle 3 = \angle 3'$	2. Why?
3.	$\therefore \quad \angle B = \angle B'$	3. Why?
4. Also	$\angle D = \angle D'$, $\angle E = \angle E'$	4. By similar proof.
5. $\therefore$	the polygons are mutually equiangular.	5. Definition.
6.	$\dfrac{AB}{A'B'} = \dfrac{AE}{A'E'} = \dfrac{BE}{B'E'}$	6. Why?
7.	$\dfrac{BE}{B'E'} = \dfrac{ED}{E'D'} = \dfrac{BD}{B'D'}$	7. Why?
8.	$\dfrac{BD}{B'D'} = \dfrac{CD}{C'D'} = \dfrac{BC}{B'C'}$	8. Why?
9.	$\therefore \dfrac{AB}{A'B'} = \dfrac{AE}{A'E'} = \dfrac{ED}{E'D'}$ $= \dfrac{CD}{C'D'} = \dfrac{BC}{B'C'}$	9. Ax. 1, p. 32
10.	$\therefore ABCDE \backsim A'B'C'D'E'$	10. §244(a), p. 213

266. *Upon a given segment, corresponding to a given side of a given polygon, a polygon similar to the given polygon can be constructed.*

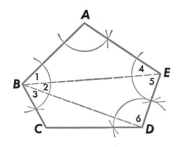

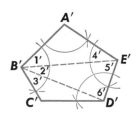

Given. Polygon $ABCDE$ and segment $A'B'$.

Required. To construct on $A'B'$ a polygon that is similar to $ABCDE$, with $A'B'$ corresponding to AB.

Construction	Authorities
1. Draw diagonals BE and BD, separating $ABCDE$ into three triangles.	1. Possible?
2. Construct $\triangle A'B'E' \backsim \triangle ABE$.	2. How?
3. Construct $\triangle B'E'D' \backsim \triangle BED$.	3. How?
4. Construct $\triangle B'D'C' \backsim \triangle BDC$.	4. How?

Statement. $A'B'C'D'E' \backsim ABCDE$
(Proof left to the pupil.)

1. $RSTV$ represents the shape of a piece of metal. Construct, full size, a quadrilateral that has this shape, making the dimensions four times those of this drawing.

2. Draw an irregular pentagon. Then enlarge it in the ratio $3 : 1$.

3. At the right, $\angle V = \angle Z = 90°$. Is $RSTV \backsim WXYZ$? Prove your conclusion.

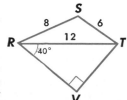

4. Draw any irregular polygon. Construct a polygon similar to it that has to it the ratio of similitude 4 to 1.

267. *Two similar polygons can be separated into the same number of triangles, similar each to each, and similarly placed.*

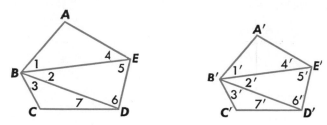

Hypothesis. Polygon $ABCDE \backsim$ polygon $A'B'C'D'E'$, corresponding vertices being indicated by corresponding letters. (Pentagons are used for convenience.)

Conclusion. The polygons can be separated into the same number of triangles, similar each to each and similarly placed.

Proof.

	Statements	Authorities
1.	Draw BE, BD, $B'E'$, and $B'D'$.	1. Why possible?
2.	$\angle A = \angle A'$	2. Why?
3.	$\dfrac{AB}{A'B'} = \dfrac{AE}{A'E'}$	3. Why?
4.	$\therefore$ $\triangle ABE \backsim \triangle A'B'E'$	4. Why?
5.	$\angle 4 = \angle 4'$, $\angle AED = \angle A'E'D'$	5. Why?
6.	$\therefore$ $\angle 5 = \angle 5'$	6. Ax. 4, p. 32
7.	$\dfrac{BE}{B'E'} = \dfrac{AE}{A'E'}$	7. Why?
	$\dfrac{ED}{E'D'} = \dfrac{AE}{A'E'}$	
8.	$\therefore$ $\dfrac{BE}{B'E'} = \dfrac{ED}{E'D'}$	8. Why?
9.	$\therefore$ $\triangle BED \backsim \triangle B'E'D'$	9. Why?
10.	Also $\triangle BDC \backsim \triangle B'D'C'$	10. By a similar proof.

1. In some other way, separate the polygons into similar triangles, similarly placed. Then prove that your way is correct.

2. Draw any rectangle, $ABCD$. Construct rectangle $A'B'C'D'$ similar to $ABCD$, with $A'B' = 2AB$. Draw the diagonals intersecting at O and O'. Prove $\triangle B'O'A' \backsim \triangle BOA$ and $A'O' = 2AO$.

DIVISION OF A SEGMENT

268. A point P on a segment AB **divides the segment internally** into two segments AP and PB.

Observe that $AP + PB = AB$.

A ——————— P ——————— B

Name AP from the beginning of AB to the division point P, then PB from P to the end of the given segment.

269. *In a triangle, the bisector of an interior angle divides the opposite side internally into segments proportional to the adjacent sides of the triangle.*

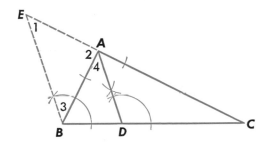

Hypothesis. AD bisects $\angle A$ of $\triangle ABC$, meeting BC at D.

Conclusion.
$$\frac{BD}{DC} = \frac{BA}{AC}$$

Plan. Draw a parallel to DA through B to find $BD : DC$.

Proof.

Statements	Authorities
1. Construct $BE \parallel DA$, meeting CA extended at E.	1. §95, p. 95
2. $\qquad$ In $\triangle EBC, \dfrac{BD}{DC} = \dfrac{EA}{AC}.$	2. Why?

(The rest of the proof is left to the pupil.)

Suggestion. In $\triangle AEB$, prove $\angle 1 = \angle 3$.

Prove $AB = AE$, and substitute in Step 2.

1. Find BD if $AB = 3$, $AC = 6$, and $DC = 5$.

2. Find AB if $BD = 2.5$, $AC = 9$, and $DC = 7.5$.

3. The sides of a triangle are 10 in., 20 in., and 12 in. respectively. Find the segments of the 12 in. side made by the bisector of the opposite angle.

270. A point P that lies on AB extended is said to **divide** AB **externally** into segments AP and PB.

FIG.1   FIG. 2

The first segment is named from A, the beginning of the given segment, to the division point. The second segment is named from the division point to B, the other end of the given segment.

The sum of AP and PB equals AB only if the algebraic sum is meant. However, in plane geometry, only the lengths, without reference to algebraic signs, are considered.

271. *The bisector of an exterior angle at a vertex of a triangle divides the opposite side externally into two segments whose ratio equals the ratio of the other two sides of the triangle.*

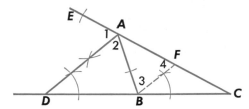

Hypothesis. AD bisects exterior $\angle BAE$ of $\triangle ABC$, meeting CB extended at D.

Conclusion. $BD:DC = BA:AC$

Plan. Draw a parallel to AD through B so that the ratio of BD to DC can be expressed.

Proof.

Statements	Authorities
1. Draw $BF \parallel DA$, meeting AC at F.	1. Why possible?
2. $\therefore$ $BD : DC = FA : AC$	2. §242, p. 211
3. $\angle 3 = \angle 2, \angle 4 = \angle 1$	3. Give the proof.
4. $\therefore$ $\angle 3 = \angle 4$	4. Give the proof.
5. $\therefore$ $BA = FA$	5. Why?
6. $\therefore$ $BD : DC = BA : AC$	6. Why?

272. A segment is **divided harmonically** if it is divided internally and externally into segments that have the same ratio.

Thus: X and Y divide AB harmonically if
$$AX : XB = AY : YB.$$
An instance occurs when $AB = 4$, $AX = 3$, and $BY = 2$.
Then $AX:XB = 3:1$; also $AY:YB = 6:2$, or $3:1$.

1. Prove that the bisector of the interior angle of a triangle at any vertex and the bisector of the exterior angle at the same vertex divide the opposite side harmonically.

Suggestion. This exercise is proved by using §269 and §271.

2. A common internal tangent of two circles divides the line joining their centers internally into two segments that have the same ratio as the radii of the circles.

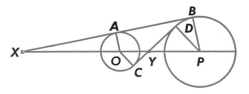

Suggestion. Prove that $OY : YP = OC : PD$.

3. A common external tangent of two circles divides the line joining their centers externally into two segments that have the same ratio as the radii of the circles.

Suggestion. Prove $OX : XP = OA : PB$.

4. Prove that a common internal and a common external tangent of two circles divide the line of centers of the circles harmonically.

5. Two circles O and P are tangent externally at A. Their common external tangent XY meets $\odot O$ at X and $\odot P$ at Y. Tangent XY meets OP extended at B. Prove A and B divide OP harmonically.

Suggestion. Draw OX and PY. Prove $OB : BP = OX : PY = OA : AP$.

6. AM is the median to BC of $\triangle ABC$. MX bisects $\angle AMB$, meeting AB at X. MY bisects $\angle CMA$, meeting CA at Y. Prove $XY \parallel BC$.

7. Two circles with centers O and P have radii that equal 4 in. and 6 in. respectively. Their line of centers is 15 in. long. A common internal tangent intersects OP at Y. Find OY and YP.

CHAPTER 8

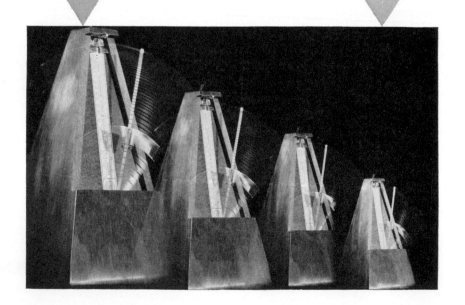

TRIGONOMETRY

Have you ever wondered how the height of the cloud ceiling at an airport is measured? Or perhaps you have seen the vertical beam of light at an airport at night and wondered what its purpose was.

The point at which the beam of light meets the clouds marks the height of the ceiling. An instrument measures this height indirectly by means of similar triangles (which you have studied) and by trigonometry which is based on similar triangles. Trigonometry is a valuable tool in surveying, in navigation on the sea and in the air, in astronomy, and in many phases of industry.

You may have studied numerical trigonometry in earlier courses in mathematics. In this chapter you will find the deductive explanations that justify the use of the tangent, the sine, and the cosine.

Three uses of trigonometric functions: the astronomer with a telescope can use spherical triangles to determine distances; the naval officer with a sextant can use triangles to determine the position of a vessel; the motion of a metronome, an inverted pendulum, can be described using sines and cosines.

TOP LEFT: EWING GALLOWAY, NEW YORK   TOP RIGHT: A. DEVANEY, INC., NEW YORK
BOTTOM: UNDERWOOD AND UNDERWOOD

273. The **tangent of an acute angle.** Let $\angle ABC$ be an acute angle. On BC take any points P_1, P_2, and P_3. Draw P_1R_1, P_2R_2, and $P_3R_3 \perp BA$. You can prove that

$$\triangle BR_1P_1 \backsim \triangle BR_2P_2 \backsim \triangle BR_3P_3$$

$$\therefore \quad \frac{R_1P_1}{BR_1} = \frac{R_2P_2}{BR_2} = \frac{R_3P_3}{BR_3} \qquad \text{(Why?)}$$

That is, the ratio of RP to BR is the same no matter where P is on BC. We say that the *ratio is constant.*

This constant ratio for an acute angle is called the **tangent of the angle.** For an $\angle B$, it is abbreviated **tan B.**

When the angle, B, is acute, the sides of the angle and the perpendicular to one of them from a point of the other form a right triangle, RBP, in which

$$\textbf{tan } B = \frac{\textbf{the leg opposite } \angle \textbf{ } B}{\textbf{the leg adjacent to } \angle \textbf{ } B}.$$

274. The *approximate value* of the tangent of an acute angle can be obtained as follows:

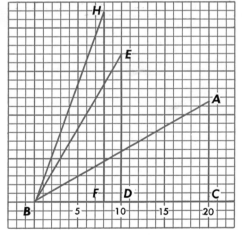

(*a*) $\angle CBA = 30°$.

$$\tan 30° = \frac{CA}{BC} = \frac{11.5}{20} = .6$$

(*b*) $\angle DBE = 60°$.

$$\tan 60° = \frac{DE}{BD} = \frac{17}{10} = 1.7$$

(*c*) $\angle FBH = 70°$.

$$\tan 70° = \frac{FH}{BF} = \frac{22}{8} = 2.8$$

These values of the tangent are *correct* to *tenths.*

Observe that *the tangent of an acute angle increases as the angle increases.*

The approximate value, correct to four decimal places, of the tangent of an angle for each angle expressed in degrees from $0°$ to $90°$ appears in the table on page 245.

Angle	Sin	Cos	Tan	Angle	Sin	Cos	Tan
1°	.0175	.9998	.0175	46°	.7193	.6947	1.0355
2°	.0349	.9994	.0349	47°	.7314	.6820	1.0724
3°	.0523	.9986	.0524	48°	.7431	.6691	1.1106
4°	.0698	.9976	.0699	49°	.7547	.6561	1.1504
5°	.0872	.9962	.0875	50°	.7660	.6428	1.1918
6°	.1045	.9945	.1051	51°	.7771	.6293	1.2349
7°	.1219	.9925	.1228	52°	.7880	.6157	1.2799
8°	.1392	.9903	.1405	53°	.7986	.6018	1.3270
9°	.1564	.9877	.1584	54°	.8090	.5878	1.3764
10°	.1736	.9848	.1763	55°	.8192	.5736	1.4281
11°	.1908	.9816	.1944	56°	.8290	.5592	1.4826
12°	.2079	.9781	.2126	57°	.8387	.5446	1.5399
13°	.2250	.9744	.2309	58°	.8480	.5299	1.6003
14°	.2419	.9703	.2493	59°	.8572	.5150	1.6643
15°	.2588	.9659	.2679	60°	.8660	.5000	1.7321
16°	.2756	.9613	.2867	61°	.8746	.4848	1.8040
17°	.2924	.9563	.3057	62°	.8829	.4695	1.8807
18°	.3090	.9511	.3249	63°	.8910	.4540	1.9626
19°	.3256	.9455	.3443	64°	.8988	.4384	2.0503
20°	.3420	.9397	.3640	65°	.9063	.4226	2.1445
21°	.3584	.9336	.3839	66°	.9135	.4067	2.2460
22°	.3746	.9272	.4040	67°	.9205	.3907	2.3559
23°	.3907	.9205	.4245	68°	.9272	.3746	2.4751
24°	.4067	.9135	.4452	69°	.9336	.3584	2.6051
25°	.4226	.9063	.4663	70°	.9397	.3420	2.7475
26°	.4384	.8988	.4877	71°	.9455	.3256	2.9042
27°	.4540	.8910	.5095	72°	.9511	.3090	3.0777
28°	.4695	.8829	.5317	73°	.9563	.2924	3.2709
29°	.4848	.8746	.5543	74°	.9613	.2756	3.4874
30°	.5000	.8660	.5774	75°	.9659	.2588	3.7321
31°	.5150	.8572	.6009	76°	.9703	.2419	4.0108
32°	.5299	.8480	.6249	77°	.9744	.2250	4.3315
33°	.5446	.8387	.6494	78°	.9781	.2079	4.7046
34°	.5592	.8290	.6745	79°	.9816	.1908	5.1446
35°	.5736	.8192	.7002	80°	.9848	.1736	5.6713
36°	.5878	.8090	.7265	81°	.9877	.1564	6.3138
37°	.6018	.7986	.7536	82°	.9903	.1392	7.1154
38°	.6157	.7880	.7813	83°	.9925	.1219	8.1443
39°	.6293	.7771	.8098	84°	.9945	.1045	9.5144
40°	.6428	.7660	.8391	85°	.9962	.0872	11.4300
41°	.6561	.7547	.8693	86°	.9976	.0698	14.3010
42°	.6691	.7431	.9004	87°	.9986	.0523	19.0810
43°	.6820	.7314	.9325	88°	.9994	.0349	28.6360
44°	.6947	.7193	.9657	89°	.9998	.0175	57.2900
45°	.7071	.7071	1.0000				

275. **Using the tangent of an angle.**

Example 1. At a point 60 ft. from the foot of a flagpole, $\angle BCA$ was measured and found to be 55°. How high was the pole?

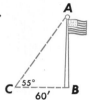

Solution. 1. $\tan 55° = \dfrac{AB}{BC}$, or $\dfrac{AB}{60} = \tan 55°$.

2. From page 245, $\tan 55° = 1.4281$.

3. $\therefore \quad AB = 60 \times 1.4281$

4. $\therefore \quad AB = 85.686$, or about 86 ft.

$\angle BCA$ is called the **angle of elevation** of A at C.

The first form of the result is 85.686. No one is interested in such a result for the height of a flagpole. In it, there are too many *significant figures.* Moreover, we cannot be sure of more than two significant figures since 60, an original measure, has only two significant figures. We round off 85.686 to 86, because 85.686 is nearer to 86 than to 85.

Note. See page 423 for computing with approximate numbers.

Example 2. An observer in a balloon at C measures $\angle DCA$ between DC, a horizontal line, and the line of sight to a point A on the ground. He finds $\angle DCA = 14°$. He is 1800 ft. above the plain on which A is located. How far is A from B on the plain directly below him?

Solution. 1. We assume that DC, AC, and AB are coplanar and that $DC \parallel AB$.

2. $\qquad\qquad \angle BAC = \angle DCA = 14°$ $\qquad\qquad$ (Why?)

3. $\qquad\qquad \tan BAC = \dfrac{BC}{AB}$ or $\tan 14° = \dfrac{1800}{AB}$

4. $\qquad\qquad \tan 14° = .2493$

5. $\qquad\qquad \therefore .2493 \times AB = 1800$ $\qquad\qquad$ (Why?)

6. $\qquad\qquad \therefore \quad AB = \dfrac{1800}{.2493}$

7. $\qquad\qquad AB = 7220.2$, or 7200 ft.

$\angle DCA$ is called the **angle of depression** of A at C.

1. 125 ft. from the foot of a building, the angle of elevation of its top is 40°. How high is the building?

2. An observer in a fire observation tower that is 100 ft. high notices smoke at a point X, the angle of depression of which is 3°. How far from a point on the ground, directly below the observer, is the point X? Express the result correct to tenths of a mile.

3. The angle of elevation of a cloud at a point on the ground that is 2000 ft. from a point directly below the cloud is 55°. How high is the cloud, correct to the nearest 100 ft.?

4. AB is a chord of a circle O. Line $OC \perp AB$ at C. $\angle BOC = 30°$. If $AB = 12$ in., how long is OC?

5. In right $\triangle ABC$, $\angle A = 90°$ and $\angle B = 70°$. Altitude AD meets BC at D, and $BD = 6$ in. Find AD and DC.

6. If T is a target and G is a gun position located so that $\angle CGT = 90°$, what would be the *range*, GT, of the target if it is known that $\angle C = 51°$ and $CG = 600$ yards?

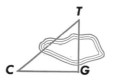

7. Find the unknown length x in each of the following figures:

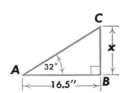 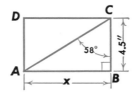 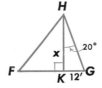

8. How long is the altitude to the base of an isosceles triangle if the base equals 24 in. and each base angle equals 65°?

9. What is the length of the altitude of an equilateral triangle whose sides equal 30 in.?

10. Construct an isosceles trapezoid whose upper base measures 24 inches, whose lower base measures 38 inches, and whose lower base angles equal 60°. Compute the length of the altitude of this trapezoid.

★11. (SG) $V-ABC$ . . . is a regular pyramid (p. 134) such that each lower-base edge is 10 in., and lower-base angles on each face equal 50°. Find the length of the altitude on each face.

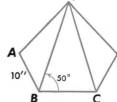

276. **Sine of an acute angle.** In the following figure recall why $\triangle BR_1P_1 \backsim \triangle BR_2P_2 \backsim \triangle BR_3P_3$ when P_1, P_2, and P_3 are any points on side BC of $\angle ABC$, and P_1R_1, P_2R_2, and P_3R_3 are perpendicular to BA.

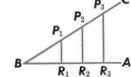

$$\therefore \quad \frac{R_1P_1}{BP_1} = \frac{R_2P_2}{BP_2} = \frac{R_3P_3}{BP_3}$$

$\therefore$ wherever P is on BC, the ratio $\dfrac{RP}{BP}$ is constant.

This ratio is called the **sine** of $\angle B$ (abbreviated **sin B**). If $\angle B$ is an acute angle, then in right triangle BRP

$$\sin B = \frac{\text{the leg opposite } \angle B}{\text{the hypotenuse}}.$$

In §274: $CA = 11.5$, $BA = 23$, $DE = 17$
$BE = 20$, $FH = 22$, $BH = 24$

$$\sin 30° = \frac{11.5}{23} = .50 \quad \sin 60° = \frac{17}{20} = .85 \quad \sin 70° = \frac{22}{24} = .92$$

The sine of an acute angle increases as the angle increases.

277. **Cosine of an acute angle.** In the same figure:

$$\frac{BR_1}{BP_1} = \frac{BR_2}{BP_2} = \frac{BR_3}{BP_3}$$

$\therefore$ wherever P is on BC, the ratio $\dfrac{BR}{BP}$ is constant.

This ratio is called the **cosine** of $\angle B$ (abbreviated **cos B**). If $\angle B$ is an acute angle, then in right triangle BRP

$$\cos B = \frac{\text{the leg adjacent to } \angle B}{\text{the hypotenuse}}.$$

In §274: $BC = 20$, $BA = 23$, $BD = 10$
$BE = 20$, $BF = 8$, $BH = 24$

$$\cos 30° = \frac{20}{23} = .87 \quad \cos 60° = \frac{10}{20} = .50 \quad \cos 70° = \frac{8}{24} = .33$$

The cosine of an acute angle decreases when the angle increases.

278. For each angle there is a definite value of the sine, the cosine, and the tangent. We say that the sine, the cosine, and the tangent are **functions** of the angle.

Example. In trapezoid $ABCD$, if $AD = 18$ in., and $\angle A = 70°$, find the length of altitude DE.

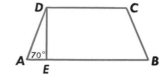

Analysis. 1. $\tan A = \dfrac{DE}{AE}$. Since AE is unknown, $\tan A$ cannot be used.

2. $\cos A = \dfrac{AE}{AD}$. Since $\cos A$ does not refer to DE, $\cos A$ is not a promising approach to DE.

3. $\sin A = \dfrac{DE}{AD}$. Since $\angle A$ and AD are known, $\sin A$ does offer a promising way to find DE.

Solution. 1. $\qquad \sin 70° = \dfrac{DE}{AD}$

$\qquad\qquad$ or $\dfrac{DE}{18} = \sin 70°$ $\qquad \left(\begin{array}{c}\sin\ 70° \\ = .9397\end{array}\right)$

2. $\qquad\qquad \therefore \quad DE = 18 \times .9397$

3. $\qquad\qquad \therefore \quad DE = 16.9146$

4. $\qquad\qquad \therefore \quad DE = 16.9$ in. (or 17 in.)

Solve the following problems.

1. $AC \perp CD$, $CD = 175$ ft.; $\angle D = 68°$. Find AC.

2. Do Ex. 1 if $\angle D = 80°$.

3. Do Ex. 1 if $CD = 250$ ft. and $\angle D = 75°$.

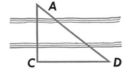

4. (a) 250 ft. from the foot of a building on level ground, the angle of elevation of the top of the building is 28°. How high is the building?

   (b) Do part (a) if the angle is 32°.

5. From the top of a cliff 240 ft. high, the angle of depression of a horseman on the plain below is 25°. How far is the horseman from a point on the level of the plain directly below the observer?

6. In the adjoining figure, if $AB \perp BC$, $BC = 16$ ft., and $BA = 8$ ft., find:

   (a) AC, correct to tenths of a foot.

   (b) $\angle ACB$, correct to the nearest degree.

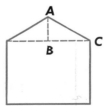

7. In a $\triangle XYZ$, base $YZ = 30$ ft., $\angle Y = 55°$, and $XY = 10$ ft. Draw altitude XW to YZ.

   (a) Find XW. (b) Find YW.

279. Approximate values of trigonometric ratios for acute angles that *do not* appear in the table on page 245 can be found.

Example 1. Find sin 27°30′.

Analysis. 1. Since 30′ = $\frac{1}{2}$ of 60′, 27°30′ is halfway between 27° and 28°.

2. Since the sine *increases when the angle increases*, we assume that sin 27°30′ is sin 27° *plus* half the difference between sine 28° and sine 27°.

Solution.

1.
$$\begin{array}{lll}
\sin 27° & = .4540 & .4695 \\
\sin 27°30′ & = \quad ? & .4540 \\
\sin 28° & = .4695 & .0155
\end{array}$$

$$30′ = \tfrac{1}{2} \text{ of } 1°$$
$$\tfrac{1}{2} \times .0155 = .00775$$
$$= .0078$$

2.   ∴   sin 27°30′ = .4540 + .0078, or .4618

Example 2. Find cos 27°15′.

Analysis. 1. Since 15′ is $\frac{1}{4}$ of 60′, 27°15′ is one quarter of the way between 27° and 28°.

2. Since the cosine *decreases when the angle increases* we assume that cos 27°15′ is cos 27° *minus* one fourth of the difference between cos 27° and cos 28°.

Solution.

1.
$$\begin{array}{lll}
\cos 27° & = .8910 & .8910 \\
\cos 27°15′ & = \quad ? & .8829 \\
\cos 28° & = .8829 & .0081
\end{array}$$

$$15′ = \tfrac{1}{4} \text{ of } 1°$$
$$\tfrac{1}{4} \times .0081 = .002025$$
$$= .0020$$

2.   ∴   cos 27°15′ = .8910 − .0020, or .8890

Example 3. Find tan 48°45′.

Analysis. 1. Since 45′ is $\frac{3}{4}$ of 60′, 48°45′ is three fourths of the way between 47° and 48°.

2. Since the tangent *increases when the angle increases*, we assume that tan 48°45′ is tan 48° *plus* three fourths of the difference between tan 49° and tan 48°.

Solution.

1.
$$\begin{array}{lll}
\tan 48° & = 1.1106 & 1.1504
\end{array}$$

$$\frac{3}{\cancel{4}} \times \cancel{0.0398}^{\,0.00995}$$

$$\begin{array}{lll}
\tan 48°45′ & = \quad ? & 1.1106 \\
\tan 49° & = 1.1504 & 0.0398
\end{array}$$

$$= 0.02985$$
$$= 0.0299$$

2.   ∴   tan 48°45′ = 1.1106 + 0.0299, or 1.1405

280. The process of finding the approximate value of a ratio for an angle that is between two angles whose values appear in the table is called *interpolation*.

Thus: To find sin 40°12′, we *interpolate* between sin 40° and sin 41°, using the obvious fact that 12′ = $\frac{1}{5}$ of 60′.

Find the value of the function in Exercises 1 to 9.

1. sin 29°45′
2. cos 36°15′
3. tan 73°30′

4. sin 25°30′
5. tan 48°15′
6. cos 62°45′

7. sin 52°15′
8. tan 37°20′
9. cos 75°12′

281. The **approximate size of an angle** can be found by using the table on page 245 when the value of one of the three trigonometric ratios is known.

Example. Find ∠X correct to the nearest degree when tan X = 1.3675.

Analysis. ∠X is between the two angles whose tangents are the nearest greater than and the nearest less than 1.3675.

Solution.

1.
$$\begin{array}{ll} \tan 53° = 1.3270 & 1.3675 \\ \tan X \ \ = 1.3675 & 1.3270 \\ \tan 54° = 1.3764 & .0405 \end{array} \ \begin{array}{l} 1.3764 \\ 1.3675 \\ .0089 \end{array}$$

2.   1.3675 is nearer to 1.3764 than to 1.3270.

∴ ∠X = 54°, correct to the nearest degree.

Note. By interpolation, the size of the angle, correct to the nearest 10′ could be computed, but, for ordinary purposes, such *precise* determination of the angle is not necessary.

By the procedure illustrated above, find ∠X correct to the nearest degree when:

10. sin X = .6293
11. tan X = .5169
12. cos X = .4384

13. sin X = .8503
14. tan X = 7.1154
15. cos X = .3175

16. tan X = 1.2215
17. sin X = .3465
18. cos X = .6749

19. sin X = .8516
20. tan X = .3750
21. cos X = .8824

22. tan X = 2.4410
23. sin X = .6975
24. cos X = .2384

In the following problems, compute angles correct to the nearest degree, and lengths of segments as directed on pages 423 and 424.

1. What is the angle of elevation of the sun when a 12 ft. pole casts a shadow 4 ft. long?

2. The radius of a circle is 12 in. What is the length of the chord of an arc of 34°?

3. Inscribed in a circle of radius 10 in. is an equilateral hexagon. Find the distance from the center of the circle to each of the sides of this hexagon, and the length of a side of the hexagon.

4. Do Ex. 3 if the polygon is an inscribed octagon with equal sides.

5. The mid-point of a 15 in. chord of a circle is 6 in. from the mid-point of the arc of this chord.
   (a) How many degrees are there in the arc of the chord?
   (b) What is the radius of this circle?

Suggestion. For (a) use §273 and §200. For (b) use §251.

6. A circle is inscribed in an equilateral triangle whose sides are 10 in. long. Find the radius of the circle.

7. A circle is circumscribed about an equilateral triangle whose sides are 12 in. long. Find the radius.

8. From the sketch, determine the length of the diameter x of the head of the screw.

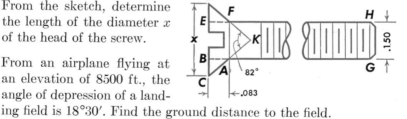

9. From an airplane flying at an elevation of 8500 ft., the angle of depression of a landing field is 18°30'. Find the ground distance to the field.

10. Find the altitude DE to the base AB of $\square ABCD$ in which $AD = 25$:
    (a) If $\angle A = 30°$.   (b) If $\angle A = 60°$.   (c) If $\angle A = 75°30'$.

11. In Ex. 10, if AD is constant, how does DE change as $\angle A$ increases?

12. $\angle x$ is $\frac{1}{2}$ the angle formed by DC and AB if they are extended to meet. Find $\angle x$ and then the angle between AB and DC, correct to the nearest degree, and find y, correct to thousandths.

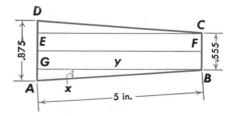

RATIOS FOR ANY ANGLE

282. So far, the trigonometric ratios have been defined only for acute angles. They will be defined now for any angle.

(*a*) Locate any angle, $\angle AOB$, on a set of rectangular coordinate axes as follows:

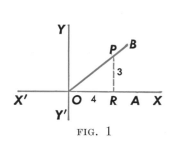

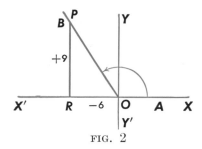

FIG. 1   FIG. 2

For the origin, take the vertex of the angle. For the *X*-axis, take the initial side, OA, of the angle. For the *Y*-axis, take a line through the vertex, perpendicular to the initial side, OA. Call this the **standard position** of the angle. The angle is read in the counterclockwise direction.

If $\angle AOB$ is acute, its terminal side, OB, falls in quadrant I as in Fig. 1; if obtuse, it falls in quadrant II as in Fig. 2; if larger than 180° but less than 360°, it falls in quadrant III or IV.

1. Represent on rectangular axes the following angles.
   (*a*) 60°   (*b*) 150°   (*c*) 90°   (*d*) 225°   (*e*) 135°

(*b*) The sign and length of a segment that is parallel to either axis is determined by the scales on the axes.
Thus: In Fig. 1, $RP = +3$, and $OR = +4$
In Fig. 2, $RP = +9$, and $OR = -6$

Segments that are not parallel to one of the axes *are considered positive*, and their lengths are expressed by the unit used on the axes.

Thus: In Fig. 1, $OP = \sqrt{3^2 + 4^2} = \sqrt{25} = +5$
In Fig. 2, $OP = \sqrt{9^2 + (-6)^2} = \sqrt{81 + 36} = \sqrt{117}$
$\therefore \quad OP = \sqrt{9 \times 13} = 3\sqrt{13}$. (See p. 418.)

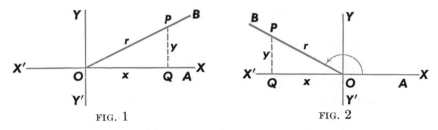

FIG. 1 FIG. 2

283. *General definitions of the trigonometric functions.*

Place $\angle AOB$ in the standard position. Take any point P on the terminal side OB. Mark its coordinates x and y as above. Let $OP = r$. Then:

$$\sin AOB = \frac{y}{r} \qquad \cos AOB = \frac{x}{r} \qquad \tan AOB = \frac{y}{x}$$

In quadrant I, x and y are both positive. Therefore the sine, cosine, and tangent of every acute angle are positive.

In quadrant II, r and ordinate y are positive, but abscissa x is negative. Therefore, when the angle is obtuse, the sine is positive, the cosine is negative, and the tangent is negative.

1. Using the results from (b), p. 253, express the sine, cosine, and tangent of $\angle AOB$:
   (a) In Figure 1. (b) In Figure 2.

2. (a) Draw in standard position an $\angle AOB$, of 45°.
   (b) On OB, take point P with ordinate $+5$.
   (c) Find the abscissa of P and the distance, r, of OP.
   (d) Express each of the three ratios for 45°.

3. Do Exercise 2 when $\angle AOB$ equals 135°.

4. Do Exercise 2 when $\angle AOB$ equals 150°.

5. Do Exercise 2 when $\angle AOB$ equals 225°, using -5 for the ordinate of P.

6. Do Exercise 2 when $\angle AOB$ equals 240°, using -5 for the ordinate of P.

7. Do Exercise 2 when $\angle AOB$ equals 315°, using -5 for the ordinate of P.

8. Do Exercise 2 when $\angle AOB$ equals 300°, using -5 for the ordinate of P.

★9. (a) As in Exercise 2, find: (1) Sin 90° (2) Cos 90°
   (b) Why must tan 90° be left undefined?

284. Place any $\angle A$ in the standard position. Let $P:(x, y)$ be any point on the terminal side of $\angle A$. Let $OP = r$.

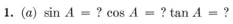

1. (a) $\sin A = ?$ $\cos A = ?$ $\tan A = ?$

   (b) Compare $\tan A$ with $\dfrac{\sin A}{\cos A}$.

   (c) Express in words the conclusion suggested by part (b).

2. (a) By $\sin^2 A$ we mean $(\sin A)^2$, or $\sin A \times \sin A$. Using the results of Ex. 1(a), find:

   (1) $\sin^2 A$ (2) $\cos^2 A$ (3) $\sin^2 A + \cos^2 A$

   (b) Simplify the result for (3) of (a).

   (c) Express the conclusion suggested by part (b).

3. Verify the conclusions of Ex. 1(c) and Ex. 2(c) when:

   (a) $\angle A = 45°$ (b) $\angle A = 60°$ (c) $\angle A = 135°$

285. **The law of sines in a triangle.**

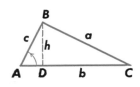 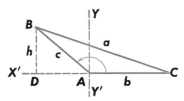

In a triangle ABC the length of a side is represented by the small letter that corresponds to the capital letter at the vertex of the opposite angle.

Using either figure:

$$\text{In } \triangle ABD,\ \sin A = \frac{h}{c}; \text{ in } \triangle BCD,\ \sin C = \frac{h}{a}$$

$$\therefore \quad c \times \sin A = ? \quad \text{and } a \times \sin C = ?$$

$$\therefore \quad c \times \sin A = a \times \sin C, \text{ or } \frac{\sin A}{a} = \frac{\sin C}{c}$$

286. **Summary.** The following conclusions appear above.

(a) $\tan A = \dfrac{\sin A}{\cos A}$ (§284, Ex. 1)

(b) $\sin^2 A + \cos^2 A = 1$ (§284, Ex. 2)

(c) $\dfrac{\sin A}{a} = \dfrac{\sin C}{c}$ (§285)

287. The **law of cosines in a triangle** expresses the length of one side in terms of the lengths of the other two sides and the angle between them.

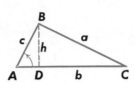
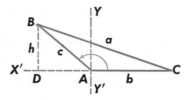

Problem. Express a in terms of b, c, and $\angle A$.

Plan. a is the distance between B and C. Use the distance formula derived in §264, p. 234, letting B be (x_1, y_1) and C be (x_2, y_2).

Solution. 1. $x_1 = AD \qquad \cos A = \dfrac{AD}{c} \qquad \therefore \quad x_1 = c \cos A$

$\qquad\qquad y_1 = DB \qquad \sin A = \dfrac{DB}{c} \qquad \therefore \quad y_1 = c \sin A$

$\qquad \therefore \quad$ the coordinates of B are $(c \cos A,\ c \sin A)$.

2. $\qquad x_2 = AC = b, \quad y_2 = 0 \quad \therefore \quad$ the coordinates of C are $(b, 0)$.

3. $\qquad\qquad a^2 = (x_1 - x_2)^2 + (y_1 - y_2)^2$

4. $\qquad \therefore \quad a^2 = (c \cos A - b)^2 + (c \sin A - 0)^2$

5. $\qquad \therefore \quad a^2 = c^2 \cos^2 A - 2bc \cos A + b^2 + c^2 \sin^2 A$

6. $\qquad \therefore \quad a^2 = b^2 + c^2(\sin^2 A + \cos^2 A) - 2bc \cos A$

7. $\qquad\qquad$ But $\sin^2 A + \cos^2 A = 1$.

8. $\qquad\qquad \therefore \quad a^2 = b^2 + c^2 - 2bc \cos A$

1. Express in words the conclusion of §287.

2. In $\triangle DEF$, $EF = 80'$, $ED = 50'$, and $\angle FED = 60°$.
  (a) Find the square of e by using the law of cosines.
  (b) Find the length of e.

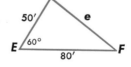

3. Do Exercise 2, if $\angle E = 120°$.

Suggestion. Remember that $\cos 120°$ is negative.

4. State and prove the converse of the Pythagorean Theorem.

Suggestion. Let $c^2 = a^2 + b^2$. Prove $\angle C = 90°$ by using §287 and Ex. 9(a), p. 254.

5. In $\triangle ABC$, $AB = 8$, $AC = 15$, and $\angle CAB = 135°$. Find BC.

1. In $\triangle RQP$, $QP = 200'$, $\angle P = 105°$, and $\angle Q = 45°$. Find the length of PR.

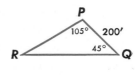

Suggestion. $\angle R = ?$ Use $\dfrac{\sin R}{PQ} = \dfrac{\sin Q}{PR}$ to find PR.

2. A triangular plot of ground is formed at the intersection of three streets. If $\angle B = 150°$, $\angle A = 20°$, and $BC = 50$ ft., find side AC.

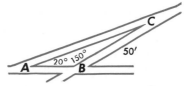

3. A polygon with five equal sides, each ten inches long, is inscribed in a circle. Find the radius of the circle.

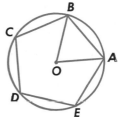

Suggestion. First find the angles in $\triangle ABO$.

4. A machine part in the shape of a $\triangle RST$ must have $RT = 35$ cm., $ST = 28$ cm., and $\angle RST = 60°$. Find $\angle SRT$.

Suggestion. Use the law of sines to find $\sin \angle SRT$. Then use the table on page 245 to find $\angle SRT$, correct to the nearest degree.

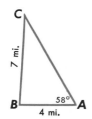

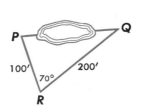

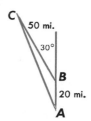

5. Two lighthouses A and B are 4 miles apart. A boat sails from A in the direction that makes $\angle BAC = 58°$. How large must $\angle BCA$ be when the boat reaches a point C which is 7 miles from B.

6. P and Q are on opposite sides of a swampy spot. If $PR = 100$ ft., $QR = 200$ ft., and $\angle R = 70°$, find PQ by the law of cosines.

7. A road from town A north 20 miles to town B turns 30° west of north and goes 50 miles to C. How long would a new road be to go directly from A to C?

8. In a $\triangle ABC$, $a = 6$, $b = 8$, and $c = 11$. Find $\angle A$.
Suggestion. Use the law of cosines.

Assume that the angles to which reference is made on this page are positive angles not greater than 180°.

1. If two angles are equal, their sines are equal.

Suggestion. Prove it when the angles are acute, and also when the angles are obtuse. Take equal segments on the terminal sides of the angles when expressing the sines.

2. The sine of an angle equals the sine of its supplement.

Suggestion. Do as for Exercise 1.

3. (*a*) Is the converse of Exercise 1 true?
(*b*) What *is* true if sin X = sin Y?

4. If $\angle A > \angle B$ but $< (180° - B)$, then sin $A >$ sin B.

Suggestions. Use the adjoining figures. $\angle B$ must be acute. Why? Assume $\angle A$ acute. By §158, p. 147, prove $CE > FD$, and then sin $\angle A >$ sin $\angle B$. Next, assume $\angle A$ obtuse.

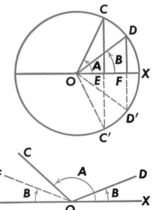

If $\angle A$ is obtuse but $< (180° - B)$, let $\angle X'OF = \angle B$. Then $\angle XOC$ or $\angle A$ must be less than $\angle XOF$. Therefore OF falls inside $\angle X'OC$. Prove sin $\angle X'OC >$ sin $\angle X'OF$; sin $\angle X'OC =$ sin $\angle A$; and then sin $\angle A >$ sin $\angle B$. Finally, assume $\angle A$ a right angle.

5. If sin $A >$ sin B and $\angle B$ is acute, then $\angle A$ must be greater than $\angle B$ but less than the supplement of $\angle B$.

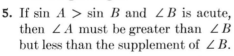

Suggestions. Give an indirect proof for (*a*) when $\angle A$ is acute, (*b*) when $\angle A$ is obtuse but less than $(180° - B)$, and (*c*) when $\angle A$ is a right angle.

6. In a $\triangle ABC$, if $\angle A = \angle B$, then $a = b$. (Use §285, p. 255.)

7. In a $\triangle ABC$, if $a = b$, then $\angle A = \angle B$.

8. In a $\triangle ABC$, if $a > b$, then $\angle A > \angle B$.

9. In a $\triangle ABC$, if $\angle A > \angle B$, then $a > b$.

10. In a $\triangle ABC$, if $a = 8$ in., $b = 10$ in., and $c = 12$ in., find the value of $\angle C$ correct to the nearest degree.

11. In a $\triangle ABC$, if $a = 10$ in., $b = 12$ in., and $\angle C = 40°$, find side c correct to tenths of an inch.

12. From §287, $c^2 = a^2 + b^2 - 2ab \cos C$ in a $\triangle ABC$.
(*a*) Solve this equation for cos C.
(*b*) Write two similar relations for $\angle A$, and for $\angle B$.

1. (a) Draw any acute angle, $\angle AOB$, in standard position with reference to a set of coordinate axes.
   (b) Choose a point P on the terminal side of $\angle AOB$. Draw its ordinate RP and indicate its abscissa OR.
   (c) What are sin $\angle AOB$, cos $\angle AOB$, and tan $\angle AOB$ in terms of OR, OP, and RP?
   (d) Why is sin $\angle AOB$ always the same number regardless of the position of P on the terminal side of $\angle AOB$?

2. Do Ex. 1 for any obtuse angle, $\angle COD$.

3. (a) In the relation $\tan A = \dfrac{y}{x}$, how many variables are there?

   (b) How many of the variables in the relation $\tan A = \dfrac{y}{x}$ must be known in order that the relation will become an equation in which there is only one unknown?

   (c) If $\tan A = \dfrac{y}{x}$, find y when $x = 2$ and $\angle A = 25°$.

   (d) If $\tan A = \dfrac{y}{x}$, find $\angle A$ when $x = 7$ and $y = 8$.

4. In $\triangle ACB$, $\angle C$ is a right angle. Write the trigonometric relation:
   (a) To find a when $\angle A$ and c are known.
   (b) To find $\angle A$ when b and c are known.
   (c) To find a when $\angle A$ and b are known.
   (d) To find $\angle B$ when a and b are known.
   (e) To find c when $\angle B$ and a are known.
   (f) To find $\angle A$ when a and c are known.

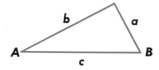

5. (a) In a $\triangle ABC$, express the trigonometric relation between $\angle A$, $\angle B$, side a, and side b.
   (b) If $\angle A = 55°$, $\angle B = 48°$, and $a = 100$, find b.
   (c) If $\angle B = 70°$, $a = 20$, and $b = 50$, find $\angle A$.

6. (a) What trigonometric relation must you have to find a leg b of a right triangle in which acute angle B and leg c are known?
   (b) If $a = 10$, $b = 15$, $c = 20$, and $\angle C = 60°$, find $\angle A$ and $\angle B$ if you can.

7. (a) What relation will be sufficient to find b when $\angle B$, c, and a are known?
   (b) Find b if $\angle B = 60°$, $c = 5$, and $a = 8$.

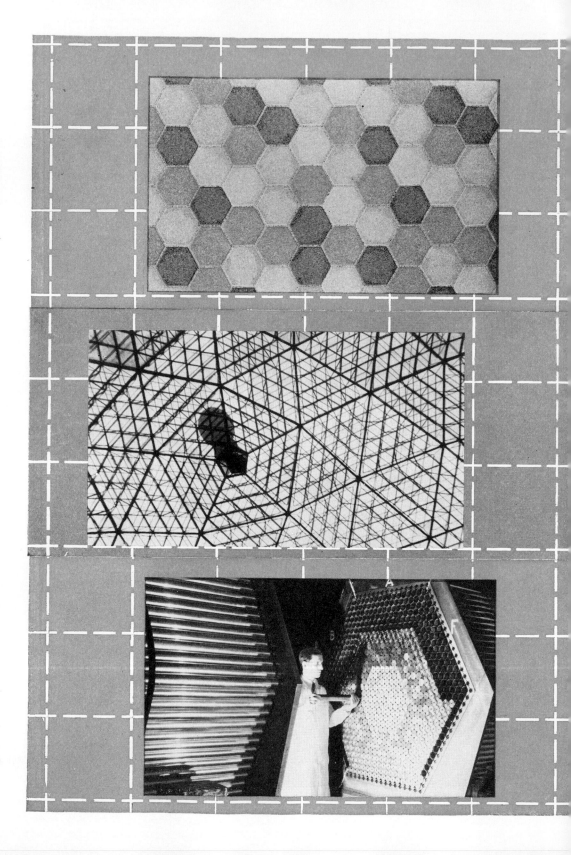

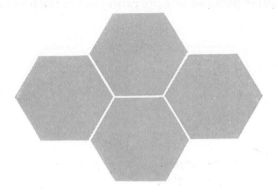

CHAPTER 9

REGULAR POLYGONS

You know some of the regular polygons, because they are used so commonly in practical and artistic designs. In particular, you readily recognize equilateral triangles, squares, and regular hexagons. In general, they are the polygons that have equal sides and equal angles. Such regularity in their shapes makes them pleasing to the eye.

Because they are used so universally, you will wish to know how to construct them, and some facts about them on which their common use depends.

You will acquire this information while studying Chapter 9, and as a result, you will have a greater appreciation of regular polygons when you see them.

Top: Regular hexagons are used for a linoleum pattern. *Center:* Triangles form a rigid structure for the Ford Rotunda. *Bottom:* A technician inserts a fuel rod into a hexagonal pile assembly for an experiment in reactor design at the Knolls Atomic Power Laboratory.

TOP: ARMSTRONG CORK COMPANY CENTER: FORD COMPANY BOTTOM: NEWS BUREAU, GENERAL ELECTRIC COMPANY

288. A **regular polygon** is a polygon that is both equilateral and equiangular.

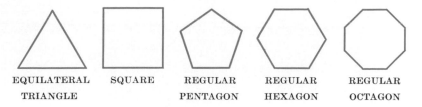

EQUILATERAL   SQUARE   REGULAR   REGULAR   REGULAR
TRIANGLE   PENTAGON   HEXAGON   OCTAGON

289. *The sum of the angles of any polygon having n sides is (n − 2) straight angles.*

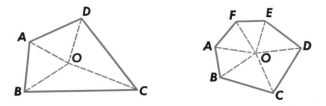

Hypothesis. Take any polygon having n sides.

Note. In $ABCD$, $n = 4$; in $ABCDEF$, $n = 6$.

Conclusion. The sum of the $\angle = (n - 2)$ st. $\angle$.

Informal proof. 1. From any interior point O, draw a segment to each vertex of the polygon, forming n $\triangle$.

2. The sum of the $\angle$ of each triangle is one st. $\angle$.

3. $\therefore$ the sum of the $\angle$ of all the $\triangle$ is n st. $\angle$.

4. The sum of the $\angle$ around $O = 2$ st. $\angle$. (§29(b), p. 28)

5. $\therefore$ the sum of the base $\angle$ of the $\triangle = (n - 2)$ st. $\angle$.

6. The sum of the base $\angle$ of the $\triangle$ = the sum of the $\angle$ of the polygon.

7. $\therefore$ the sum of the $\angle$ of the polygon is $(n - 2)$ st. $\angle$.

290. Cor. *Each angle of a regular polygon having n sides equals* $\left(\dfrac{n - 2}{n}\right)$ *straight angles.*

1. What is the sum of all the angles, and how large is each angle in each polygon in §288?

★2. If the sides of a regular n-gon, in order, be extended beyond each vertex, the sum of the exterior angles is a *perigon*. Prove it when $n = 6$.

295. *A circle can be circumscribed about a regular polygon.*

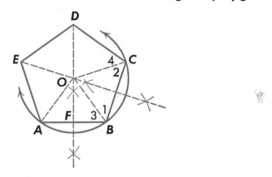

Hypothesis. $ABCDE$ is a regular polygon.

Conclusion. A circle can be circumscribed about $ABCDE$.

Plan. Prove that the circle through A, B, and C passes through D and E, by proving OD and OE equal to OA.

Proof.

Statements	Authorities
1. A ⊙ can be drawn through A, B, and C. Let O be its center, and OA its radius.	1. §216, p. 194
2. $\qquad \angle 1 = \angle 2 \quad \therefore \quad \angle 3 = \angle 4$	2. Give proof.
3. $\qquad \triangle ODC \cong \triangle OBA$	3. Give proof.
4. $\qquad \therefore \quad OD = OA$	4. Why?
5. $\qquad \therefore \quad \odot ABC$ goes through D.	5. §167(c), p. 161
6. Similarly $\odot ABC$ can be proved to pass through E.	

296. Cor. *A circle can be inscribed in a regular polygon.*

The sides of $ABCDE$ are equidistant from O. (Why?) Therefore, the circle with center O and radius OF will be tangent to each side of $ABCDE$. (§188, p. 172)

297. Definitions. The **center** of a regular polygon is the center of its inscribed and its circumscribed circles, as O. Its **radius** is the distance from its center to any of its vertices, as OA. Its **apothem** is the distance from its center to any of its sides, as OF. Its **central angle** is the angle between any two consecutive radii, as $\angle AOB$.

298. In *practical geometry*, a polygon of any number of sides, approximately regular, can be constructed by using a protractor to draw at the center of the circle central angles of proper size. In *classical geometry*, however, only the straightedge and compasses are used for constructions.

299. A square can be inscribed in a circle.

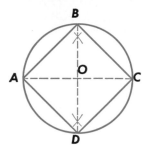

Given. Circle O.

Required. To inscribe a square in circle O.

Construction	Authorities
1. Construct ⊥ diameters AC and BD.	1. §75, p. 76
2. Draw chords AB, BC, CD, and AD.	2. Why possible?

Statement. $ABCD$ is an inscribed square.
(Proof left to the pupil. Use §291, p. 263.)

300. Regular polygons of 8, 16, 32, etc., sides can be inscribed in a circle by repeatedly bisecting the arcs and drawing their chords. The proof is based on §292, p. 263.

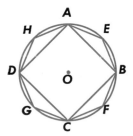

1. Inscribe a square in a circle with radius 2 in.

2. Inscribe in a circle with radius 2 in. a regular octagon and a regular 16-gon.

3. Prove that the opposite sides of the adjoining regular octagon are parallel.

4. Prove HB parallel to DF.

5. Prove $ABFH$ is an isosceles trapezoid.

6. Prove AC the ⊥-bisector of HE.

7. How large is each angle of $\triangle AHD$?

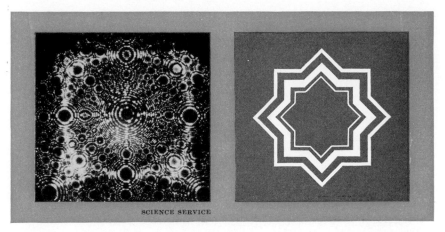

Atomic lace and designs reflect patterns of inscribed squares and hexagons.

8. How large are the vertex $\angle H$ and the central $\angle AOH$ in the figure for Ex. 3, p. 266?

9. Does radius OH bisect $\angle AHD$?

★ **10.** Construct a regular octagon with 1-in. sides.

★ **11.** *Inscribing a regular octagon in a square.*

Construction. 1. With center O and radius equal to apothem OR, locate points X, Y, Z, W on the diagonals of the square.

2. Construct $\perp$s to the diagonals at X, Y, Z, and W, thus locating E, F, G, H, etc.

Statement. $EFGH$ . . . is a regular octagon.

Suggestions. 1. Prove the circle with center O and radius OR is tangent to each side of $EFGH$ . . . .

2. Prove $\angle ROX = \angle XOP = \angle POY$, etc. $= 45°$.

3. Prove $EFGH$ . . . is a regular octagon by §293.

12. In the figure for Ex. 3, p. 266:

(*a*) Prove that the diagonals from A divide $\angle HAE$ into six equal parts.

(*b*) Let AG cut DB at X, and AF cut DB at Y. Then prove that $\triangle DAX \cong \triangle BAY$, and $\triangle AXY$ is isosceles.

(*c*) Prove $\triangle DGX$ is an isosceles triangle.

★ **13.** A square and a regular octagon are inscribed in a circle. Prove that the apothem of the octagon is greater than that of the square.

301. *A regular hexagon can be inscribed in a circle.*

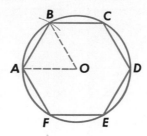

Given. Circle O.

Required. To inscribe a regular hexagon in circle O.

Analysis. The central angle must be a 60° angle.

Construction. Draw any radius OA. With OA as radius, and A as center, draw an arc cutting the circle at B.

Statement. $\overset{\frown}{AB} = \dfrac{1}{6}$ of the circle. The circle can be divided into six arcs equal to $\overset{\frown}{AB}$. Polygon $ABCDEF$ formed by the chords of the arcs is a regular hexagon.

Proof.

Statements	Authorities
1. Draw OB. Then $\triangle OAB$ is equilateral.	1. Prove it.
2. $\therefore$ $\angle AOB = 60°$.	2. Why?
3. $\therefore$ $\overset{\frown}{AB} = \frac{1}{6}$ of the circle.	3. Prove it.
4. $\therefore$ $ABCDEF$ is a regular inscribed hexagon.	4. §291, p. 263

302. Regular polygons of 3, 6, 12, 24, . . . , sides can be inscribed in a circle.

(*a*) The equilateral triangle can be made by joining alternate vertices of a regular inscribed hexagon.

(*b*) The 12-gon, 24-gon, etc., can be inscribed by §292, p. 263.

1. (*a*) Inscribe a regular hexagon in a circle having a radius of 1 in.
    (*b*) What is the perimeter of this hexagon?

2. Construct a regular hexagon whose side is 1.5 in. long.

3. In a circle having a 2-in. diameter, inscribe an equilateral triangle and also a regular 12-gon.

BYZANTINE   MOORISH   MODERN

Designs based upon regular hexagons

ABCDEF is a regular hexagon.

1. Prove AC is the perpendicular-bisector of OB.

2. Prove AD must be a diameter of the circle.

3. Prove opposite sides of $ABCDEF$ are parallel.

4. Prove FC is parallel to AB and to DE.

5. Prove AD is the perpendicular-bisector of BF and of CE.

6. Prove $BF \parallel CE$.

7. Prove $BCEF$ is a rectangle.

8. Prove $\triangle BHC$, CKD, DLE, etc., are congruent.

9. Prove $\triangle CHK$, DKL, ELM, etc., are congruent.

10. Prove $GHKLMN$ is a regular hexagon.

11. How large is each angle of $\triangle ABG$?

12. How large is each angle of $\triangle BHG$?

13. Prove $AC = BD = CE$.

14. How large is each angle of $\triangle ABC$?

15. In a circle having a 4-inch diameter, construct the modern design shown at the top of the page, omitting the small figure at the center of it.

16. Construct a Maltese cross having the dimensions indicated.

Suggestion. First construct a regular octagon.

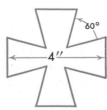

★17. In a given equilateral triangle, construct a regular hexagon having two vertices on each side of the triangle.

303. *Regular polygons having the same number of sides are similar.*

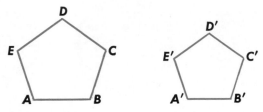

Hypothesis. $ABCDE$ and $A'B'C'D'E'$ are regular polygons having the same number of sides.

Conclusion. $ABCDE \backsim A'B'C'D'E'$

Plan. Prove corresponding $\angle$ are equal and corresponding sides are proportional.

Note. The proof is given for regular *pentagons*.

Proof.

Statements	Authorities
1. Each $\angle$ of each polygon $= \left(\dfrac{5-2}{5}\right)180°$.	1. §290
2. ∴ the polygons are mutually equiangular.	2. Definition.
3. $AB = BC = CD$, etc. $A'B' = B'C' = C'D'$, etc.	3. Hyp.; §288
4. ∴ $\dfrac{AB}{A'B'} = \dfrac{BC}{B'C'} = \dfrac{CD}{C'D'}$, etc.	4. Ax. 6, p. 32
5. ∴ $ABCDE \backsim A'B'C'D'E'$	5. Why?

1. If AD is the perpendicular from A to BC of $\triangle ABC$, prove that $\overline{AB}^2 - \overline{AC}^2 = \overline{BD}^2 - \overline{CD}^2$.

2. XY, YZ, ZW, and WX are tangents to a circle, O, at points A, B, C, and D that divide the circle into four equal arcs. Prove that $XYZW$ is similar to inscribed quadrilateral $ABCD$, and that the ratio of similitude is $\sqrt{2}:1$.

Suggestion. Let OX cut AD at E. Assume $OA = r$.

3. If tangents are drawn to a circle O at the vertices of an inscribed regular hexagon, prove that they form a circumscribed polygon that is similar to the inscribed polygon and that the ratio of similitude is $2:\sqrt{3}$.

1. Derive a formula for the exterior angle at the vertex of a regular polygon that has n sides.

2. Prove that any central angle of a regular polygon is the supplement of any vertex angle of the polygon.

3. Why is it that the polygons used in the following mosaic pattern completely cover the surface?

4. In a regular pentagon $ABCDE$, prove that $AC = BD = DA = BE = CE$.

5. In $ABCDE$, prove AD and AC trisect $\angle BAE$.

6. In $ABCDE$ prove $CE \parallel AB$.

7. If a circle circumscribes $ABCDE$, prove that the diameter of it that is perpendicular to CD passes through A.

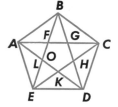

8. Prove $\triangle ABF$ is isosceles.

9. Prove $\triangle AEF$ is isosceles.

10. Prove $\triangle BFG$ is isosceles.

11. Prove $\triangle ABF \cong \triangle BGC$.

12. Prove $FGHKL$ is a regular pentagon.

13. How many degrees are there in each angle of $\triangle ABF$?

14. How many degrees are there in each angle of $\triangle AFL$?

15. What is the sum of any central angle of $ABCDE$ and the exterior angle at any vertex?

★16. The radius of a circle is 8 in. Use trigonometry to find:
(a) The length of a side of an inscribed square.
(b) The length of the apothem of an inscribed square.

★17. Do Ex. 16 if the polygon is:
(a) An inscribed equilateral triangle.
(b) An inscribed regular hexagon.
(c) An inscribed regular pentagon.

Use trigonometry if necessary to solve the following exercises. Obtain the results correct to tenths of an inch.

1. If the length of the radius of a circle is 12 in. what is the length of a side of a regular circumscribed polygon that has:

    (*a*) 3 sides?   (*b*) 4 sides?   (*c*) 5 sides?
    (*d*) 6 sides?   (*e*) 8 sides?   (*f*) 10 sides?

2. In Ex. 1, with constant radius, how does the length of the side change when the number of the sides increases?

3. What is the length of the radius of the circle that circumscribes a regular polygon with 1-in. sides, when the polygon has:

    (*a*) 3 sides?   (*b*) 4 sides?   (*c*) 5 sides?

4. (*a*) How long is the altitude of an equilateral triangle that has sides 12 in. long?
   (*b*) How long is the side of an equilateral triangle when the altitude is 12 in. long?

5. How long is the apothem of a regular polygon inscribed in a 10-in. circle, when the polygon has:

    (*a*) 3 sides?   (*b*) 4 sides?   (*c*) 5 sides?
    (*d*) 6 sides?   (*e*) 9 sides?   (*f*) 10 sides?

6. In Ex. 5, if the radius of the circle is constant, how does the apothem change when the number of sides increases?

7. If a regular polygon having n sides is inscribed in a circle with radius r, express by a formula the length of:
   (*a*) The side of the polygon.
   (*b*) The apothem of the polygon.

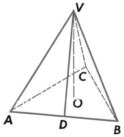

8. V–ABC is a triangular pyramid whose edges all equal 10 in. and whose altitude is perpendicular to its base at the center of gravity (§146, p. 130) of the triangle.
   (*a*) What is the length of its altitude, VO?
   (*b*) VD is called its slant height. How long is VD?

9. (*a*) Draw a figure to represent a square pyramid whose base edges equal 10 in., whose vertex is in the perpendicular to the base at the center of the base, and whose lateral edges equal 15 in.
   (*b*) Find the length of the altitude of the pyramid.
   (*c*) Find the length of the slant height of the pyramid.

CONSTRUCTING OTHER REGULAR POLYGONS

304. You have been taught how to construct a regular polygon by use of straightedge and compasses alone if the number of its sides is one of the numbers of either of the two following sets:

(a) 4, 8, 16, 32, . . .   (b) 3, 6, 12, 24, . . .

There are two other sets of polygons that are constructible by straightedge and compasses alone. It is necessary to study first a topic of historical interest and of practical use in ornamental design.

305. Golden Rectangle. Which of the following rectangles do you think has the most pleasing proportions? Why?

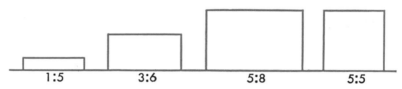

1:5   3:6   5:8   5:5

Most people would select the third rectangle.

The Greeks answered that question by dividing a segment in *extreme and mean ratio.*

Def. A segment is divided in **extreme and mean ratio** when it is divided into two segments such that *the whole segment is to the longer part as the longer part is to the shorter;* that is, $AB : AC = AC : CB$.

A———————————C————————B

Problem. Let $AB = 10$ in. Find AC and CB.

1.   Let $AC = x$. Then $CB = 10 - x$.
2.   ∴ $10 : x = x : (10 - x)$, or $x^2 = 10(10 - x)$
3.   ∴ $x^2 = 100 - 10x$, or $x^2 + 10x = 100$
4.   ∴ $x^2 + 10x + 25 = 100 + 25$, or $(x + 5)^2 = 125$
5.   ∴ $x + 5 = \pm\sqrt{125}$, or $x = -5 \pm 5\sqrt{5}$
6.   ∴ $x = 5\sqrt{5} - 5$, or $11.18 - 5$, or 6.18
          and $10 - x = 10 - 6.18$, or 3.82.

Observe that 6.18 is more than $\frac{1}{2}$ of and less than $\frac{2}{3}$ of 10.

A rectangle with base about 6.2 and altitude 3.8 has a pleasing shape.

306. *A segment can be divided in extreme and mean ratio.*

Given. Segment AB.

Divide. AB in extreme and mean ratio.

Construction. 1. Construct $BE \perp AB$ and make $BE = \frac{1}{2}AB$.

2. Construct $\odot E$ with center E and radius EB or $\frac{1}{2}AB$.

3. Draw AE cutting the circle at F and G.

4. On AB, take $AC = AF$.

Statement. $\dfrac{AB}{AC} = \dfrac{AC}{CB}$

Proof.

	Statements	Authorities
1.	AB is tangent to $\odot E$ at B.	1. Why?
2.	$\therefore \dfrac{AG}{AB} = \dfrac{AB}{AF}$	2. §257, p. 224
3.	$\therefore \dfrac{AG}{AB} = \dfrac{AB}{AC}$	3. Why?
4.	$\therefore \dfrac{AG - AB}{AB} = \dfrac{AB - AC}{AC}$	4. §236, p. 207
5.	But $AB = 2BE$ and therefore $= FG$.	5. Construction.
6.	$\therefore \ \ AG - AB = AG - FG = AF$, or AC	6. Ax. 2, p. 32
7.	$\therefore \dfrac{AC}{AB} = \dfrac{CB}{AC}$	7. Ax. 2
8.	$\therefore \dfrac{AB}{AC} = \dfrac{AC}{CB}$	8. §234, p. 207

307. On page 273, it is proved that $\dfrac{AC}{AB} = $ about $\dfrac{6.18}{10}$, or about

.618 when $AB = 10$. This decimal is near .625 which equals $\dfrac{5}{8}$.

The ratio 5 : 8 has been called the *golden ratio*. If the ratio of the altitude of a rectangle to its base is 5 : 8, the rectangle has pleasing dimensions. It may be called the *golden rectangle*. Such rectangles, either alone or in combination with others having pleasing dimensions, were much favored by Greek designers.

308. A good example of the use of the golden rectangle in conjunction with others is the design of the water jar below. This is an ancient Greek kalpis, now in possession of the Metropolitan Museum, New York. It is described in *Dynamic Symmetry* by Mr. Jay Hambidge.

ANCIENT GREEK VASE

1. Given a segment AB. Construct a segment AF such that
   $AF:AB = AB:BF$.
   Construction. 1. Construct square $ABCD$ having side AB.
   2. With O, the mid-point of AB, as center and OC as radius, draw semicircle $EDCF$.
   Statement. AF is the required segment.

Suggestions. 1. Prove $AF : AD = AD : AE$.
   2. Prove $BF = AE$, and $AB = AD$.

★**2.** If $RSTV$ is a golden rectangle (with base RS and with $ST = RW$, where $RS:RW = RW:WS$); if SX, perpendicular to RT, meets VT at X; if XY, perpendicular to RS, meets RS at Y; then $RYXV$ is a square.

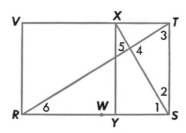

Suggestion. Find SY by similar triangles. Prove $SY = SW$, so that Y should be at W.

309. *A regular decagon can be inscribed in a circle.*

Given. Circle O.

Inscribe. A regular decagon.

Construction. 1. Draw OA. Divide it in extreme and mean ratio so that
$$OA:OM = OM:MA.$$
2. Make chord $AB = OM$.

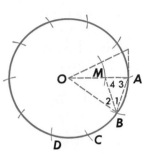

Statement. $\overset{\frown}{AB} = \frac{1}{10}$ of circle O.

Proof.

Statements	Authorities
1. In $\triangle OAB$ and $\triangle ABM$, $\angle A = \angle A$.	1. Why?
2. Since $OA:OM = OM:AM$, then $OA:AB = AB:AM$.	2. Construction. Ax. 2, p. 32
3. $\therefore \triangle OAB \backsim \triangle ABM$	3. §248, p. 218
4. Since $\triangle OAB$ is isosceles, then $\triangle ABM$ also is isosceles.	4. Why?
5. $\therefore BM = BA = OM$	5. Ax. 1, p. 32
6. $\angle 4 = 2\angle AOB$	6. Prove it.
7. $\therefore \angle 3 = 2\angle AOB$	7. Prove it.
8. $\therefore \angle ABO = \angle 3 = 2\angle AOB$	8. Prove it.
9. $\angle AOB + \angle 3 + \angle ABO = 180°$	9. Why?
10. $\therefore 5\angle AOB = 180°$	10. Why?
11. $\therefore \angle AOB = 36°$	11. Why?
12. $\therefore \overset{\frown}{AB} = \dfrac{1}{10}$ of the circle.	12. §198(c), p. 179
13. $\therefore$ AB is one side of an inscribed regular decagon.	

310. Cor. 1. *Chords joining the alternate vertices of a regular inscribed decagon, starting with any vertex, form a regular inscribed pentagon.*

311. Cor. 2. *Regular inscribed polygons of 20, 40, 80, etc. sides can be constructed with straightedge and compasses alone.*

312. *A regular 15-gon can be inscribed in a circle.*

Given. A circle.

Inscribe. A regular 15-gon.

Analysis. 1. The central ∠ of

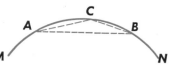

$$\text{a } 15\text{-gon} = \frac{360°}{15} = 24°.$$

2. But $24° = 60° - 36°$.

3. ∴ combine the constructions of §301 and §309.

Construction. Construct AB, a side of a regular inscribed hexagon, and AC, a side of a regular inscribed decagon. Draw chord BC.

Statement. BC is a side of the regular inscribed 15-gon.

Proof. $\overset{\frown}{BC} = (\frac{1}{6} - \frac{1}{10})$, or $\frac{1}{15}$ of the circle. Why?

313. Cor. *Regular polygons of* 30, 60, *etc., sides can be inscribed in a circle by straightedge and compasses alone.*

314. Summary. You have now learned (in §300, §302, §309, §311, §312, and §313) that a regular polygon can be constructed *by means of straightedge and compasses alone* if the number of its sides is one of the numbers of the following sets of numbers:

(a) 4, 8, 16, 32, ...   (b) 3, 6, 12, 24, ...
(c) 5, 10, 20, 40, ...   (d) 15, 30, 60, ...

Observe that many of the integers are missing even when these four lists are combined; for example, 7, 9, 11, 13. Gauss, one of the great mathematicians of the past, proved that a regular 17-gon can be constructed.

Regular polygons are used for a basis for designs.

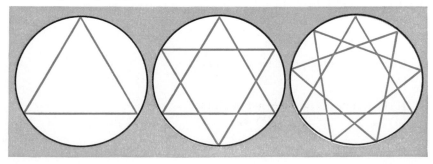

SEQUENCES OF REGULAR POLYGONS

315. A square (4-gon), the regular octagon (8-gon), the regular 16-gon, etc. inscribed in a circle by the methods described in §291 and §292 form one sequence of inscribed regular polygons.

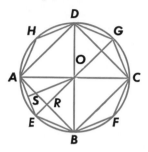

In the figure above, AB is the side of a square, and AE the side of a regular 8-gon inscribed in the circle O, whose radius OA is r. OR is the apothem of the square (4-gon), and OS the apothem of the 8-gon. OA is the radius (§297, p. 265) of each of the polygons as well as of the circle.

Let s_4, s_8, s_{16}, . . . be the lengths of the sides of this sequence of polygons; a_4, a_8, a_{16}, . . . the lengths of their respective apothems; p_4, p_8, p_{16}, . . . their perimeters; and K_4, K_8, K_{16}, etc., the surfaces enclosed by them, respectively.

1. In any circle prove:
   (a) $s_8 < s_4$ (b) $a_8 > a_4$ (c) $p_8 > p_4$ (d) $K_8 > K_4$

2. If r is the radius of the circle prove:
   (a) $s_4 = 2r \sin 45°$ (b) $a_4 = r \cos 45°$ (c) $p_4 = 8r \sin 45°$

3. If r is the radius of the circle, prove:
   (a) $s_8 = 2r \sin 22.5°$ (b) $a_8 = r \cos 22.5°$ (c) $p_8 = 16r \sin 22.5°$

4. If r is the radius of the circle, prove:
   (a) $s_n = 2r \sin \dfrac{180°}{n}$ (b) $a_n = r \cos \dfrac{180°}{n}$ (c) $p_n = 2nr \sin \dfrac{180°}{n}$

5. If the radius of the circle is 1 in., find:
   (a) s_4 (b) a_4 (c) p_4

6. If the radius of the circle is 1 in., find:
   (a) s_8 (b) a_8 (c) p_8

7. For each part of Ex. 4, what happens when n is increased?

8. Let $r = 10$ in. Using your results from Ex. 2, 3, and 4, compute correct to hundredths:

  (a) s_4, s_8, and s_{16}

  (b) a_4, a_8, and a_{16}

  (c) p_4, p_8, and p_{16}

9. Let $r = 10$ in. Using the formulas you have proved in Ex. 4, compute, correct to hundredths:

  (a) s_3, s_6, and s_{12}

  (b) a_3, a_6, and a_{12}

  (c) p_3, p_6, and p_{12}

316. Summary. Exercises 1 to 9 suggest the following:

If a sequence of regular polygons is inscribed in a circle, by successively doubling the number of sides of the polygons (§292, p. 263):

(a) *The radius of the circle is also the radius of each of the polygons.*

(b) *The sides, successively, become smaller and, ultimately, in length differ little from zero.*

(c) *The perimeters, successively, become larger and, ultimately, differ little from the circumference of the circle itself.*

(d) *The apothems, successively, become longer and, ultimately, differ little from the radius of the circle.*

(e) *The surface within the polygons, successively, becomes larger and, ultimately, differs little from the surface inside the circle.*

10. According to the statement in §316 (c), both p_{12}, obtained in Ex. 9 (c), and p_{16}, obtained in Ex. 8 (c), should approximate the length of the circle.

  (a) Which of these perimeters is the larger?

  (b) What is the approximate length of the circle, correct to tenths?

Note. If a sequence of regular polygons is inscribed in a circle as described above, we say:

  (a) The perimeters *approach as limit* (an undefined expression) the length of the circle.

  (b) The apothems approach the radius as limit.

  (c) The interiors of the polygons approach the interior of the circle as limit.

These statements enable us later to define and compute the length of the circle and the area of the circle.

REGULAR PYRAMIDS AND POLYHEDRONS

317. The definition of a regular pyramid that appears in SG 33, p. 133 can be restated as follows:

SG 58. Def. A **regular pyramid** is a pyramid whose base is enclosed by a regular polygon and whose vertex lies in the perpendicular to its base at the center of its base. Thus $V{-}ABCDEF$ below is a regular pyramid if $ABCDEF$ is a regular hexagon, and if VO is perpendicular to the base at O the center of $ABCDEF$.

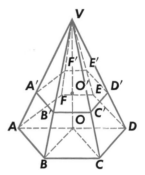

1. In the adjoining figure:
   (a) What kind of angle does VO make with $OA, OB, OC, \ldots$?
   (b) How do $OA, OB, OC, \ldots$ compare?
   (c) How do $VA, VB, VC, \ldots$ compare in length?
   (d) What kind of triangle is $\triangle AVB$, $\triangle BVC, \triangle CVD, \ldots$?
   (e) Prove $\triangle AVB, BVC, CVD, \ldots$ are congruent.

2. In a figure like that for Ex. 1, draw $VM \perp AB, VN \perp BC, \ldots$.
   (a) Where is M on AB? N on $BC, \ldots$?
   (b) Prove $VM = VN, \ldots$.
   (c) Prove $OM \perp AB, ON \perp BC, \ldots$.
   (d) In $ABCDEF$, what is $OM, ON, \ldots$?

3. If $A'B'C'D'E'F'$ is a section of the pyramid made by a plane that is parallel to the base:
   (a) What kind of triangles are $\triangle AVB$ and $\triangle A'VB', \ldots$?
   (b) Prove $VA : VA' = VB : VB' = VC : VC' = VO : VO'$.
   (c) Prove $A'B' : AB = B'C' : BC, \ldots$.
   (d) Prove $\angle A'B'C' = \angle ABC, \angle B'C'D' = \angle BCD, \ldots$.
   (e) Prove $ABCDEF \backsim A'B'C'D'E'F'$. (§244(a), p. 213)

SG 59. Summary. In a regular pyramid:

(a) *The altitude is perpendicular to each radius of the base.*

(b) *The lateral edges are equal.*

(c) *The lateral faces are enclosed by congruent isosceles triangles.*

(d) *The altitudes of the face triangles are equal. Their common length is the* **slant height** *of the pyramid.*

318. In the figure on page 280, observe the polyhedron (p. 133) that is enclosed by the part of a plane within a section of the pyramid made by a plane parallel to the base, the base of the pyramid, and the parts of the lateral faces of the pyramid that are between the base and the parallel section. The polyhedron $A'D$ consists of the *lower base AD*, the *upper base $A'D'$*, and the lateral faces such as $A'B$, $B'C$, $C'D$, $\ldots$.

1. If VO is the altitude of $V–ABCDEF$, at what angle does VO intersect the upper base $A'D'$?

2. Prove that $A'B'BA$ is an isosceles trapezoid; also $B'C'CB$, $C'D'DC$, $\ldots$.

3. If $VM \perp AB$, meeting $A'B'$ at M', at what angle does VM' intersect $A'B'$? What is MM' in trapezoid $A'B'BA$?

4. Prove that $A'B'BA \cong B'C'CB$, etc.

Suggestion. Prove they are mutually equilateral and equiangular.

5. If also $VN \perp CD$, intersecting $C'D'$ in N', what is $N'N$ in $C'D'DC$?

6. Prove that $M'M = N'N$.

7. If O' bisects VO, what is the ratio of $M'M$ to VM?

8. If VO' is one third of VO, what part of the slant height VM is the segment $M'M$?

9. Prove that the perimeter of the upper base $A'D'$ of the polyhedron $A'D$ has the same ratio to the perimeter of lower base AD as the upper section, VO', of the altitude has to the altitude VO.

SG 60. Summary. (*a*) **Def.** If a plane parallel to the base of a pyramid intersects all the lateral faces, it, the parts of the faces of the pyramid that lie below it, and the base of the pyramid form a **frustum** of the pyramid.

(*b*) *The lateral faces of a frustum of a regular pyramid are enclosed by congruent isosceles trapezoids.*

(*c*) *The altitudes of the lateral faces of a frustum of a regular pyramid are equal* and any one is the **slant height** of the frustum.

(*d*) *The two bases of a frustum of a regular pyramid are enclosed by similar polygons, whose ratio of similitude equals the ratio of the upper segment of the altitude of the pyramid to the whole altitude.*

319. Def. A **regular polyhedron** is a polyhedron whose faces are enclosed by congruent regular polygons, and whose polyhedral angles are all equal. (Pp. 133, 157)

320. *There are not more than five convex regular polyhedrons.* These are represented by the following figures:

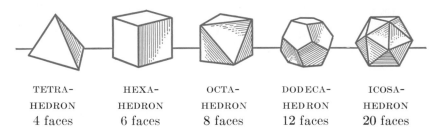

TETRA-	HEXA-	OCTA-	DODECA-	ICOSA-
HEDRON	HEDRON	HEDRON	HEDRON	HEDRON
4 faces	6 faces	8 faces	12 faces	20 faces

(a) *A polyhedron may be formed with faces enclosed by equilateral triangles.*

Proof.

1. Each angle of an equilateral triangle is 60°. Therefore a convex polyhedral angle can be formed having three, four, or five, but not more than five, faces enclosed by equilateral triangles. (SG 45, p. 157)

2. Therefore, not more than three regular convex polyhedrons can be formed with faces enclosed by equilateral triangles. These are the first, third, and fifth of the figures above.

Note. To check this statement, construct on stiff paper three lines AOB, COD, and EOF through a point O, so that $\angle AOC = \angle COF = \angle FOB = 60°$. Draw polygon $ACFBDE$. Try to form a polyhedral angle as directed in §160, p. 153.

(b) *A polyhedron may be formed with faces enclosed by squares.*

Proof.

1. Each angle of a square is 90°. Therefore, a convex polyhedral angle can be formed by three, but not more than three, faces enclosed by squares.

2. Therefore, not more than one regular convex polyhedron can be formed with faces enclosed by squares.
   This is the *cube*, the second figure above.

(c) *A polyhedron may be formed with faces enclosed by regular pentagons.*

Proof.

1. Each angle of a regular pentagon is 108°. Therefore, a convex polyhedral angle can be formed having three, but not more than three, faces inclosed by a regular pentagon.

2. Therefore, not more than one regular convex polyhedron can be formed with faces inclosed by regular pentagons. This is a polyhedron having twelve faces. It is a **dodecahedron,** the fourth figure at the top of page 282.

(d) *No regular polyhedrons can be formed with faces enclosed by other regular polygons.*

Proof.

Regular polygons with six or more faces have angles that measure 120° or more. A polyhedral angle must have at least three faces. Therefore the sum of the face angles would be 360° or more if polygons having six or more sides are used. This is impossible. (Why?)

(e) Steps (a) to (d) prove that *there are not more than five regular polyhedrons.*

Patterns for models of the five regular polyhedrons may be constructed. The patterns are shown below.

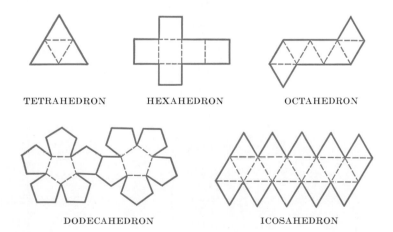

TETRAHEDRON   HEXAHEDRON   OCTAHEDRON

DODECAHEDRON   ICOSAHEDRON

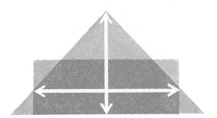

MEASUREMENT OF PLANE FIGURES

Recent tremendous scientific progress depends in part on new and more precise methods of measurement. Most of these are based primarily upon properties of simple geometric figures.

Many examples of the need for measuring common geometrical figures can be found in our immediate surroundings. We see measurement involved in the construction of every building, automobile, and airplane. Some measurements are relatively easy to make since they can be made directly. Others are more difficult either because they must be computed, as areas and volumes, or because they must be made indirectly, as the depth of the ocean by means of sound waves.

You have learned how to measure rectangles, triangles, and rectangular solids by formulas that were derived inductively. In this chapter you will learn how to measure other figures and to develop proofs for the formulas.

Plane surfaces play an important role in the design of modern buildings as illustrated by the Lodge Hall at Elizabethtown, Pennsylvania, and by Rockefeller Center, New York. Architects need to know the area of such surfaces to make specifications for the material required.

TOP: PROGRESSIVE ARCHITECTURE MAGAZINE   BOTTOM: A. DEVANEY, INC., NEW YORK

321. (*a*) **To measure a segment:**

(1) A **unit of linear measure** is selected, such as an inch, or a yard, or a centimeter.

(2) The **length** of a segment is the number of the selected linear units that the segment contains.

Thus: The length of your classroom may be 32 (ft.). Strictly, the measure is 32, but that statement is not intelligible unless the kind of linear unit is named, so we say that the length is 32 ft.

(*b*) The **perimeter,** or length, of a polygon is the sum of the lengths of its sides.

(*c*) To **measure a bounded plane surface:**

(1) A **unit of surface measure** is selected, such as a square foot, or a square meter.

(2) The **area** of a polygon means the area of the interior of the polygon. It is the number of units of surface measure enclosed by the polygon.

Thus: The area of a room may be 360 sq. ft.

Caution. The *area* is a *number* of surface units. It is *not* the interior.

At the right, if the unit of measure is a small square, the area of *ABCD* is 15 of the squares; if the unit is △*FEC*, the area is 30 of the triangles.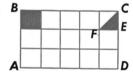

1. Below, use a small square as the *unit of measure.* Give the exact or the approximate area of each figure, counting each square of which all or at least half is inside the figure.

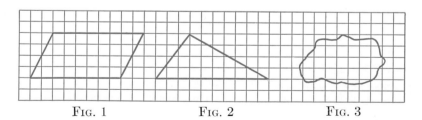

FIG. 1   FIG. 2   FIG. 3

322. **Bounded plane surfaces are equal** if their areas are equal *when they are measured by the same unit of surface.*

Thus: Rectangles $ADCB$ and $XWZY$ are equal since each contains 12 square units like that which is shaded.

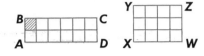

Observe that $ADCB$ and $XWZY$ are not congruent since they do not have the same shape.

Since equal figures have the same area, then equal figures can be added or subtracted or can be multiplied or divided by the same number, in accordance with the axioms of page 32.

Thus: If equal figures are added to equal figures, the sums are equal. Halves of equal figures are equal, etc.

323. (*a*) *Congruent polygons are equal* since they enclose the same amount of plane surface.

(*b*) *Polygons are equal but are not necessarily congruent,* if they are composed of parts that are respectively congruent or equal.

Thus: The parallelogram and the kite-shaped figure at the right are *equal* because $\triangle A \cong \triangle A'$, and $\triangle B \cong \triangle B'$, but $XYZW$ *is not* $\cong RSTV$.

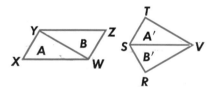

1. Hyp. $RSXY$ is a $\square$.
      $XW = WY$
      TV, through W, forms
      trapezoid $RSTV$.
   Con. $RSTV = RSXY$

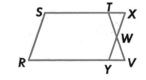

Suggestion. Prove $\triangle TXW \cong \triangle VYW$. Then use §323(*b*).

2. Hyp. $ABCD$ is a trapezoid.
      $BE = AE$, $CF = FD$
      $XEY \perp AD$, $WFZ \perp AD$
   Con. $XYZW = ABCD$

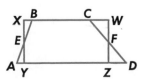

Note. Ex. 217 through Ex. 219, pp. 404–405, can be done now.

324. **Area of a rectangle.** If the base of a rectangle measures 6 linear units and its altitude 5, its area is 6 × 5 or 30 *corresponding surface units.*

If its base measures 6 units and its altitude 3½ units, the figure at the right shows that its area is 21 or 6 × 3.5 surface units.

These two examples suggest the following:

325. **Post. 25.** *The area of a rectangle is the product of the number of linear units in its base and the number in its altitude.*

The usual brief statement of this postulate is:
The area of a rectangle is the product of its base and its altitude.

This statement is taken as a postulate since:
(*a*) It gives the area when the base and the altitude can each be expressed exactly in terms of the same linear unit.

(*b*) It gives the approximate area when the base or the altitude, or both, can be expressed only approximately in terms of the same linear unit.

Thus: If *AB* is a little more than .6 in., and *AE* = .6 in.; if *AD* is a little more than 1.5 in., and *AG* = 1.5 in.; then .6 × 1.5 or .90 sq. in., the area of *AEFG*, is *approximately* the area of *ABCD*.

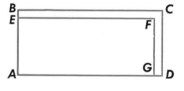

If *h* equals the number of linear units in the altitude, *b* equals the number of the *same units* in the base, and *A* equals the number of *corresponding surface units* in the interior, then

$A = hb$ **is the formula for the area of a rectangle.**

Example. What is the area of the rectangle whose base is 2.5 in. and whose altitude is 3.5 in.?

Solution.

1.   The formula is $A = hb$.
2. $h = 3.5$ in.; $b = 2.5$ in.; $A = \underline{\ ?\ }$ sq. in.
3. $\therefore A = 3.5 \times 2.5$
4. $\therefore A = 8.75$ sq. in. or 8.8 sq. in.

1. How many acres of ground are there in a field that is 80 rd. long and 40 rd. wide? (160 sq. rd. = 1 acre)

2. How many square yards of linoleum are needed for a room that is 12 ft. wide and 15 ft. long?

3. How many square feet of surface are there on the ceiling and four walls of a room that is 12 ft. long, 11 ft. wide, and 8 ft. high, including doors and windows?

4. How many square feet of floor space are there in a building that is 25 ft. wide and 70 ft. long if there are four floors in the building?

5. What is the cost of a concrete sidewalk 5 ft. wide along the two sides and corner of a corner lot that is 35 ft. wide and 120 ft. deep, at 40¢ a square foot?

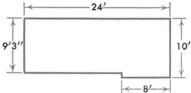

6. What is the cost of a concrete floor for a porch having the shape and dimensions shown in the adjoining figure, at 45¢ a square foot?

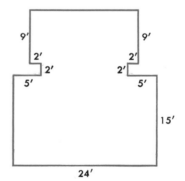

7. What is the cost of decorating the ceiling of a room having the shape and dimensions shown in the adjoining figure, at $1.50 a square yard?

8. What is the cost of a tile floor for a bathroom that is 7 ft. 6 in. wide and 9 ft. long at $2.25 a square foot?

9. The charge for insulating an attic floor is 24¢ a square foot. How much will it cost to insulate a floor that is 24 ft. wide and 35 ft. long?

10. A piece of sheet metal is 4.50 ft. long and 2.25 ft. wide. What will the piece weigh if one square foot of the metal weighs 4.375 lb.?

11. How many square feet of glass are there in 4 windows each of which contains two pieces of 24 in. by 28 in. glass?

12. How many tiles that are 1-ft. square will be needed for the floor of a patio that is 8 yd. long and 10 ft. wide?

Note. Ex. 220 through Ex. 224, p. 405, can be done now.

326. *The area of a parallelogram equals the product of the lengths of its base and altitude.*

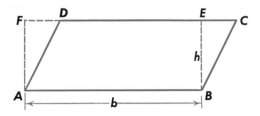

Hypothesis. $ABCD$ is a parallelogram.

Its base $AB = b$ units. Its altitude $BE = h$ units.

Conclusion. Area of $ABCD = hb$ square units.

Note. Usually "units" and "square units" as used above are omitted, and will be hereafter.

Plan. Change $ABCD$ into an equal rectangle.

Proof.

Statements	Authorities
1. Draw $AF \perp CD$, $BE \perp CD$.	1. Why possible?
2. $ABEF$ is a rectangle.	2. Prove in full.
3. $\triangle AFD \cong \triangle BEC$	3. Prove.
4. $\therefore$ $ABCD = ABEF$	4. Prove.
5. Area $ABEF = hb$	5. Why?
6. $\therefore$ Area $ABCD = hb$	6. Ax. 2, p. 32

1. What is the area of the parallelogram:
   (*a*) With altitude 8 in. and base 12 in.?
   (*b*) With altitude 3 yd. and base 4 ft.?

2. Construct parallelogram $XYZW$ having $XY = 3$ in., $XW = 2$ in., and $\angle X - 45°$. What is the area of $\square XYZW$?

Suggestion. Draw altitude WR. Find WR.

3. (*a*) Do Exercise 2 when $\angle X = 30°$. (§117)
   (*b*) Do Exercise 2 when $\angle X = 60°$.
   (*c*) How does the area of $XYZW$ change when the sides XY and XW remain unchanged and $\angle X$ increases?

★4. In $\square ABCD$, $AB = 15$ in., $AD = 9$ in., and $\angle A = 80°$. $DG \perp AB$ at G. Using §276, p. 248, find area of $ABCD$.

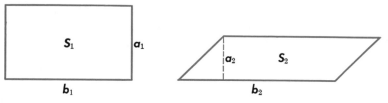

327. Consider two rectangles, or two parallelograms, or a rectangle and a parallelogram having altitudes a_1 and a_2, bases b_1 and b_2, and areas S_1 and S_2.

$$\text{Then } S_1 = a_1b_1 \quad \text{and} \quad S_2 = a_2b_2. \qquad \text{(Why?)}$$

(a) *Two rectangles or parallelograms having equal bases and equal altitudes are equal.*

Proof. If $a_1 = a_2$ and $b_1 = b_2$, then $a_1b_1 = a_2b_2$. (Ax. 5, p. 32)

$$\therefore \quad S_1 = S_2.$$

Example. If rectangle R has base 24 and altitude 6, and parallelogram T has base 24 and altitude 6, then:

$$R = T$$

(b) *Two rectangles or parallelograms are to each other as the products of their bases and altitudes.*

Proof. $\qquad \dfrac{S_1}{S_2} = \dfrac{a_1b_1}{a_2b_2} \qquad$ (Why?)

Example. If rectangle R has base 20 and altitude 15, and parallelogram T has base 15 and altitude 24, then:

$$\frac{R}{T} = \frac{20 \times 15}{15 \times 24}, \text{ or } \frac{5}{6} \qquad \text{(Prove it.)}$$

(c) *Two rectangles or parallelograms having equal altitudes are to each other as their bases.*

Proof. Since $\dfrac{S_1}{S_2} = \dfrac{a_1b_1}{a_2b_2}$, then $\dfrac{S_1}{S_2} = \dfrac{b_1}{b_2}$ if $a_1 = a_2$. (Why?)

Example. If R has base 24 and altitude 17, and T has base 36 and altitude 17, then $R:T = 24:36$, or $2:3$.

(d) *Two rectangles or parallelograms having equal bases are to each other as their altitudes.*

Proof. Since $\dfrac{S_1}{S_2} = \dfrac{a_1b_1}{a_2b_2}$, then $\dfrac{S_1}{S_2} = \dfrac{a_1}{a_2}$ if $b_1 = b_2$. (Why?)

1. Rectangles or parallelograms R, S, T, X, and Y have the dimensions given in the following table.

Compare:

(a) R with S.   (b) R with T.

(c) S with T.   (d) S with X.

(e) T with X.   (f) T with Y.

(g) R with Y.   (h) X with S.

(i) Y with X.   (j) Y with T.

Figure	Altitude	Base
R	12 in.	18 in.
S	6 in.	9 in.
T	24 in.	18 in.
X	15 in.	9 in.
Y	12 in.	24 in.

2. (a) Construct a rectangle $ABCD$ having base 4 in. and altitude 3 in.
   (b) Construct a rectangle $XYZW$ having base 4 in. that will equal $\frac{2}{3}$ of $ABCD$.

3. Prove that the segment joining the mid-points of two bases of $\square RSTX$ separates $RSTX$ into two equal parallelograms.

4. Draw any parallelogram $DEFG$. Construct from points on GF two lines parallel to DG that will separate $DEFG$ into three equal parallelograms.

★5. $\square ABCD$ has a base AB 20 in. long, $\angle A = 40°$, and side $AD = 12$ in. Using trigonometry, find the length of the altitude from D to AB, and then find the area of $ABCD$, getting the result correct to tenths.

6. A path that is 3 ft. wide surrounds a rectangular flower bed that is 25 ft. long and 12 ft. wide. What is the area of the path?

7. All the lots on a street are rectangular and 125 ft. deep. Compare two lots A and B if their frontages are 40 ft. and 60 ft. respectively.

8. What is the area, correct to tenths, of the parallelogram whose sides are 18 in. and 24 in. long if these sides include an angle of:
   (a) 30°?   (b) 45°?   (c) 60°?

9. (a) Find the area of the cross section of an H-beam as represented by the drawing at the right when $b = .5$ in., $a = 4.5$ in., and $w = 10$ in.
   (b) Prepare a formula for the area of the cross section of this H-beam, using the dimensions a, b, and w.

10. How long must the sides of a square be to make the area of the square equal that of a rectangle with base 75 ft. and altitude 15 ft.?

328. *The area of a triangle equals one half the product of the lengths of its base and altitude.*

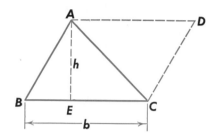

Hypothesis. $\triangle ABC$ has altitude $AE = h$ and base $BC = b$.

Conclusion.   Area of $\triangle ABC = \frac{1}{2}bh$.

Plan. Compare $\triangle ABC$ with a related parallelogram.

(Proof suggested by the figure.)

1. What is the area of the triangle:
   (*a*) Whose base is 10 in. and altitude is 7 in.?
   (*b*) Whose base is 2 ft. and altitude is 15 in.?

2. The diagonals of a rhombus measure 8 in. and 14 in. respectively. What is the area of the rhombus?

3. The base of a triangle is 30 in. and its altitude is 15 in. What is the length of the side of the square whose area equals that of the triangle?

4. What is the area of the equilateral triangle whose sides are each 12 in. long?

Suggestion. Draw an altitude. Find its length, using §259, p. 228.

5. Find the weight of a triangular steel plate of which the base is 30.5 in. and the altitude 15.5 in., if the steel weighs .028 lb. per sq. in. Give the result correct to the nearest tenth of a pound.

6. *ABCDE* is the outline of the front of a garage that is 24 ft. long.
   (*a*) How many sq. ft. of surface are there on the walls? On the roof?
   (*b*) How many rolls of roofing paper will it take for the roof if one roll covers 100 sq. ft.?

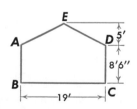

7. What is the area of an isosceles right triangle whose sides are 8 in. long?

329. (*a*) *A triangle is one half a parallelogram that has the same base and altitude.*

Proof. If $\triangle T$ and $\square P$ both have base b and altitude h, then:

$$\frac{\triangle T}{\square P} = \frac{\frac{1}{2}hb}{hb} = \tfrac{1}{2}; \text{ or } \triangle T = \tfrac{1}{2}\square P$$

(*b*) *Two triangles are to each other as the products of their bases and altitudes.* (See §327, p. 291.)

Proof. If $\triangle R$ has base b and altitude h, and $\triangle T$ has base c and altitude d, then

$$\frac{\triangle R}{\triangle T} = \frac{\frac{1}{2}hb}{\frac{1}{2}cd} = \frac{hb}{cd} \qquad\qquad \text{(Why?)}$$

(*c*) *Two triangles having the same base are to each other as their altitudes.*

(*d*) *Two triangles having the same altitudes are to each other as their bases.*

(*e*) *Two triangles having equal bases and equal altitudes are equal.*

1. Using the theorems above:

(*a*) Compare A with B.
(*b*) Compare A with C.
(*c*) Compare A with D.
(*d*) Compare A with E.
(*e*) Compare B with C.

Figure	Alt.	Base
$\triangle A$	12	15
$\square B$	12	15
$\triangle C$	18	15
$\triangle D$	18	30
$\triangle E$	12	24

2. (*a*) Compare $\square ABCD$ with $\triangle BCE$.
(*b*) Compare $\triangle BCX$ with $\triangle BCE$.
(*c*) If X is the mid-point of AD, compare $\triangle ABX$ with $\triangle CDX$.
(*d*) In (*c*), also compare $\triangle CXD$ with $\triangle BCE$ and with $\square ABCD$.

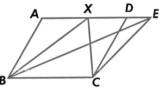

3. In $\triangle XYZ$, YW is the median to side XZ. Prove that $\triangle XYW = \triangle ZYW$.

4. In $\triangle RST$, RD is the median to ST. E is the mid-point of RD. Prove that $\triangle EST = \tfrac{1}{2}\triangle RST$.

Note. Ex. 225 through Ex. 251, pp. 405 through 408, can be done now.

330. The area of a triangle in terms of its sides.

Solution. 1. If a, b, and c are the lengths of the sides of $\triangle ABC$ and $s = \frac{1}{2}(a + b + c)$, it can be proved that the altitude drawn to side a is given by the formula:

$$h_a = \frac{2}{a}\sqrt{s(s-a)(s-b)(s-c)} \qquad \text{(See note.)}$$

2. \hspace{2cm} Area of $\triangle ABC = \frac{1}{2}a \times h_a$

3. $\therefore$ area of $\triangle ABC = \frac{1}{2}a \times \frac{2}{a}\sqrt{s(s-a)(s-b)(s-c)}$

4. $\therefore$ area of $\triangle ABC = \sqrt{s(s-a)(s-b)(s-c)}$

Pause for a moment to appreciate how remarkable this formula is. It is attributed to Hero of Alexandria, who lived in the first century A.D.

Example. Find the area of the triangle whose sides are 13, 14, and 15.

Solution. 1. Let $a = 13$, $b = 14$, and $c = 15$.

2. \hspace{2cm} $\therefore$ $s = \frac{1}{2}(13 + 14 + 15)$, or $s = 21$

3. \hspace{1cm} $\therefore$ area of the $\triangle = \sqrt{21 \times 8 \times 7 \times 6}$ sq. in.

or $\sqrt{3 \times 7 \times 2 \times 4 \times 7 \times 2 \times 3}$ sq. in.

4. \hspace{1cm} $\therefore$ area of the $\triangle = 3 \times 7 \times 2 \times 2$ or 84 sq. in.

1. Find the areas of the triangles whose sides are:
   (a) 12, 16, and 20 \hspace{1cm} (b) 15, 18, and 21 \hspace{1cm} (c) 20, 30, and 40

2. The sides of the lots A and B in the figure have the lengths indicated. Find the area of each lot.

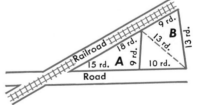

3. By the formula of §330 find the area of the equilateral triangle whose side is 14 in. long.

4. (a) By the same formula, prove that the area of the equilateral triangle with side a is $\frac{a^2}{4}\sqrt{3}$.

   (b) By this new formula, find the area of the equilateral triangle whose side is: (1) 12 in. (2) 15 in. (3) 20 in.

5. Determine the area of the triangle whose sides are 25, 17, and 28 inches respectively.

Note. See comments for p. 295 in the Teacher's Manual.

331. *The area of a trapezoid equals one half the product of the length of its altitude multiplied by the sum of the lengths of its bases.*

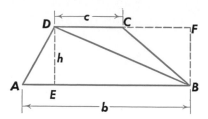

Hypothesis. Trapezoid $ABCD$ has altitude $DE = h$, base $AB = b$, and base $CD = c$.

Conclusion.   Area $ABCD = \frac{1}{2}h(b + c)$

Proof.

	Statements	Authorities
1.	Draw BD and alt. DE of $ABCD$.	1. Why possible?
2.	$ABCD = \triangle ABD + \triangle BCD$	2. Why?
3.	Area $\triangle ABD = \frac{1}{2}hb$	3. Why?
4.	Area $\triangle BCD = \frac{1}{2}hc$	4. Prove.
5.	$\therefore$ Area $ABCD = \frac{1}{2}hb + \frac{1}{2}hc$	5. Why?
6.	$\therefore$ Area $ABCD = \frac{1}{2}h(b + c)$	6. Factoring.

332. **Cor.** *The area of a trapezoid equals the product of the lengths of its altitude and its median.* Recall §142, p. 128.

Find the area of the trapezoid if:

Exercise	1.	2.	3.	4.
Altitude	12 in.	4 ft.	30 in.	1 yd. 6 in.
Lower base	18 in.	3 yd.	$2\frac{1}{2}$ yd.	4 yd. 1 ft.
Upper base	10 in.	2 yd.	5 ft.	2 yd. 2 ft.

Find the area of each of these trapezoids:

5.

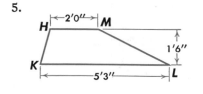

6.

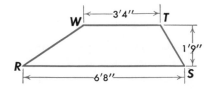

1. The nonparallel sides AB and CD of trapezoid $ABCD$ are 25 in., AD is 33 in., and BC is 19 in. What is the area of $ABCD$?

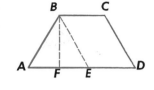

Suggestion. Draw $BE \parallel CD$ and $BF \perp AD$. Prove $\triangle ABE$ is isosceles. Find the length of BF.

2. In trapezoid $XYZW$, base $XY = 25$ in., base $WZ = 15$ in., $XW = 12$ in., and $\angle X = 30°$. What is the area of $XYZW$?

3. In isosceles trapezoid $DEFG$, the nonparallel sides DE and GF make 45° angles with the lower base EF. The bases measure 12 in. and 30 in. respectively. What is the area of trapezoid $DEFG$?

4. On an irregular field bounded by $ABCDE$, $AD = 44$ rd. The perpendiculars to AD from B, C, and E are 20 rd., 16 rd., and 15 rd., respectively. $AB = 25$ rd., and $CD = 20$ rd. What is the area of $ABCDE$?

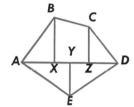

Suggestion. Use the Pythagorean Theorem to find AX and ZD, so that you can find XZ. Then find the area of each part of $ABCDE$, correct to tenths.

5. Base RT of $\triangle RST$ is 30 in. and altitude SW is 16 in. Point Z on SW is 4 in. from S. A line through Z, parallel to RT, meets SR at X and ST at Y. Find the area of $XRTY$.

Suggestion. To find XY, use §250.

6. What is the length of the side of a square that equals:
   (a) A parallelogram whose base and height are 18 in. and 30 in.?
   (b) A triangle whose base and height are 24 in. and 12 in., respectively?
   (c) A trapezoid whose bases are 15 in. and 35 in., respectively, and whose altitude is 20 in.?

Suggestion. In each part, if necessary, express the result first as a radical, and then correct to tenths. (See p. 419.)

★ 7. In trapezoid $RSTK$, bases RK and ST are 20 in. and 30 in. respectively. RS is 18 in. and makes a 45° angle with ST. Find the area of $RSTK$ correct to tenths of a square inch.

★ 8. Do Exercise 7 when $\angle S = 60°$.

★ 9. Develop a formula for the area of $RSTK$ of Exercise 7, using b for the lower base, c for the upper base, d for side RS, and $X°$ for the angle formed by RS and ST.

Note. Ex. 252 through 257, p. 408, can be done now.

333. *The square on the hypotenuse of a right triangle is equal to the sum of the squares on the legs.*

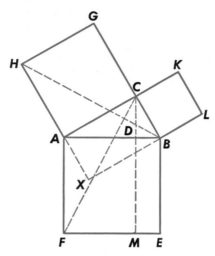

Hypothesis. $\angle C$ of $\triangle ABC$ is a right angle.

$ABEF$, $ACGH$, and $BCKL$ are squares.

Conclusion. $ABEF = ACGH + BCKL$

Plan. Separate $\square AE$ into two rectangles; prove the larger rectangle equal to $\square AG$ and the smaller equal to $\square CL$.

Proof.

	Statements	Authorities
1.	Draw $CD \perp AB$, meeting FE at M. Draw BH and CF.	1. Why possible?
2.	BCG is a straight line.	2. Prove it.
3.	$\triangle ABH \cong \triangle ACF$	3. Prove it.
4.	From B draw $BX \perp HA$ extended. Then $BX = CA$.	4. Possible? Prove it.
5.	$\therefore \;\; \square AG = 2\triangle AHB$	5. §329(a)
6.	Similarly $\square AM = 2\triangle AFC$.	6. Prove it.
7.	$\therefore \;\; \square AG = \square AM$	7. Why?
8.	Similarly $\square CL = \square BM$.	8. Prove it.
9.	$\therefore \;\; \square AG + \square CL = \square AM + \square BM$	9. Ax. 3, p. 32
10.	$\therefore \;\; \square AG + \square CL = \square AE$	10. Ax. 7, Ax. 2

The Greek scholar Pythagoras is associated with the theorem on page 298 since he was said to have given the first proof of the theorem.

Efforts to originate other proofs of the Pythagorean Theorem have been a favorite pursuit of students of geometry. Two more geometric proofs appear below.

1. In the adjoining figure, $\square AH$ is turned over AB on $\triangle ABC$.

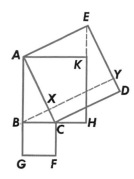

> **Prove.** $\square AD = \square AH + \square BF$
>
> **Plan.** 1. Prove BH must fall on BC.
>
> 2. Prove HKE is a st. line by proving that $\angle HKE$ is a st. $\angle$.
>
> 3. Prove $\square AH = \square AXYE$ by comparing each with $\triangle ABE$.
>
> 4. Prove $\square BF = \square XCDY$ after proving that $\triangle ACF \cong \triangle BCD$.
>
> 5. Then prove $\square AD = \square BF + \square AH$.

Note. Other proofs are obtained by turning the other squares over $\triangle ABC$ one at a time, or two at a time, or all at one time. See also the Teacher's Manual.

2. A proof attributed to President James A. Garfield.

> **Prove.** $b^2 = a^2 + c^2$.

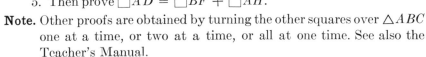

> **Plan.** 1. Extend BC to D making $CD = AB$. Draw $ED \perp BCD$ making $ED = BC$. Draw CE and AE.
>
> 2. Prove $ABDE$ is a trapezoid.
>
> 3. Express the area of $ABDE$ in terms of a and c.
>
> 4. Prove $\angle ACE$ is a rt. $\angle$ and $CE = b$.
>
> 5. Express the areas of $\triangle ABC$, CDE, and ACE.
>
> 6. Substitute in the equation
> trapezoid $ABDE = \triangle ABC + \triangle CDE + \triangle ACE$.
>
> 7. Simplify and you will get the conclusion.

3. In §333 prove that H, C, and L lie in a st. line.
Suggestion. Prove that $\angle HCL$ is a st. angle.

4. Prove $AG \parallel BK$.

5. Prove that $\triangle GCK \cong \triangle ABC$.

334. *If* s = *the length of a side of a regular polygon having n sides, and* p = *the perimeter, then:*

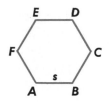

$$p = ns \qquad \text{(Why?)}$$

Thus: In regular hexagon $ABCDEF$,
$$p = 6s.$$

335. The area of a regular polygon equals one half the product of its apothem and its perimeter.

Hypothesis. Let the apothem of a regular polygon $XYZW \ldots$ be r, the perimeter be p, and the area be A.

Conclusion. $$A = \frac{1}{2}rp$$

Proof.

1. Let the polygon have n sides.
2. Draw radii OX, OY, OZ, etc., forming △ OXY, OYZ, OZW, etc.
3.   △OXY, OYZ, OZW, etc., are congruent.   (Prove.)
4.   ∴ $XYZW \ldots = n \times △OXY$
5.   Area of $△OXY = \frac{1}{2}r \times XY$ (Prove.)
6.   ∴ $XYZW \ldots = n \times \frac{1}{2}r \times XY$ (Ax. 2.)
7.   ∴ $A = \frac{1}{2}r \times nXY$
8.   But $p = nXY$ (Why?)
9.   ∴ $A = \frac{1}{2}rp$ (Ax. 2.)

1. (*a*) In a circle having a 2-in. radius, inscribe a square as taught in §299.
   (*b*) Compute correct to tenths of an inch the length of a side of the square and also the apothem.
Suggestion. Use trigonometry or the Pythagorean Theorem.
   (*c*) Compute the area of the square to tenths.

2. (*a*) In a 2.5 in. circle inscribe a regular hexagon.
   (*b*) Compute to tenths the length of a side and of an apothem.
   (*c*) Compute the area correct to tenths.

3. Do Exercise 2 for a regular octagon.

4. Do Exercise 2 for an equilateral triangle.

Assume that the dimensions given below are exact. The trigonometric ratios are correct to 4 places. Express final results, first, to 4 places; then round off correct to tenths.

1. If AC is a side of a regular 10-gon inscribed in a circle of radius 12 in., how long are AC and the apothem BD?

Solution. 1. Since $\overset{\frown}{AC} = \frac{1}{10} \times 360°$,
$$\angle DBA = 18°.$$

2. $\therefore \quad \dfrac{BD}{AB} = \cos \angle DBA$
  or $BD = 12 \times \cos 18°$

3. $\therefore \quad BD = 12 \times .9511$
  $BD = 11.41''$ or $11.4''$

4. $\dfrac{AD}{AB} = \sin \angle DBA$
  or $AD = 12 \times \sin 18°$

5. $\therefore \quad AD = 12 \times .3090$ or $AD = 3.708$

6. Since $AD = 3.708''$, $AC = 7.416''$ or $7.4''$.

2. Find the apothem and a side of the regular pentagon inscribed in a circle of radius 15 in.

3. Find the side and apothem of the regular octagon inscribed in a circle of radius 9 in.

In Exercises 4 to 9, find the perimeter and the area of:

4. A regular 12-gon inscribed in a circle of radius 8 in.

5. A regular 10-gon inscribed in a circle of radius 5 in.

6. A regular octagon circumscribed about a circle of radius 8 in.

7. A regular pentagon circumscribed about the circle of radius 9 in.

8. A regular 10-gon circumscribed about the circle of radius 10 in.

9. A regular 12-gon circumscribed about the circle of radius 7 in.

10. Find the side of a regular hexagon whose apothem is 4.

11. Find the side of a regular octagon whose apothem is 5.

12. Find the side of a regular 10-gon whose apothem is 6.

13. Find the side of an equilateral triangle whose altitude is 8.

14. Derive formulas for the perimeter and the area of an equilateral triangle inscribed in a circle with radius r.

336. **Finding the length and the area of a circle** have been two of the interesting problems of mathematics.

The **circumference of a circle** means the length of the circle.

The problem is to find the circumference when the length of the radius or of the diameter of the circle is known.

An *inductive solution* of this problem follows.

A class measured the diameter and the circumference of each of several circular objects. They found:

Object	Diameter d	Circumference C
Lampshade	5.5 in.	17.25 in.
Plate	8.25 in.	26.00 in.
Pail	9.5 in.	29.75 in.
Tire	28.0 in.	88.00 in.

It was obvious that the circumference of each circle was more than three times the diameter. Dividing, they found:

For the	$C \div d$ was:
Lampshade	3.136, or 3.14
Plate	3.151, or 3.15
Pail	3.131, or 3.13
Tire	3.142, or 3.14

The average of 3.14, 3.15, 3.13, and 3.14 is 3.14. The class decided that C was about $3.14d$.

The *constant ratio of the circumference to the diameter of a circle* is represented by the Greek letter π, so that

$$C = \pi d \text{ where } \pi \text{ is about } 3.14.$$

Since $d = 2r$, then $C = \pi \times 2r$, or $C = 2\pi r$.

By other methods it has been found that π is about 3.1416.

Archimedes proved that π is about $3\frac{1}{7}$, although he did not have the Hindu-Arabic numerals with which to write the result in this simple form. $3\frac{1}{7}$ is convenient for use when the radius can be divided by 7.

Thus: If $d = 21$, $C = 3\frac{1}{7} \times 21 = \frac{22}{7} \times 21$, or 66.

337. For centuries, mathematicians tried to determine what kind of number π is.

A number like 3 is an *integer*. Early it was decided that π is not an integer.

Presently mathematicians found ways to compute the value of π decimally. Vieta (1540–1603) gave 3.141592653 as the value of π to nine decimal places. D. E. Ferguson has carried out the computation to 808 places. With an electronic computer the value of π can be carried out to any number of places. It has been computed to 10,000 places. However, it has been proved that π cannot be expressed *exactly* by either a common or a decimal fraction. This means that π *is an irrational number*. In 1882 it was proved that π is a special kind of irrational number.

We use an approximate value of π that is suited to the conditions of the problem. The three common values are:

$$\pi = 3\tfrac{1}{7}, \ \pi = 3.14, \ \pi = 3.1416$$

Of these 3.1416 is the *most precise*, because it is expressed in terms of the smallest *unit*, namely, ten-thousandths of an inch.   3.1416 contains five significant digits.

If a very precise result is not needed, use either of the first two values. Use the first if the diameter is divisible by 7.

Thus: If the diameter of a track is 140 ft., the circumference is about $3\tfrac{1}{7} \times 140$ ft. or 440 ft.

If the diameter or radius contains only two significant digits, use 3.14 for π, and round off the result to two significant digits.

Thus: If $d = 2.5$, then $C = 3.14 \times 2.5$ or 7.85.

Therefore $C = 7.85$, or about 7.9.

If the diameter contains more than two significant digits, use 3.1416 for π and round off the result to the number of significant digits in the diameter, but at most to five significant digits since 3.1416 has only five such digits.

Thus: If $r = 2.15$, then $C = 2 \times 3.1416 \times 2.15$.
$$C = 13.50888, \text{ or about } 13.5.$$

1. What is the circumference of the circle whose diameter is:
   (a) 14 in.?   (b) 12 in.?   (c) 28 in.?   (d) 25 in.?

2. How many feet of lace edging are needed for the outside edge of a circular centerpiece whose radius is 20 in.?

Suggestion. Secure the result correct to the nearest larger integer. Why?

3. A circular lake is $\frac{1}{2}$ mi. in diameter. What is its circumference, correct to the nearest rod? (1 mi. = 320 rd.)

4. The radius of a wheel is 10.5 in. How long is an arc:
   (a) Of 60°?   (b) Of 90°?   (c) Of 72°?   (d) Of 36°?

5. The diameter of the *tread* of the rear-wheel tires of a car is 28 in. How far, correct to tenths of a foot, does the car move when the rear wheel makes one revolution?

6. The *rim speed* of a wheel is the distance through which a point on the rim passes in one minute. What is the rim speed, in feet, of the flywheel of an engine that has a diameter of 12 ft. if the wheel revolves 200 times per minute?

7. The side of a square is 10 in. What is the circumference:
   (a) Of its inscribed circle?
   (b) Of its circumscribed circle?

8. Find the circumferences of the inscribed and circumscribed circles of a regular hexagon if the sides of the hexagon measure 16 in.

9. A circular running track is to be $\frac{1}{2}$ mi. in length. Find its diameter correct to the nearest foot. (1 mi. = 5280 ft.)

★10. For a certain emery wheel, a maximum desirable rim speed is 5000 ft. per minute.
   (a) What is the rim speed of an emery wheel 7 in. in diameter that revolves 1750 times per minute?
   (b) How fast may an emery wheel be revolved in order that its rim speed shall not be more than 5000 ft. per minute if the diameter of the wheel is 10 in.?

★11. Find the length of the tube needed to make the bent tube shown at the right.

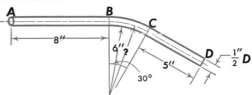

12. Derive a formula for the radius of the circle that circumscribes a square whose side measures *s* inches.

Note. Ex. 258 through Ex. 264, pp. 408 and 409, can be done now.

338. **Informal proof** *that the area of a circle equals one half the product of its radius and its circumference.*

In the figure at the right are shown an inscribed square and a regular octagon. Imagine also an inscribed regular 16-gon, 32-gon, etc.

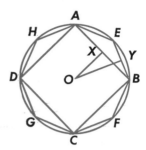

When the number of sides increases, the polygons come closer and closer to the circle. Therefore their perimeters come closer and closer to the circumference of the circle and their areas come closer and closer to the area of the circle.

Notice also that the lengths of the apothems (like OX and OY) come closer and closer to the length of the radius, so much so, that even in the case of the 16-gon it would be difficult to distinguish between the length of the apothem and that of the radius.

Note. At this point read again the note that appears after §316, p. 279.

The area of each polygon = $\frac{1}{2}$ apothem × perimeter. (§335)

This makes it reasonable to conclude that:

The area of the circle = $\frac{1}{2}$ radius × circumference.

$$\therefore \quad A = \tfrac{1}{2}rC$$

339. **Cor.** (*a*) Since $C = 2\pi r$, $A = \frac{1}{2}r \times 2\pi r$, or $A = \pi r^2$.

(*b*) *Since* $r = \frac{1}{2}d$, $A = \pi\left(\dfrac{d^2}{4}\right)$, *or* $A = \frac{1}{4}\pi d^2$.

Example. The piston of a locomotive has a diameter of 15 in. What is the total pressure exerted on it by the steam when the steam pressure is 90 lb. per sq. in.?

Solution. 1. Here $d = 15$; $A = \frac{1}{4}\pi d^2$.

2. $\qquad\qquad \therefore \quad A = \frac{1}{4} \times 3.14 \times 15 \times 15$,
   or 176.62 sq. in.

3. $\qquad\qquad \therefore \quad$ the pressure = 176.62 × 90 lbs.,
   or 15,895.8 lb.

4. $\qquad\qquad \therefore \quad$ the pressure is about 16,000 lb.

1. What is the area of the circle whose radius is 14 in.?

2. Find the area of the circle whose diameter is 21 in.

3. A circular pond is $\frac{1}{2}$ mi. in diameter. What is its area in acres, correct to tenths? (1 mi. = 320 rd., 160 sq. rd. = 1 acre)

4. In a park is a circular flower bed 25 ft. in diameter. How many square feet of surface are there in the flower bed?

5. Around the flower bed described in Ex. 4 is a footpath 4 ft. wide. What is the area of the footpath?

6. A circular doily 10 in. in diameter has a border of lace that is 2 in. wide. How many square inches of lace are there in the border?

7. How many tulip bulbs are needed for a circular flower bed that is 10 ft. in diameter if 24 sq. in. on the average are allowed for each bulb?

8. What is the area between the circle that is inscribed in and the one that is circumscribed about the square whose side is 10 in.?

9. The larger of two circles has a radius that is three times that of the smaller. Compare the area of the first circle with that of the second circle.

10. The pipes running from a furnace to the rooms of a house have circular cross sections. Which will carry more heated air to a room, one 12-in. pipe, or two 8-in. pipes?

★11. In a well-installed air heating system, the area of the cross section of the cold-air supply pipe must be about as much as the sum of the cross sections of the warm-air pipes.

If there are three 9-in. and four 10-in. warm-air pipes, what must be the approximate diameter of the cold-air pipe?

★12. Prove that the area of a circle equals four times the area of the circle drawn on its radius as diameter.

★13. Around a circle of radius 6 in. is circumscribed a regular hexagon. How much more than the circumference and area of the circle are the perimeter and area of the hexagon?

★14. How many times as much gas will flow through a 24-in. main as through a 16-in. main, if the pressure and temperature are the same?

15. If the radius of a circle is changed from 3″ to 6″:
   (a) How is the circumference changed?
   (b) How is the area changed?

1. What is the ratio of the circumferences of two circles if the radius of the second is:
   (a) Double that of the first?
   (b) Five times that of the first?
   (c) One half that of the first?
   (d) One third that of the first?

2. An automobile is traveling at the rate of 50 m.p.h. The outside diameter of the tires of the car is 29 in. How many times do the wheels of the car revolve in a minute?

Suggestion. Express the result correct to the nearest whole number.

3. In the adjoining semicircular arch constructed about center O, AB is 10 ft. If the arch is to be constructed of 15 stones of equal size at their bases, how long is each of the arcs like arc DE?

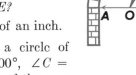

Suggestion. Express DE correct to tenths of an inch.

4. Quadrilateral $ABCD$ is inscribed in a circle of radius 8 in. If $\angle A = 60°$, $\angle B = 100°$, $\angle C = 120°$, and $\angle D = 80°$, how long is each of the arcs if arc $AB = 60°$?

5. Prove that the area of the ring included between two concentric circles is equal to the area of a circle whose diameter is that chord of the outer circle that is tangent to the inner.

Suggestion. Prove the area of the ring $= \frac{1}{4}\pi \overline{AC^2}$.

6. Prove that the area of the square inscribed in a sector whose central angle is a right angle is equal to one half the area of the square on the radius.

Note. BOA is the *sector*. Prove that the area of square $OECD$ equals one half the area of the square whose side equals the radius.

7. Find the area of the shaded part of each of the following figures if they are squares in which AB equals 12 inches.

Note. Ex. 265 through 282, pp. 409 and 410, can be done now.

1. Draw any $\triangle ABC$. On BC take MN so that $MN = 3BC$. Draw AM and AN. How does $\triangle AMN$ compare with $\triangle ABC$?

2. Construct an isosceles triangle twice as large as $\triangle ABC$ having:
(a) The same base as $\triangle ABC$.
(b) The same altitude as $\triangle ABC$.

3. Construct a square equal to the sum of two squares.

4. Given two squares. Construct a square equal to the larger minus the smaller.

5. Draw trapezoid $ABCD$, of which AD is one base. Draw diagonals AC and BD intersecting at E. Prove $\triangle ABE = \triangle DEC$.

6. X is any point on diagonal BD of $\square ABCD$. Prove $\triangle ADX = \triangle CDX$.

7. In Ex. 6, if $XD = \frac{1}{3}BD$, compare $AXCD$ with $ABCD$.

8. If $\angle A$ of $\triangle ABC = 30°$, prove $\triangle ABC = \frac{1}{4}AB \times AC$.

Suggestion. Draw $BX \perp AC$.

9. Prove the square whose side is a diagonal of a given square equals twice the given square.

10. In the following square $ABCD$, $AB = 9$ in. EF and GH join the mid-points of opposite sides. R and T trisect EF. W and S trisect GH. Find the area of the shaded star-shaped figure.

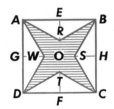
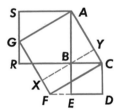

For Exercises 11–14 use the right-hand figure above. In $\triangle ABC$, $\angle B = 90°$. $BCDE$, $ABRS$, and $ACFG$ are squares on the sides.

11. Prove that SR passes through G and that DE extended passes through F.

Suggestion. Draw GS. Prove that $\angle GSA = $ rt. $\angle$ by proving $\triangle GSA$ congruent to $\triangle ABC$. Then GS coincides with RS.
    Draw DF. Prove $\angle FDC = $ rt. $\angle$, and FD coincides with ED.

12. Compare square SB with rectangle $XGAY$.

13. Compare square BD with rectangle $XFCY$.

14. Prove square $FGAC = $ square $SB + $ square BD.

MEASURING COMMON FIGURES

1. Tell the difference between the interior and area of a polygon.

2. A square has sides that are 2 yd. long. What is its area:
   (a) When the unit of measure is a square yard?
   (b) When the unit of measure is a square foot?

3. What are the differences between equal figures, congruent figures, and similar figures?

4. If figures are congruent, then they are . . . .

5. If congruent figures be added to congruent figures, the sums are . . . .

6. Rectangles A and B have equal bases, and altitudes of 9 and 12 respectively. What is the ratio of A to B?

7. Parallelograms R and S have equal altitudes, and bases of 8 and 24 respectively. What is the ratio of R to S?

8. Triangle C and parallelogram D have equal altitudes, and bases of 6 and 12 respectively. What part of D is C?

9. In trapezoid $ABCD$, $BC = 2AD$.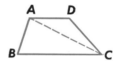
   (a) How does $\triangle ABC$ compare with $\triangle ADC$?
   (b) How does $\triangle ADC$ compare with $ABCD$?

10. In Ex. 9, if $AD = 5$ in., $BC = 15$ in., and the distance between AD and BC is 10 in., what is the area of $ABCD$?

11. In right $\triangle ABC$, $\angle B = 90°$, $AB = 6$ in., and $BC = 8$ in. What is the length of AC?

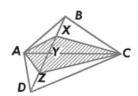

12. In square $ABCD$, $AB = 6$ in. X and Y trisect AB. Z and W trisect AD. What is the total area of the colored triangles in $ABCD$?

13. In quadrilateral $ABCD$, points X, Y, and Z divide BD into four equal parts. What part of $ABCD$ is quadrilateral $AXCZ$?

14. Construct equilateral $\triangle ABC$ and its altitude AD. Extend DA through A to X, so that $AX = AD$. Draw $XY \parallel AB$ and $XZ \parallel AC$, meeting BC at Y and Z respectively.
    (a) Prove $\triangle XYZ$ is equilateral.
    (b) Find the ratio of $\triangle XYZ$ to $\triangle ABC$.

MEASURING REGULAR POLYGONS AND CIRCLES

1. (a) What is a regular polygon?
   (b) What is: (1) Its apothem? (2) Its radius?

2. What is the perimeter of a regular octagon when the length of a side is 8 in.?

3. What is the area of a regular pentagon whose sides are 5 in. and whose apothem is 3.44 in.?

4. (a) How long is the apothem of a regular hexagon whose side is 10 in.?
   (b) What is the area of this hexagon?

5. (a) What is the circumference of a circle having a 12 in. diameter?
   (b) What is the area of this circle?

6. If the area of a circle is 75 sq. in., what is the area of the interior of the circle that is inside a central angle of 60°?

7. The perimeter of one regular polygon is 64 in. A second regular polygon of the same number of sides has sides that are one half as long as those of the first polygon. What is the perimeter of the second polygon?

★ 8. Polygons P and Q are similar. The sides of Q are three times those of P. What is the perimeter of Q if the perimeter of P is 80 in.?

9. The radius of circle X is half that of circle Y.
   (a) What is the circumference of circle Y if that of circle X is k in.?
   (b) What is the area of circle Y if that of circle X is z square inches?

10. Given a regular hexagon having 8-inch sides.
    (a) What is the area of its circumscribed circle?
    (b) What is the area of its inscribed circle?

11. A square is inscribed in a circle having 10-inch radius.
    (a) What is the perimeter of this square?
    (b) What is the area of this square?
    (c) Do parts (a) and (b) if the square is circumscribed about the circle.

12. Do Ex. 11 if the inscribed polygon is an equilateral triangle.

13. Do Ex. 11 if the inscribed polygon is a regular hexagon.

14. $\triangle ABC$ is inscribed in the semicircle on AB as diameter. $AC = 12$ in. and $BC = 5$ in.
    (a) What is the area of $\triangle ABC$?
    (b) What is the area of the semicircle?

AREA OF A SECTOR AND SEGMENT

340. (*a*) **A sector of a circle** is the part of the interior of the circle that lies between the sides of a central angle. The central angle is called the *angle of the sector.*

(*b*) *The area of a sector of a circle is to the area of the circle as its angle is to* 360°.

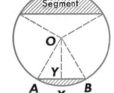

Example. What is the area of a sector of a circle with 7-in. radius if the angle of the sector is 36°?

Solution. 1. $A = \pi \times 7^2$, $A = \frac{22}{7} \times 7^2$, $A = 154$ sq. in.

2.   ∴   area of sector $= \frac{36}{360} \times 154$.

3. ∴   the area of the sector is 15.4 sq. in. or about 15 sq. in.

341. **A segment of a circle** is the part of the interior of the circle that lies between a chord and its arc, as segment AXB.

To find the area of a segment, subtract from the area of the corresponding sector the area of the triangle formed by the chord and the radii drawn to its ends.

Example. What is the area of a segment of a circle of radius 7 in. that is bounded by a 7-in. chord and its arc?

Solution. 1. Area of circle $= 154$ sq. in. (See Ex. above.)

2.   Since $AB = AO = OB = 7$ in., $\angle O = 60°$.

3. ∴   area sector $OAXB = \frac{1}{6} \times 154$, or $25\frac{2}{3}$ sq. in.

4.   In $\triangle OAB$, draw $OY \perp AB$. ∴ $YB = \frac{7}{2}$ in.

5.   ∴ $\overline{OY}^2 = 7^2 - (\frac{7}{2})^2$ ∴ $\overline{OY}^2 = 49 - \frac{49}{4}$

$$\therefore \overline{OY}^2 = 49 \times \tfrac{3}{4}$$
$$OY = \tfrac{7}{2}\sqrt{3}$$

6.   ∴   area $\triangle OAB = \frac{1}{2} \times \frac{7}{2}\sqrt{3} \times 7$, or $\frac{49}{4}\sqrt{3}$
$$= 21.22 \text{ sq. in.}$$

7.   ∴   area of segment $AXB = (25.67 - 21.22)$ sq. in.
     ∴   segment $AXB = 4.45$ sq. in. or about 4.5 sq. in.

COMPARING SIMILAR FIGURES

342. The perimeters and areas of similar polygons often can be compared without actually finding the perimeters or the areas.

343. **Fundamental theorem about equal ratios.** *If several ratios are equal, the sum of the numerators is to the sum of the denominators as any numerator is to its denominator.*

Hypothesis. $\dfrac{a}{b} = \dfrac{c}{d} = \dfrac{e}{f} = \dfrac{g}{h}$

Conclusion. $\dfrac{a + c + e + g}{b + d + f + h} = \dfrac{a}{b}$ or $\dfrac{c}{d}, \ldots$

Proof.

1. Let $r = \dfrac{a}{b} = \dfrac{c}{d} = \dfrac{e}{f} = \dfrac{g}{h}.$

2. $\therefore\quad br = a,\ dr = c,\ fr = e,\ hr = g$ (Why?)

3. $\therefore\quad br + dr + fr + hr = a + c + e + g$ (Why?)

4. $\therefore\quad r(b + d + f + h) = a + c + e + g$ (Factoring.)

5. $\therefore\quad r = \dfrac{a + c + e + g}{b + d + f + h}$ (Why?)

6. $\therefore\ \dfrac{a + c + e + g}{b + d + f + h} = \dfrac{a}{b} = \dfrac{c}{d} = \dfrac{e}{f} = \dfrac{g}{h}$ (Why?)

344. *The perimeters of two similar polygons have the same ratio as any two corresponding sides.*

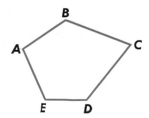 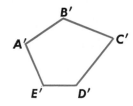

If $ABCDE \backsim A'B'C'D'E'$, then

$$\frac{AB}{A'B'} = \frac{BC}{B'C'} = \frac{CD}{C'D'} = \frac{DE}{D'E'} = \frac{EA}{E'A'}$$

$\therefore\ \dfrac{AB + BC + CD + DE + EA}{A'B' + B'C' + C'D' + D'E' + E'A'} = \dfrac{AB}{A'B'}$ or $\dfrac{BC}{B'C'}, \ldots$

345. *The areas of two similar triangles are to each other as the squares of any two corresponding sides.*

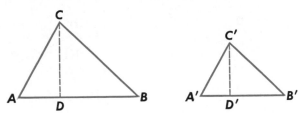

Hypothesis. AB and $A'B'$ are corresponding sides of similar $\triangle ABC$ and $A'B'C'$ respectively.

Conclusion. $\dfrac{\triangle ABC}{\triangle A'B'C'} = \dfrac{\overline{AB}^2}{\overline{A'B'}^2} = \dfrac{\overline{BC}^2}{\overline{B'C'}^2} = \dfrac{\overline{AC}^2}{\overline{A'C'}^2}$

Proof.

Statements	Authorities
1. Draw altitudes CD and $C'D'$.	1. Why possible?
2. $\therefore$ $\dfrac{\triangle ABC}{\triangle A'B'C'} = \dfrac{AB \times CD}{A'B' \times C'D'}$	2. §329(*b*), p. 294
3. But $\dfrac{CD}{C'D'} = \dfrac{AB}{A'B'}$.	3. §250, p. 220
4. $\therefore$ $\dfrac{\triangle ABC}{\triangle A'B'C'} = \dfrac{AB}{A'B'} \cdot \dfrac{AB}{A'B'}$, or $\dfrac{\overline{AB}^2}{\overline{A'B'}^2}$	4. Ax. 2, p. 32
5. But $\dfrac{BC}{B'C'} = \dfrac{AC}{A'C'} = \dfrac{AB}{A'B'}$.	5. Why?
6. $\therefore$ $\dfrac{\triangle ABC}{\triangle A'B'C'} = \dfrac{\overline{BC}^2}{\overline{B'C'}^2} = \dfrac{\overline{AC}^2}{\overline{A'C'}^2}$	6. Why?

1. $\triangle ABC \backsim \triangle A'B'C'$, $AB = 2A'B'$
   Compare the area of $\triangle ABC$ with that of $\triangle A'B'C'$.

2. What is the ratio of the areas of two equilateral triangles whose sides measure 6 in. and 9 in. respectively?

3. $\triangle ABC$ and $\triangle XYZ$ are equilateral. $\triangle XYZ$ is three times $\triangle ABC$. If $AB = 4$ in., how long is XY?

4. One side of $\triangle RST = 6$ in. How long must the corresponding side of similar $\triangle XYZ$ be to make the area of $\triangle XYZ$ four times that of $\triangle RST$?

346. *The areas of two similar polygons are to each other as the squares of any two corresponding sides.*

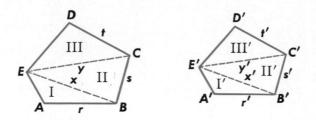

Hypothesis. r and r' are corresponding sides of similar polygons AC and $A'C'$.

Conclusion. $\dfrac{\text{Area of polygon } AC}{\text{Area of polygon } A'C'} = \dfrac{r^2}{r'^2} = \dfrac{s^2}{s'^2} = \dfrac{t^2}{t'^2},$ etc.

Proof.

	Statements	Authorities
1.	Draw diagonals x, x', y, and y'.	1. Post. 1, p. 34
2.	$\triangle \text{I} \backsim \triangle \text{I}',\ \triangle \text{II} \backsim \triangle \text{II}',\ \triangle \text{III} \backsim \triangle \text{III}'$	2. §267, p. 238
3.	$\dfrac{\triangle I}{\triangle I'} = \dfrac{r^2}{r'^2},\ \dfrac{\triangle II}{\triangle II'} = \dfrac{s^2}{s'^2},\ \dfrac{\triangle III}{\triangle III'} = \dfrac{t^2}{t'^2}$	3. §345
4.	$\dfrac{r}{r'} = \dfrac{s}{s'} = \dfrac{t}{t'},\ \ \therefore\ \dfrac{r^2}{r'^2} = \dfrac{s^2}{s'^2} = \dfrac{t}{t'^2}$	4. Why?
5.	$\therefore\ \dfrac{\triangle I}{\triangle I'} = \dfrac{\triangle II}{\triangle II'} = \dfrac{\triangle III}{\triangle III'}$	5. Why?
6.	$\therefore\ \dfrac{\triangle I + \triangle II + \triangle III}{\triangle I' + \triangle II' + \triangle III'} = \dfrac{\triangle I}{\triangle I'}$	6. §343, p. 312
7.	$\therefore\ \dfrac{\text{area } ABCDE}{\text{area } A'B'C'D'E'} = \dfrac{\triangle I}{\triangle I'} = \dfrac{r^2}{r'^2},$ etc.	7. Why?

1. The side of one square is double that of another. How many times as large as the smaller is the larger?

2. The corresponding sides of two similar pentagons measure 3 in. and 12 in. respectively. Compare their areas.

3. Two hexagons are similar. The shortest sides measure 2 in. and 6 in. respectively. How do their areas compare?

4. In Ex. 3, how long must the side of the larger hexagon be to make the area twice that of the smaller?

1. $\triangle ABC$ is a given triangle. XY is a segment that is four times as long as AB. If $\triangle XYZ$ is constructed similar to $\triangle ABC$ so that XY corresponds to AB, how many times as large as $\triangle ABC$ is $\triangle XYZ$?

2. In Ex. 1, if $XY = \frac{2}{3}AB$, what is the ratio of $\triangle XYZ$ to $\triangle ABC$?

3. The bases of two similar triangles measure 3 in. and 9 in. respectively.
   (a) How do their perimeters compare?
   (b) Compare their areas.

4. Prove that the areas of two similar triangles are to each other as:
   (a) The squares of any two corresponding altitudes.
   (b) The squares of any two corresponding medians.
   (c) The squares of their perimeters.

5. Two polygons are similar. A side of one equals 8 in. If the second is four times as large as the first, how long is the corresponding side of the second?

Suggestion. Let $x =$ the no. of in. in the corresponding side of the second.

6. Repeat Ex. 5 if the second polygon is:
   (a) Twice as large as the first.   (b) Three times as large.

7. AB of $\triangle ABC$ is 12 in. long. DE is to be drawn parallel to BC from D on AB to E on AC. Where must D be located on AB in order that $\triangle ADE$ shall equal one half $\triangle ABC$?

Suggestion. Let $AD = x$.

8. A pennant shaped like an isosceles triangle has its equal sides 24 in. long. How long should the sides be in order that a pennant of the same shape shall require just half as much cloth?

9. On an architect's drawing, the area of the foundation of a house is 56 sq. in. The drawing is to the scale $\frac{1}{4}'' = 1'$, or $1:48$. What will the area of the foundation be in square feet?

10. On a pictograph the amount of wheat produced in a certain year is represented by a square whose side is of length s. How long must the side of a square be that will correctly represent a crop twice as large?

11. A plane parallel to the base of a regular pyramid whose base measures 60 sq. in. cuts one third from the top of the lateral edges. What is the area of the section of the pyramid made by the plane?

Note. Ex. 283 and 284, p. 410, can be done now.

347. *The perimeters of two regular polygons of the same number of sides have the same ratio as any two corresponding sides, or their radii, or their apothems.*

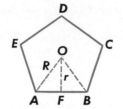
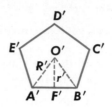

Hypothesis. AC and $A'C'$ are regular polygons having the same number of sides. AB and $A'B'$ are two corresponding sides. O and O' are their centers. R and R' are radii. r and r' are apothems. P and P' are their perimeters.

Conclusion. $\dfrac{P}{P'} = \dfrac{R}{R'} = \dfrac{r}{r'} = \dfrac{AB}{A'B'}$

Proof.

Statements	Authorities
1. Draw radii OA, OB, $O'A'$, $O'B'$, and apothems OF and $O'F'$.	1. Why possible?
2. Polygon $AC \backsim$ polygon $A'C'$	2. §303, p. 270
3. $\therefore \dfrac{P}{P'} = \dfrac{AB}{A'B'}$	3. §344, p. 312
4. $OA = OB$, and $O'A' = O'B'$	4. Why?
5. $\therefore \dfrac{OA}{O'A'} = \dfrac{OB}{O B'}$	5. Ax. 6, p. 32
6. $\angle AOB = \angle A'O'B'$	6. Why?
7. $\therefore \triangle AOB \backsim \triangle A'O'B'$	7. §248, p. 218
8. $\therefore \dfrac{AB}{A'B'} = \dfrac{R}{R'} = \dfrac{r}{r'}$	8. Why?
9. $\therefore \dfrac{P}{P'} = \dfrac{R}{R'} = \dfrac{r}{r'}$	9. Ax. 1, p. 32

1. Regular hexagons are inscribed in circles of radii 4 in. and 8 in. respectively. How do their perimeters compare?

2. In Ex. 11, p. 315, the perimeter of the section made by the cutting is what part of the perimeter of the base?

348. *The areas of two regular polygons having the same number of sides are to each other as the squares of any two corresponding sides, or of their radii, or of their apothems.*

Proof. 1. In the figure for §347, if polygons AC and $A'C'$ are regular and have the same number of sides, they are similar.

2. $\therefore \dfrac{\text{area of } AC}{\text{area of } A'C'} = \dfrac{\overline{AB}^2}{\overline{A'B'}^2}$ (§346)

3.   But $AB : A'B' = R : R' = r : r'$.   (Prove it.)

4. $\therefore \dfrac{\text{area of } AC}{\text{area of } A'C'} = \dfrac{\overline{AB}^2}{\overline{A'B'}^2} = \dfrac{R^2}{R'^2} = \dfrac{r^2}{r'^2}$ (Why?)

349. *The areas of two circles are to each other as the squares of their radii or of their diameters.*

Suggestion. Use the theorem of §339 and the method of proof employed in §327(b), p. 291.

1. The side of one equilateral triangle is 1 in. long; that of another is 2 in. long.
   (a) How do their perimeters compare? Their areas?
   (b) How many of the smaller will it take to cover the larger?

2. Repeat Ex. 1, if the side of the larger is:
   (a) 3 in.   (b) 4 in.   (c) 5 in.

3. Two regular pentagons have sides that measure 2 in. and 6 in. respectively. How does:
   (a) The perimeter of the first compare with that of the second?
   (b) The area of the first compare with that of the second?

4. In a circle of diameter 2 in., the perimeter of a regular inscribed hexagon is 6 in. and its area is 2.6 sq. in. What are the perimeter and the area of a regular inscribed hexagon in a circle of diameter:
   (a) 4 in.?   (b) 1 in.?   (c) 3 in.?

5. The adjoining set of squares is suggested in a book on design as a desirable background. How does the area of each square compare with the next larger if the sides have the measures indicated?

6. The perimeter of an inscribed regular octagon is 40 in. What is the perimeter of a regular octagon inscribed in a circle that is twice as large in diameter?

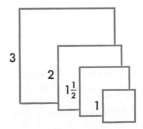

Note. Leave radical results in simplest radical form.

1. The perimeter of the equilateral triangle circumscribed about a circle of radius 1 in. is $6\sqrt{3}$ in. and its area is $3\sqrt{3}$ sq. in. What are the perimeter and area of the equilateral triangle circumscribed about a circle whose radius is:
   (*a*) 2 in.?   (*b*) 3 in.?   (*c*) $\frac{1}{2}$ in.?

2. In the figure below, $ABCDEF$ is an inscribed regular hexagon and $XYZWRS$ is a circumscribed regular hexagon.
   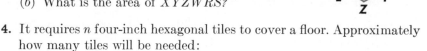
   (*a*) OA is the apothem of $XYZW$ .... If $OA = 6$ in., how long is the apothem OK?
   (*b*) What is the perimeter of $ABCDEF$?
   (*c*) What then is the perimeter of $XYZWRS$?

3. (*a*) In Ex. 2, find the area of $ABCDEF$.
   (*b*) What is the area of $XYZWRS$?

4. It requires n four-inch hexagonal tiles to cover a floor. Approximately how many tiles will be needed:
   (*a*) If 2-in. hexagonal tiles are used?
   (*b*) If 6-in. hexagonal tiles are used?

5. For a patchwork quilt pattern, Mrs. Ames estimates that she needs 1 yd. of material for certain circular disks that are 1 in. in diameter. How much of the same material will she require if she makes the same number of disks 2 in. in diameter?

6. How much of the interior of a circle is there in a sector angle with:
   (*a*) 60°?   (*b*) 90°?   (*c*) 270°?

7. A pictograph is being constructed to represent the distribution of the income of a city. If the interior of a circle represents the whole income, and if the amount expended for schools is 40% of the total, what must the central angle of the sector be to represent fairly the expenditure for schools?

8. If the interior of a circle with 1-in. radius represents the enrollment of a school ten years ago, what radius must be used to represent the enrollment now if it now is double that of ten years ago?

9. Find the radius of the circle whose area equals the sum of the areas of circles with radii 3 in. and 4 in.

10. Some regular hexagonal tile have six-inch sides, others have four-inch sides. About how many of the larger tile are needed to cover the same surface as 100 of the smaller?

CONSTRUCTING SPECIFIED POLYGONS

350. It is possible to construct a polygon that has a certain relation to a given polygon without having the dimensions of the given polygon specified. Two preliminary constructions are needed.

351. The **fourth proportional** to three given segments, or numbers, a, b, and c is the segment x of the proportion $a : b = c : x$.

The numbers a, b, and c must be used in the order in which they are named. The fourth proportional to 2, 3, and 4 is x, if $\frac{2}{3} = \frac{4}{x}$. $2x = 12$, and $x = 6$.

352. *The fourth proportional to three given segments can be constructed.*

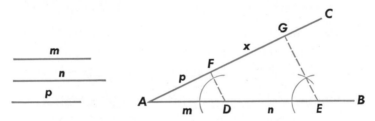

Given. Segments m, n, and p.

Required. To construct the fourth proportional to m, n, and p.

Analysis. 1. Let x represent the fourth proportional.
Then $m : n = p : x$.
2. This suggests construction of a triangle with a line parallel to its base in order to use §239, p. 210.

Construction. 1. On side AB of a convenient angle, $\angle BAC$, take $AD = m$, and $DE = n$. On AC, take $AF = p$.
2. Draw DF and construct $EG \parallel DF$, meeting AC at G.

Statement. FG is the fourth proportional to m, n, and p.
(Proof to be given by the pupil.)

1. Construct the fourth proportional to segments n, m, and p given above.
2. Construct x so that $m : n = n : x$ if m and n are the segments given above.

353. *The mean proportional between two segments can be constructed.*

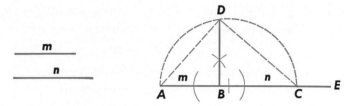

Given. Segments m and n.

Construct. The mean proportional between m and n.

Analysis. 1. Let x be the mean proportional.

2.   Then $m : x = x : n$ (§255, p. 224)

3.   This proportion suggests use of §258, p. 226.

Construction. 1. On AE take $AB = m$, and $BC = n$.

2.   Construct a semicircle on AC as diameter.

3.   Construct $BD \perp AC$, meeting the semicircle at D.

Statement. BD is the mean proportional between m and n.

Plan. Draw AD and DC. Prove $AB:DB = DB:BC$.
          (Proof left to the pupil.)

1. Using the same segments m and n, construct the mean proportional between:
   (a) $2m$ and n (b) m and $2n$ (c) $2m$ and $3m$
2. (a) Construct the mean proportional between 1 in. and 4 in.
   (b) How long should the result in (a) be? Is it?
3. Construct the segment that equals $r\sqrt{3}$ when r is a given segment.
   Analysis. Let $x = r\sqrt{3}.$ $\therefore$ $x^2 = 3r^2$ and $\therefore$ $r : x = x : 3r$, or x is the mean proportional between r and $3r$.
   (Construct it as above.)
4. Using the segment r from Ex. 3, construct:
   (a) $r\sqrt{2}$ (b) $r\sqrt{5}$ (c) $r\sqrt{12}$ (d) $r\sqrt{6}$
5. Let x be the fourth proportional to three given segments r, s, and t.
   (a) Write the proportion for x and then construct x.
   (b) Write the proportion of part (a) by alternation, and again find x.
   (c) Measure and compare the results for (a) and (b).
6. Construct x so that $m : x = n : p$, given segments m, n, and p.

Example. Construct a square that equals twice a given parallelogram.

Given. $\square ABCD$ having base b and altitude h.

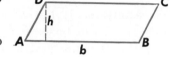

Construct. A square equal to twice $ABCD$.

Analysis. 1. Let $x =$ the side of the required square.

2. $\therefore$ $x^2 =$ the area of the square,
              and $hb =$ the area of $\square ABCD$.

3. $\therefore$ $x^2 = 2hb$, or $x^2 = (2h)b$

4. $\therefore$ $2h : x = x : b$

5. $\therefore$ x is the mean proportional between $2h$ and b.

Construction. 1. Construct x as in §353, p. 320.

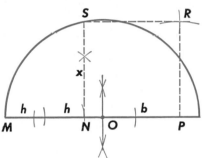

2. Construct the square $NPRS$ having side x.

Statement.

$NPRS = 2\,\square ABCD$

Proof. 1. Area $NPRS = x^2$; $x^2 = (2h)(b)$; $\square ABCD = hb$.

2. $\therefore$ $NPRS = 2\,\square ABCD$

Note. This proof is given as a check. The analysis is sufficient reason to expect that the solution is correct.

In Ex. 1 to 8, construct a square that equals:

1. A given rectangle
2. Twice a given triangle
3. Twice a given square
4. Half of a given square
5. Twice a given parallelogram
6. Two thirds of a given rectangle
7. A given trapezoid
8. Twice a given trapezoid

354. One of the famous problems of elementary geometry is to *construct a square that equals a given circle, using only a straightedge and compasses.* This construction has been proved impossible.

Example. Construct a $\triangle DBC$ having the same area and the same base BC as that of $\triangle ABC$, and $\angle DBC = 45°$.

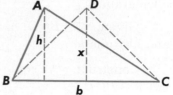

Analysis. 1. Let h be the altitude and b the base of $\triangle ABC$. Let x be the altitude and b the base of $\triangle DBC$.

2. $\therefore$ $\frac{1}{2}xb = \frac{1}{2}hb$, or $x = h$.

That is, the altitude of DBC must equal the altitude of ABC. We could have inferred this fact by using §329(c).

Construction. 1. Through A, construct ZY parallel to BC. Then all points on ZY are at the distance h from BC (§125, p. 121). One must be the third vertex of the required $\triangle DBC$.

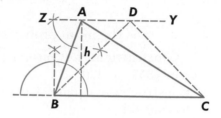

2. Since $\angle DBC$ must be 45°, construct $\angle CBD = 45°$, meeting ZY at D.

3. Draw CD, forming $\triangle DBC$.

Statement. $\triangle DBC$ is the required triangle.

Proof. 1. The altitudes of $\triangle DBC$ and $\triangle ABC$ are equal.

2. $\therefore$ $\triangle DBC = \triangle ABC$ (Why?)

3. $\triangle DBC$ has the required 45° angle at B.   (Why?)

In Ex. 1, 2, and 3, construct $\triangle XBC$ *equal to* $\triangle ABC$:

1. Having the same base BC and $\angle XBC = 90°$.
2. Having the same base BC and $\angle XCB = 60°$.
3. Having the same base BC and $XB = $ segment n.

In Ex. 4, 5, and 6, construct $\square XBCY$ *equal to a given* $\square ABCD$.

4. Having the same base BC and $\angle XBC = 45°$.
5. Having the same base BC and $BX = $ segment n.
6. Having the same base BC and $BY = $ segment m.

In Ex. 7, 8 and 9, construct $\square XBCY$ (*having base* BC):

7. Equal to twice a $\square ABCD$.
8. Equal to three times a $\triangle ABC$.
9. Equal to $\frac{2}{3}$ of given $\square ABCD$, and having $\angle XBC = 60°$.

355. *Construct a triangle equal to a given polygon.*

Note. The solution will be illustrated by constructing a triangle equal to a given pentagon.

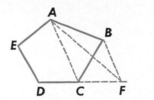 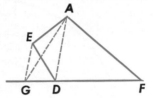

Given. Pentagon $ABCDE$.

Required. To construct a triangle equal to $ABCDE$.
   (*a*) *Change $ABCDE$ into an equal quadrilateral.*

Construction. 1. Draw AC, cutting off $\triangle ABC$.
2. To get a $\triangle$ on base AC that equals $\triangle ACB$, we must have an altitude equal to that of $\triangle ACB$. Therefore draw $BF \parallel AC$, meeting DC extended at F. Draw AF.

   Statement. $AFDE = ABCDE$

   Plan. (1) Prove $\triangle ACF = \triangle ACB$.
         (2) Prove $AFDE = ABCDE$.

   (*b*) *Change $AFDE$ into an equal triangle.*

Construction. Draw AD cutting off $\triangle ADE$. To get a triangle on base AD that equals $\triangle ADE$, draw $GE \parallel AD$, meeting FD extended at G. Draw AG.

   Statement. $\triangle AGF = AFDE = ABCDE$

   Plan. Prove $\triangle ADG = \triangle ADE$ and prove $\triangle AGF = AFDE$.

1. Draw a reasonably large quadrilateral. Construct a triangle equal to it. Then construct a square equal to the triangle.
2. Construct an isosceles triangle having a given base, equal to the quadrilateral with which you started in Exercise 1.
3. Construct a rectangle having a given base, equal to the quadrilateral of Exercise 1.
4. Construct a square equal to twice the given quadrilateral.
5. Draw two irregular quadrilaterals. Construct a square equal to their sum. (First construct squares equal to the quadrilaterals.)
6. Construct a square equal to a given pentagon.

CHAPTER 11

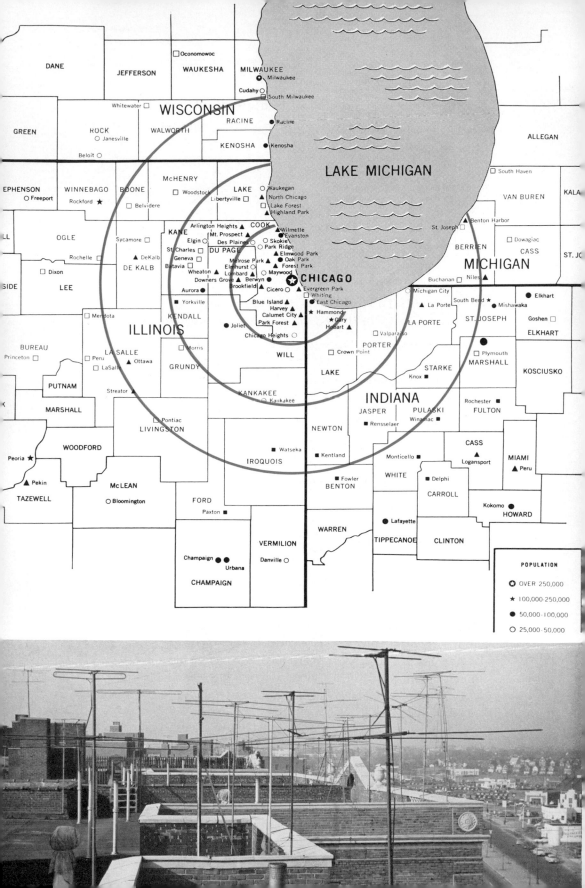

LOCI

In applications of geometry, the location of a point often is described by references to some fixed points or lines.

Thus, the N.W. corner of a farm was described as being 45 ft. S.W. of a certain tree, marked by T at the right.

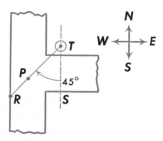

Clearly TR is the location of *all* *points* that are S.W. of T if TR makes a 45° angle with the south direction indicated by line TS.

The surveyor set up his *transit* at T, and found the south direction by use of his compass. Then he turned his transit to point 45° west of south. This gave him the line TR. On TR he measured off 45 ft. to P. He now had the northwest corner that he desired.

Loci of points are studied in this chapter.

Advertisers are interested in the area within the effective range of a TV station—essentially a locus problem. The circles have radii representing approximately 20, 40, and 60 miles and show which population centers are within areas served by a Chicago station.

TOP: WBBM-TV   BOTTOM: H. ARMSTRONG ROBERTS, PHILADELPHIA

356. Another problem illustrates the subject of this chapter.

An architect wants to place a door in wall AB, near A, to swing toward window CD. What is the point on AB nearest to A at which he can place the post to which the door hinges are to be attached, and avoid having a 3 ft. door reach the window?

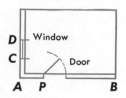

He thinks thus: The post P must be 3 ft. or more from C.

Where are all points that are 3 ft. from C?

Answer: On a circle with center C and radius 3 ft. This circle cuts AB at P.

He can place the post between A and B not closer to A than P.

The general problem is to *find where a point is located when the point must satisfy some given condition or conditions.*

Example. Where are all points that are $\frac{1}{2}$ in. from O? Several points placed $\frac{1}{2}$ in. from O *suggest* that all such points lie on the circle with center O and radius $\frac{1}{2}$ in.

This is just like drawing a graph.

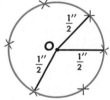

Instead of using the word "place" or the word "graph," we use the word *locus* which is the Latin word for place.

The question is stated thus:

What is the locus of points $\dfrac{1}{2}$ in. from O?

Answer: *The locus of points $\dfrac{1}{2}$ in. from O is the circle with center O and radius $\dfrac{1}{2}$ in.*

The *condition* which the points must satisfy is that they be "$\frac{1}{2}$ in. from O."

We know it to be true that:

(*a*) Every point $\frac{1}{2}$ in. from O is on the circle described.

(*b*) Every point on the circle described is $\frac{1}{2}$ in. from O.

Learn at once the correct meaning and use of the word "locus." It merely means place.

Do not say: "the locus is on." Instead, say: "the locus is."

1. Locate a point O. Draw the locus of points 2 in. from O.

2. (a) Draw a circle with radius 1 in. Place five points outside the circle, each of them $\frac{1}{2}$ in. from the nearest point of the circle.
   (b) Draw the locus of points outside the circle $\frac{1}{2}$ in. from the given circle.

3. (a) Draw a circle with radius 1 in. Place five points inside the circle each of them $\frac{1}{4}$ in. from the nearest point of the circle.
   (b) Draw the locus of points inside the circle $\frac{1}{4}$ in. from the given circle.

4. Draw a straight line. (For practical purposes make it about 3″.)
   (a) Freehand, locate five points that are above the line and $\frac{1}{2}$ in. from it. Draw the locus of points above the line and $\frac{1}{2}$ in. from it.
   (b) Locate five points that are below the line and $\frac{1}{2}$ in. from it. Draw the locus of points below the line and $\frac{1}{2}$ in. from it.

5. What is the locus of points on this page that are $\frac{1}{2}$ in. from the right-hand edge of the page?

6. (a) Draw two parallel lines. Freehand, locate five points that are equidistant from them.
   (b) Draw the locus of points on your paper that are equidistant from the two parallel lines.

7. By a drawing represent a rectangular flower bed. Draw the locus of plants that are equidistant from the two long sides.

8. Assume that a wheel like an automobile wheel rolls along a straight line. Draw three circles tangent to a line to represent three different positions of the wheel, marking the center of each circle. Draw the locus of the center of this moving wheel.

9. (a) Draw a segment AB. At C on it, draw a circle that is tangent to AB. Mark its center.
   (b) Draw three more circles all tangent to AB at C, and mark their centers. Draw the locus of the centers of such circles.
   (c) After you complete part (b), take any point on the locus. Using it as center, draw the circle that is tangent to AB at C.
   (d) Can any point not on the locus be used as center of a circle tangent to AB at C?

10. (a) Draw a large acute angle.
    (b) Freehand, locate three points each of which is approximately as far from one side as from the other.
    (c) What is the locus of such points?

357. The **locus of points satisfying a given condition** is the set of points satisfying the condition. It is such that:

(*a*) Every point in the locus satisfies the condition.

(*b*) Every point that satisfies the condition is in the locus.

358. *The locus of points equidistant from two points.*

Given. Points A and B.

Find. The locus of points equidistant from A and B.

A − − − − −B

Solution. 1. Locate R, S, and T so that $RA = RB$, $SA = SB$, and $TA = TB$.

$\times T$

2. The positions of R, S, and T *suggest* that the locus of such points is the perpendicular-bisector of AB.

Statement. *The locus of points equidistant from two points is the perpendicular-bisector of the segment joining the points.*

Hypothesis. CD is the $\perp$-bisector of AB.

Conclusion. CD is the locus of points equidistant from A and B.

Proof.

Statements	Authorities
1. Every point on CD is equidistant from A and B.	1. §113(*a*), p. 112
2. Every point that is equidistant from A and B is on CD.	2. §113(*b*), p. 112
3. $\therefore$ CD is the locus of points equidistant from A and B.	3. §357

1. (*a*) Locate a line m and two points A and B that are not on m. Construct the locus of points equidistant from A and B.

(*b*) Are there any points in your figure that are on m and are also equidistant from A and B? How many?

(*c*) Can you place A and B so that there will not be any points that are on m and also equidistant from A and B?

(*d*) Can you place A and B so that every point of m will be equidistant from A and B?

359. *The locus of points equidistant from the sides of an angle.*

Given. $\angle CBA$

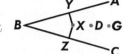

Find. The locus of points equidistant from BC and BA.

Solution. 1. Freehand, place points X, D, and G so that each is approximately equidistant from BC and BA.

2. The positions of X, D, and G suggest that the locus of such points is the bisector of $\angle CBA$.

Statement. *The locus of points equidistant from the sides of an angle is the bisector of the angle.*

Hypothesis. BR is the bisector of $\angle CBA$.

Conclusion. BR is the locus of points equidistant from BC and BA.

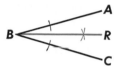

Proof.

Statements	Authorities
1. Every point on BR is equidistant from BC and BA.	1. §114(a), p. 112
2. Every point that is equidistant from BC and BA is on BR.	2. §114(b), p. 112
3. ∴ BR is the locus of points equidistant from BC and BA.	3. §357, p. 328

1. (a) Draw two intersecting lines. Construct the locus of points equidistant from the sides of each of the four angles.
   (b) Of what does the complete locus consist?

2. (a) Draw line m, and an angle A neither of whose sides is line m; construct the locus of points equidistant from the sides of $\angle A$.
   (b) Are there any points that are on m and also equidistant from the sides of $\angle A$? How many?
   (c) Can you place $\angle A$ in such position that there will not be any points that are on m and also equidistant from the sides of $\angle A$?
   (d) Can you place $\angle A$ so that every point of m is equidistant from the sides of $\angle A$?

3. Draw an obtuse angle XYZ. Construct the locus of points inside the angle, equidistant from the sides of the angle.

360. Directions for solving locus problems.

(1) Locate freehand or by construction three or more points
that satisfy the given condition. These points will suggest
the probable locus. Draw this probable locus.

(2) To prove that the probable locus is the real locus, prove
either (*a*) and (*b*) below, or (*a*) and (*c*).

   (*a*) *Every point on the locus satisfies the condition.*

   (*b*) *Every point that satisfies the condition is on the locus.*

   (*c*) *Every point not on the locus does not satisfy the condition.*
     (This is the inverse of (*a*).)

The inverse of statement (*b*) is:

   (*d*) *Every point that does not satisfy the condition is not on
the locus.*

If statements (*a*) and (*b*) are true, then (*c*) and (*d*) can be
proved true by the indirect method.

If statements (*a*) and (*c*) are true, then (*b*) and (*d*) can be
proved true by the indirect method.

Every locus theorem, therefore, is a short way of expressing
these four statements for a given condition.

361. What is the locus of the vertex of the right angle of a
right triangle having a given segment as hypotenuse?

Solution. Rt. ⊿ *ACB* suggest that vertex *C* lies on a circle with hypotenuse *AB*
as diameter.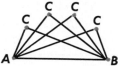

Statement. *The locus of the vertex of the right angle of a right
triangle having a given hypotenuse is the circle whose diameter
is the hypotenuse (except for the ends of the diameter).*

Proof. 1. If *X* is any point on the circle with diameter *AB*,
except *A* and *B*, then ∠ *AXB* is a right
angle. (§201, p. 182)

2. If *Y* is any point not on ⊙ *Y*, then ∠ *Y*
is acute or obtuse according as *Y* is outside or inside ⊙ *O*. (§206, §205, pp. 185,
184)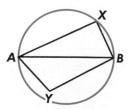

3. ∴   ⊙ *O* (except for *A* and *B*) is the
required locus. (§357, p. 328)

362. Summary of fundamental loci.

Locus 1. *The locus of points at a given distance d from a given point O is the circle with center O and radius d.*

This is a consequence of §167(c), p. 161.

Locus 2. *The locus of points at a given distance d from a fixed line a is the pair of parallels to a at the distance d from it.*

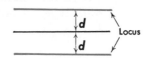

This is a consequence of §125, p. 121.

Locus 3. *The locus of points equidistant from two parallel lines is the line parallel to them and midway between them.*

This is a consequence of §125.

Locus 4. *The locus of points equidistant from two points is the perpendicular-bisector of the segment joining the points.* (§358, p. 328)

Locus 5. *The locus of points equidistant from two intersecting straight lines is the set of bisectors of their included angles.* (§359, p. 329)

These bisectors form two perpendicular straight lines.

★**Locus 6.** *The locus of the vertex of the right angle of a right triangle having a given hypotenuse is the circle whose diameter is the hypotenuse (except for the ends of the diameter).* (§361, p. 330)

1. Draw a line AB. Construct the locus of points $\frac{1}{2}$ in. from AB.

2. Draw two parallels AB and CD. Construct the locus of points equidistant from AB and CD.

3. Draw a line XY, and also two intersecting lines AB and CD.
   (a) Construct the locus of points equidistant from AB and CD. Mark the lines of this locus a and b.
   (b) Extend a and b until one or both intersect XY.
   (c) Are there in your figure any points that are on XY and that also are equidistant from AB and CD?

363. Intersection of loci. Sometimes a point must satisfy each of two given conditions, as in Ex. 3, p. 331. Each condition determines a locus. The required points are the intersections of the two loci.

Illustrative example. Find all points that are:

(1) Equidistant from two intersecting lines

(2) Also equidistant from two fixed points

Given. Intersecting lines AB and CD, and points R and S.

Find. All points equidistant from AB and CD and also equidistant from R and S.

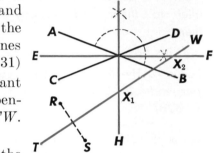

Solution. 1. The locus of points equidistant from AB and CD is the set of bisectors of the angles formed by them, lines EF and GH. (Locus 5, p. 331)

2. The locus of points equidistant from R and S is the perpen-dicular-bisector of RS, line TW. (Locus 4, p. 331)

3. The required points are the intersections of TW with EF and GH.

Discussion. 1. There may be two points, as X_1 and X_2, above.

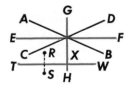
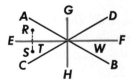

2. There may be only one point, however, since TW may be parallel to EF or GH.

3. There may be a line of points, since TW may coincide with EF or GH.

4. There must be at least one point, because TW cannot be parallel to both EF and GH.

Note. The solution of such a locus problem should always in-clude an *illustrated* discussion such as that above.

TEST A

1. On a given line, find all points that are equidistant from two parallel lines.

2. Find all points that are at a given distance from a given point and also equidistant from two other given points.

3. Find all points that are equidistant from two given parallels and also equidistant from two given points.

4. Find all points that are at a given distance from a given line and also at another given distance from a point.

5. Find all points that are equidistant from two intersecting lines and also at a given distance from a given point.

6. What is the locus of the centers of circles that have a given radius and pass through a given point?

7. What is the locus of the mid-points of parallel chords of a circle?

8. What is the locus of the points such that the tangents from them to a given circle have a given length?

TEST B

1. On a given circle, find all points that are equidistant from two parallel lines.

2. Find all points that are at a given distance from a given line and also equidistant from two given points.

3. Find all points that are equidistant from two given parallels and at a given distance from a given point.

4. Find all points that are equidistant from two parallels and also equidistant from two intersecting lines.

5. What is the locus of the centers of circles that are tangent to a given line and have a given radius?

Suggestion. The centers of the circles are at the distance of the radius from the line. What is the locus of points at a distance r from a line?

6. What is the locus of the centers of circles that are tangent to each of two parallel lines?

7. What is the locus of the centers of chords of a circle that have a given length?

8. Segment AC, of fixed length m, has its ends A and C on the sides of right angle XYZ. What is the locus of the mid-point B of AC?

364. In aeronautics, the **bearing** of a point X from a point O is $\angle NOX$, where ON is the north direction from O.

$\angle NOX$ is always read in clockwise direction.

Thus: The bearing of X from O is 310°. The bearing of O from X is $\angle N'XO$, read clockwise.

Since $N'X \parallel NO$, $\angle N'XO$ is the supplement of $\angle XON$.

$$\angle XON = 360° - 310°, \text{ or } 50°$$
$$\therefore \quad \angle N'XO = 180° - 50°, \text{ or } 130°$$

1. Locate a point A and, at the end of a 2-in. segment, locate a point B whose bearing from A is:
   (a) 40°   (b) 160°   (c) 290°   (d) 85°

2. In each part of Ex. 1, compute the bearing of A from B.

3. (a) Locate points R and S at the ends of a 2-in. segment when the bearing of S from R is 90°.
   (b) Draw the locus of Y whose bearing from R is 80°.
   (c) If the bearing of Y from S is 40°, draw a second locus for Y.
   (d) The intersection of the two loci determines Y. Find the distance of Y from R if RS represents 10 miles.

4. Do Ex. 3 if the bearing of S from R is 180°, that of Y from R is 80°, and of Y from S is 40°.

5. Do Ex. 3 if the bearing of S from R is 140°, that of Y from R is 75°, and of Y from S is 20°.

6. At X, the bearing of A is 90° and of B is 120°. It is known that the bearing of B from A is 180°, and that B is 20 miles from A.
   (a) What is the bearing of X from A? From B?
   Suggestion. First draw a *trial* figure at X, *freehand*. On it find the answers for part (a).
   (b) Locate A and B at the ends of a 2-in. segment. Draw two loci for X. Determine the position of X. Find the distance of X from A and from B.

7. Do Ex. 6 if the bearing of B from A is 160°, that of A from X is 80°, and that of B from X is 120°.

8. Do Ex. 6 if the bearing of B from A is 210°, that of A from X is 80°, and that of B from X is 140°.

LOCI IN ANALYTIC GEOMETRY

1. (a) Draw on graph paper two rectangular axes.
   (b) Locate point A whose abscissa is $+6$ and ordinate is $+8$. (p. 136)

2. Locate each of the following points:
   (a) B: $(+5, -3)$ (b) C: $(-5, -4)$ (c) D: $(-6, +10)$

3. In Exercises 1 and 2, in what *quadrant* of the XY-plane did you locate:
   (a) Point A?   (b) Point B?   (c) Point C?   (d) Point D?

4. (a) What is the abscissa of a point?
   (b) What is the ordinate of a point?
   (c) What are the coordinates of a point?

365. **Sets of points** in a plane may be described by the sets of coordinates of the points. There are two problems.
(a) Given the description of the points by means of coordinates. Find the locus of the points.
(b) Given a locus in an XY-plane. Describe the points of the locus by means of their coordinates.

5. (a) Locate five points that have the ordinate $(+4)$.
Suggestion. You may select for them any abscissas.
   (b) Draw the locus of the points for which $y = +4$.
Note. This is the locus of the set of points having $y = +4$.
   $y = +4$ *is the equation* of this locus because it is obvious that $y < 4$ or $y > 4$ for any points not on this graph.

6. On the axes used for Ex. 5, draw also the locus of points for which:
   (a) $y = -5$ (b) $y = +8$ (c) $y = -10$ (d) $y = +12$

7. (a) Locate five points that have the abscissa $+6$.
   (b) Draw the locus of the set of points for which $x = +6$.

8. On the axes used for Ex. 7, draw also the locus of points for which:
   (a) $x = +9$ (b) $x = -10$ (c) $x = -6$ (d) $x = +12$

9. (a) Draw $M'M$ parallel to the X-axis, through $(0, +12)$.
   (b) $M'M$ is the locus of what set of points?

10. (a) Draw RR' parallel to the Y-axis through $(+15, 0)$.
    (b) RR' is the locus of what set of points?

11. If the lines for Ex. 9 and Ex. 10 are drawn on the same axes, describe the locus of their intersection.

1. (*a*) Locate four points for each of which the ordinate equals the abscissa.

Suggestion. Select an abscissa, then the ordinate, then locate the point.

  (*b*) Draw the locus of the points described in part (*a*).

366. The locus for Ex. 1 obviously is the set of points for which the ordinate, y, equals the abscissa, x.

  We say that this graph:

(1) Is the locus of the set of points for which $y = x$; or

(2) Is the locus of the equation $y = x$.

  This fundamental locus can be used in sketching related loci, as suggested in Ex. 2.

2. (*a*) Obtain four points whose ordinates equal twice their abscissas.

Suggestion. Take any point on the locus of $y = x$. Keep its abscissa, but double its ordinate. It will be a point of the locus for Ex. 2. Do this four times.

  (*b*) Draw the locus of the points described in part (*a*).

  (*c*) What is the equation of the locus you obtain in part (*b*).

3. Do all parts of Ex. 2 when the ordinate of each point is:

  (*a*) Half the abscissa   (*b*) Three times the abscissa

4. What does each of the following equations tell about the ordinate of each point:

  (*a*) $y = \frac{1}{4}x$?   (*b*) $y = 4x$?   (*c*) $y = \frac{2}{3}x$?   (*d*) $y = \frac{3}{2}x$?

5. (*a*) On rectangular axes, select a large unit.

  (*b*) Guided by Ex. 2(*a*), draw on the same XY-plane the locus for each of the following equations:

    (1) $y = x$ (2) $y = \frac{1}{2}x$ (3) $y = \frac{1}{3}x$ (4) $y = \frac{1}{4}x$

    (5) $y = 2x$ (6) $y = 3x$ (7) $y = 4x$

6. Through what point do all the loci in Ex. 5 pass?

7. How does the position of the locus in Ex. 5 change when the co-efficient of x changes?

8. In Ex. 5, in each part, state in words the relation of the ordinate to the abscissa.

367. **Summary.** (*a*) The locus (or graph) of $y = ax$ is a straight line through the origin, $(0, 0)$.

(*b*) As a changes, the direction of the locus from the positive X-axis changes. In particular, if $a = 1$, the locus makes a $45°$ angle with the X-axis.

1. (a) What relation between the ordinate and the abscissa of a point is described by $y = x + 2$?
   (b) Sketch the locus of points for which $y = x + 2$, thus:

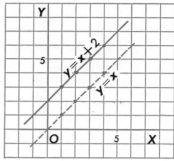

      (1) Sketch the locus of $y = x$.
      (2) Taking any point of $y = x$, add 2 to *its* ordinate. This gives a point of $y = x + 2$.
      (3) Locate four points in this manner.
      (4) Draw the locus of $y = x + 2$.
   (c) Through what point of the Y-axis does the locus pass?

2. (a) What relation of ordinate and abscissa is described by the equation $y = x + 5$?
   (b) Guided by part (b) of Ex. 1, sketch the locus of $y = x + 5$ on the axes used for Ex. 1.
   (c) Through what point on the Y-axis does the locus of $y = x + 5$ pass?

3. Do all parts of Ex. 2 for points described by:
   (a) $y = x - 5$ (b) $y = x + 10$ (c) $y = x - 10$

4. (a) On new axes, sketch the loci (1) of $y = x$ and then (2) of $y = \frac{1}{2}x$.
   (b) What relation of ordinate and abscissa is described by the equation $y = \frac{1}{2}x + 5$?
   (c) As in Ex. 1(b) sketch the locus of $y = \frac{1}{2}x + 5$.
   (d) On the same axes, sketch the loci of:
      (1) $y = \frac{1}{2}x - 5$ (2) $y = \frac{1}{2}x + 10$ (3) $y = \frac{1}{2}x - 10$

5. On new axes, sketch the loci for:
   (a) $y = 2x + 5$ (b) $y = 2x - 10$ (c) $y = 2x + 10$

6. On new axes, sketch the loci for:
   (a) $y = 3x + 5$ (b) $y = 3x + 10$ (c) $y = 3x - 10$

368. Summary. (a) The loci for equations of the form $y = ax + b$ are straight lines if a and b are constants.
(b) For a given value of a, the loci are parallel.
(c) For a given value of b the loci pass through the point $(0, b)$.

Note. The symbol $\{(x, y)\}$ is being introduced for the phrase *the set* of points (x, y); the symbol $|$, for the phrase *such that*.
      Thus: $\{(x, y) \mid y = ax - b\}$ means *the set of points* (x, y) *such that* $y = ax - b$.

369. The conclusions on pages 336 and 337 were reached inductively. They can be proved.

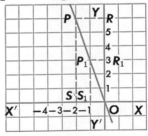

(a) Consider any line EOF through the origin. Let $R_1:(x_1, y_1)$ and $R_2:(x_2, y_2)$ be any two points of EOF.

$$\triangle T_1OR_1 \backsim \triangle T_2OR_2$$

$$\therefore \quad \frac{y_1}{y_2} = \frac{x_1}{x_2}, \text{ or } \frac{y_1}{x_1} = \frac{y_2}{x_2}$$

∴ for any point on EOF, the ratio of the ordinate to the abscissa is constant.

(b) If $R_3:(x_2,y_3)$ is not on EOF, $\dfrac{y_3}{x_2} < \dfrac{y_2}{x_2}$ or $\dfrac{y_3}{x_2} > \dfrac{y_2}{x_2}$ according as R_3 is below or above EOF.

(c) ∴ if $\dfrac{y_1}{x_1} = m$ for any point on EOF, line EOF is the locus of all such points and **$y = mx$ is the equation of the locus.**

(d) m, which equals $\dfrac{y}{x}$, is the **slope** of the locus. *It is the tangent of the angle formed by the line with the positive X-axis.* In the equation $y = mx$, it is the coefficient of x.

370. Lines through the origin having negative slope.

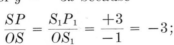

Consider $y = -3x$, or $\dfrac{y}{x} = -3$.

One point of this locus is the point $P_1:(-1,+3)$. Draw P_1O. This gives the locus of $y = -3x$ because

$$\frac{SP}{OS} = \frac{S_1P_1}{OS_1} = \frac{+3}{-1} = -3;$$

or $y = -3x$. PO forms, with the positive X-axis $\angle XOP$ whose tangent is $\dfrac{+3}{-1}$ or -3.

371. To sketch the locus $y = mx$.

(a) If m is positive, draw OP through the origin O and the point $P:(+1, +m)$. The angle from the X-axis is acute.

(b) If m is negative, let $|m|$ represent the absolute value of m. Draw OP through O and the point $P:(-1, |m|)$. The angle from the X-axis is obtuse.

Example. Write the equation of the line through the origin, draw the line, and find the angle, correct to the nearest degree, that the line makes with the positive X-axis when the slope is $-.8$.

Solution. 1. The equation is $y = -.8x$.

2. Locate $P:(-1,+.8)$. Draw OP.
3. $\angle XOP$ indicates the direction angle of line OP.

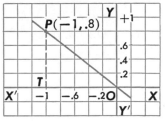

4. In $\triangle OTP$, $\tan \angle TOP = \dfrac{.8}{1} = .8$.

5. From p. 245, $\angle TOP$ equals $39°$.
   $\therefore \quad \angle XOP = 180° - 39°$, or $141°$.

1. Do as above, when the slope is:
   (a) $-.6$ (b) -1.2 (c) $+1.8$ (d) $-.4$

2. Through the origin, draw the line that forms with the positive X-axis each of the following angles, and then write the equation of the line, with slope correct to tenths.
   (a) $60°$ (b) $120°$ (c) $30°$ (d) $135°$ (e) $150°$

372. Another meaning of the slope of a line.

In §369, we agreed that the slope of a line is the tangent of the angle formed by the line with the positive X-axis.

Let P_1 and P_2 be any two points on straight line CD.

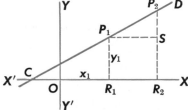

Draw $R_1P_1 \perp CX$, $R_2P_2 \perp CX$ and $P_1S \parallel OX$.

$\angle XCD = \angle SP_1P_2$; $\therefore \tan \angle XCD = \tan \angle SP_1P_2$

$$\tan \angle SP_1P_2 = \frac{SP_2}{P_1S} = \frac{R_2P_2 - R_2S}{OR_2 - OR_1} = \frac{y_2 - y_1}{x_2 - x_1}$$

$$\therefore \quad \tan \angle XCD = \frac{y_2 - y_1}{x_2 - x_1}$$

$(y_2 - y_1)$ is the difference of the ordinates and $(x_2 - x_1)$ is the difference of the abscissas of any two points of CD.

$\therefore$ *the slope of a straight line is the ratio of the difference of the ordinates to the difference of the abscissas of any two points of the line.*

373. The equation for the straight line through a given point, in a given direction from that point.

Consider CD through $P_1:(x_1, y_1)$, forming $\angle XCP$ with the X-axis. Let $P:(x, y)$ be any point on CD. Draw $P_1R_1 \perp OX$, $PR \perp OX$, and $P_1S \parallel OX$.

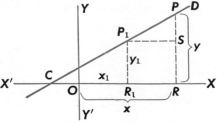

$$\therefore \quad \tan \angle SP_1P = \frac{SP}{P_1S} = \frac{y - y_1}{x - x_1}$$

Let $\tan \angle SP_1P = m$. Then $m = \dfrac{y - y_1}{x - x_1}$.

$$\therefore \quad y - y_1 = m(x - x_1)$$

is the equation of the straight line through (x_1, y_1) having the slope m.

Example 1. Write the equation of the line through the point $(+4, -5)$ that makes an angle of $60°$ with $X'OX$.

Solution. 1. $m = \tan 60° = 1.7321$, $(x_1, y_1) = (+4, -5)$

2. $\qquad\qquad y - y_1 = m(x - x_1)$

3. $\qquad \therefore \quad y - (-5) = 1.7321(x - 4)$

4. $\qquad\qquad \therefore \quad y = 1.7321x - 6.9284 - 5$

5. $\therefore \quad y = 1.7321x - 11.9284$, or $y = 1.73x - 11.93$

Example 2. Through the point $(-4, +5)$ draw the line whose slope is -2. Write the equation of the line and find the angle between the X-axis and the line.

Solution. 1. Locate $P:(-4, +5)$.

2. Draw RP, having the slope -2. To do this:

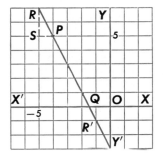

Draw $PS \parallel X'OX$, and equal to -1.
Draw $SR \parallel Y'OY$ and equal to $+2$.
Then the slope of RP will be -2.
RPR' is the required line.

3. The equation of RPR' is:

$y - 5 = -2[x - (-4)]$.

$y - 5 = -2x - 8$

$y = -2x - 3$

4. In $\triangle PSR$, $\tan \angle SPR = 2$. $\quad \therefore \quad \angle SPR = 63°$

$\therefore \quad \angle XQP = 180° - 63°$, or $117°$

In Examples 1 to 4: (a) Draw the line. (b) Write the equation of the line. (c) Find the direction of the line from OX.

1. The line through $(+5, +3)$ with slope $+3$.

2. The line through $(+4, -5)$ with slope $+1$.

3. The line through $(-4, +6)$ with slope $+\frac{1}{2}$.

4. The line through $(-3, -5)$ with slope $+\frac{3}{4}$.

In Examples 5 to 8, draw the line and write the equation of the line.

5. The line through $(+3, +5)$ whose direction angle is $60°$.

6. The line through $(-3, -5)$ whose direction angle is $30°$.

7. The line through $(-5, +5)$ whose direction angle is $120°$.

8. The line through $(+5, -5)$ whose direction angle is $150°$.

374. **The equation of the straight line through two given points.**

Let $P:(x, y)$ be any point on the straight line QP through the given points $P_1:(x_1, y_1)$ and $P_2:(x_2, y_2)$. Draw $R_1P_1 \perp OX$, $R_2P_2 \perp OX$, $PR \perp OX$ and $P_1ST \parallel X'OX$.

$$\triangle P_1SP_2 \backsim \triangle P_1TP$$

$$\frac{SP_2}{P_1S} = \frac{TP}{P_1T} \text{ or}$$

$$\frac{y_2 - y_1}{x_2 - x_1} = \frac{y - y_1}{x - x_1}$$

$$\therefore \quad y - y_1 = \frac{y_2 - y_1}{x_2 - x_1}(x - x_1)$$

The slope of the line is $\dfrac{y_2 - y_1}{x_2 - x_1}$.

Thus: For the line through $(+3, +5)$ and $(+6, -2)$ think of $(+3, +5)$ as (x_1, y_1) and $(+6, -2)$ as (x_2, y_2).

$$\therefore \quad y - 5 = \frac{-2 - 5}{6 - 3}(x - 3)$$

$$\therefore \quad y - 5 = \frac{-7}{3}(x - 3), \text{ or } y - 5 = \frac{-7}{3}x + 7$$

$$\therefore \quad y = -\frac{7}{3}x + 12. \text{ The line has slope } -\tfrac{7}{3}.$$

In Examples 1 *to* 6: (*a*) *Draw the line.* (*b*) *Write and simplify the equation of the line.* (*c*) *Find the direction of the line from* X'OX. *In Examples* 7 *and* 8, *draw the line and write its equation.*

1. The line through (+8, +6) and (+4, +1).

2. The line through (+6, +5) and (+1, +7).

3. The line through (+5, −4) and (+2, −5).

4. The line through (−5, +4) and (+4, −5).

5. The line through (−6, −2) and (−2, +6).

6. The line through (+5, +6) and (0, 0).

7. The line through (+a, 0) and (0, +b). (a ≠ 0, b ≠ 0)

8. The line through (0, +b) having the slope m.

375. **Intercept form of the equation.** From Ex. 7, $bx + ay = ab$. Assume $a \ne 0$ and $b \ne 0$. Dividing by ab,

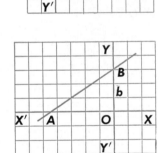

$$\frac{bx}{ab} + \frac{ay}{ab} = 1,$$

or $\dfrac{x}{a} + \dfrac{y}{b} = 1.$

a is called the **x-intercept** and b is called the **y-intercept** of the line.

376. **Slope-intercept form of the equation.** From Ex. 8, $y = mx + b$.

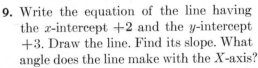

In this case, the y-intercept is b, and the slope is m.

9. Write the equation of the line having the x-intercept +2 and the y-intercept +3. Draw the line. Find its slope. What angle does the line make with the X-axis?

10. Write the equation when the x-intercept is +5 and the y-intercept is −6. Draw the line. Find its slope. What angle does the line make with the X-axis?

11. Write the equation of the line having slope ½ and y-intercept +5. What angle does the line make with X'OX?

12. Do Ex. 11 if the slope is −3 and the y-intercept −2.

13. Do Ex. 11 if the slope is −½ and the y-intercept +6.

14. Draw the line through (−5, +5) and (+6, −4). Write its equation. Find its direction from X'OX.

377. Circle with center at the origin.

Let $P: (x, y)$ be any point on $\odot O$, having radius r. Draw $PR \perp OX$. In rt. $\triangle ORP$, $x^2 + y^2 = r^2$. This is the required equation.

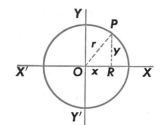

Thus: The equation of the $\odot O$ with radius $+6$ is $x^2 + y^2 = 36$.

378. The circle with center (a, b) and radius r.

Let $P: (x, y)$ be any point on the circle with center $C: (a, b)$ and radius r. Draw $CD \perp OX$, $PS \perp OX$, and $CK \perp PS$.

Then $KP = y - b$, $CK = x - a$.

In $\triangle CKP$: $\overline{CK}^2 + \overline{KP}^2 = \overline{CP}^2$.

$\therefore \quad (x - a)^2 + (y - b)^2 = r^2$

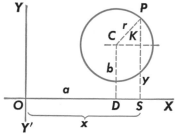

This is the required equation.

Thus: The equation with center $(5, -2)$ and radius 4 is
$$(x - 5)^2 + (y + 2)^2 = 16.$$

Example 1. What is the locus of points at distance 2 from the circle with center $(0, 0)$ and radius 5?

Solution. The locus consists of two circles, concentric with the given circle, one with radius $(5 + 2)$ or 7 and the other with radius $(5 - 2)$ or 3. The equations of these circles are: (1) $x^2 + y^2 = 7^2$ and (2) $x^2 + y^2 = 3^2$.

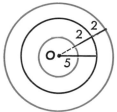

Example 2. Find all points at the distance 5 from the X-axis and at the distance 8 from the origin.

Solution. 1. The locus of points at distance 5 from the X-axis is $y = +5$.

2. The locus of points at distance 8 from the origin is $x^2 + y^2 = 64$.

3. The required points are the common solutions of these two equations. Substituting 5 for y,

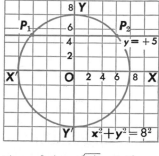

$x^2 + 25 = 64, x^2 = 39, x = \pm\sqrt{39}$

The required points are: $(+\sqrt{39}, +5)$ and $(-\sqrt{39}, +5)$

379. *The product of the slopes of two perpendicular lines is negative 1; or, if m and n are the slopes, mn = −1.*

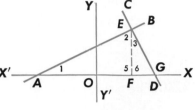

Let AB have positive slope m.

Then $m = \dfrac{FE}{AF}$, is positive.

Let $GE \perp AB$, intersect AB at E and $X'OX$ at G. Then $\angle XGE > 90°$. (Why?)

∴ n, the tan $\angle XGE$, must be negative or $\dfrac{FE}{GF}$ is negative.

∴ $mn = \dfrac{FE}{AF} \times \dfrac{FE}{GF}$, is negative.

In $\triangle AFE$ and $\triangle GFE$: $\angle 5 = \angle 6$ and $\angle 1 = \angle 3$. (Prove.)
∴ $\triangle AFE \backsim \triangle GFE$

∴ $\dfrac{FE}{AF} = \dfrac{GF}{FE}$, *neglecting their signs.*

∴ $mn = \dfrac{FE}{AF} \times \dfrac{FE}{GF} = \dfrac{GF}{FE} \times \dfrac{FE}{GF}$, or 1, neglecting signs.

Since mn is negative, $mn = -1$, or $n = -\dfrac{1}{m}$.

Example 1. If $y = x + 5$ is the equation of the line AB at the right, its slope is $+1$. If $CD \perp AB$ at E, its slope must be $-\dfrac{1}{1}$, or -1.

∴ the equation of CD is $y = -x + 5$.

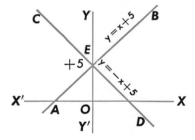

Example 2. (*a*) The equation of the line AB through $P:(5, -3)$ with slope -2 is
$$(y + 3) = -2(x - 5) \text{ or } y = -2x + 7.$$
The y-intercept is $+7$, and the x-intercept is 3.5.

(*b*) CD, through P, $\perp AB$, must have the slope $-\dfrac{1}{-2}$, or $+\dfrac{1}{2}$.

∴ the equation is $(y + 3) = \tfrac{1}{2}(x - 5)$ or $y = \tfrac{1}{2}x - \tfrac{11}{2}$.
The y-intercept is $-\tfrac{11}{2}$. The x-intercept is 11.

1. (a) Write the equation of the locus of points through the point $(5, 3)$ that is parallel to the line $y = 4x - 10$.
   (b) $3x + y = 18$ is the equation of another line in the same plane. Find the coordinates of the points where it intersects the given line in part (a) and the locus described in part (a).

2. Describe the locus of points for which:
   (a) $x = -7$ (b) $x = \frac{1}{2}y$ (c) $x + y = 0$
   (d) $x < +3$ (e) $3 < y < 4$ (f) $x > 0, y > 0$

3. (a) Write the equation of:
      (1) The line through $A:(0, 6)$ and $B:(12, 0)$
      (2) The perpendicular bisector of AB
   (b) Find the coordinates of all points that are equidistant from A and B and:
      (1) On the X-axis   (2) On the Y-axis

4. (a) Draw the locus of points for which $x^2 + y^2 = 100$.
   (b) Sketch the locus of points for which the ordinates equal half the corresponding ordinates in part (a).
   (c) Sketch the locus of points for which the ordinates equal twice the corresponding ordinates in part (a).

5. (a) Write the equation of the line AB through $R:(0, 6)$ with slope $.75$.
   (b) Write the equation of the line CD through $S:(0, -8)$ that is parallel to line AB.
   (c) Write the equation of the locus of points that are equidistant from AB and CD.

6. (a) Write the equation of the locus of points whose ordinates are $+5$.
   (b) Write the equation of the locus of points at the distance 8 from the locus in part (a).

7. Find the coordinates of all points that are at distance 6 from the origin and:
   (a) At distance 3 from the X-axis
   (b) At distance 6 from the Y-axis
   (c) At distance 8 from the X-axis

8. Write the equation of the locus of points:
   (a) At distance 9 from the origin
   (b) At distance 2 from the locus in part (a)

9. (a) Draw the $\triangle ABC$ having $A:(0, 0)$, $B:(12, 0)$, and $C:(6, 8)$.
   (b) Write the equation of RS, the perpendicular-bisector of AB.
   (c) Does C lie on RS? Should it? Why?

CHAPTER 12

MEASURING THE COMMON SOLIDS

Theorems and formulas for measuring the common solids are needed in our daily affairs, in science, and in industry. For example, gas and oil companies need to know the volumes of spherical and cylindrical containers like these shown on the opposite page.

To use the formulas effectively you must know many facts about the solids. Some of these have been given in earlier chapters of this book; others will appear in this chapter.

Although you *can* use the formulas without knowing how they are derived, having studied demonstrative geometry you will want to know why the theorems are true and how the formulas are obtained. The proofs appear in this chapter.

The proofs use facts that you have studied during this year so they are an excellent review of such parts of the earlier chapters. Some new ideas are introduced that are especially appropriate as a culmination of your course in geometry. Reading and completing these proofs will be a challenge to the knowledge of geometry and the skill in demonstration that you have acquired.

Top: This all-steel spherical container for natural gas in Savannah is 60 feet in diameter and is the largest atlas, constructed to scale, in the world. *Bottom:* A cracking unit at a Toledo refinery.

380. Recall that the *common solids* are *closed surfaces* that consist of parts of planes or curved surfaces, bounded by polygons or circles, and that enclose a part of space called the *interior* of the solid.

Recall that "altitude" and "base" in measurement problems are used as abbreviations for *length of the altitude* and *area of the base;* also that "area" of a polygon is an abbreviation for *area of the interior of the polygon.* Similarly "volume" of a solid will be used as the abbreviation for the *volume of the interior of a solid.*

381. The **lateral area** of a prism, including the rectangular solid, is the sum of the areas of its lateral faces (SG 33, p. 133). The total area is the sum of the areas of all its faces.

1. (*a*) What is the lateral area of a rectangular
      solid whose altitude is 4 ft. and whose
      base is enclosed by a rectangle with
      length 5 ft. and width 3 ft.
   (*b*) What is the total area of this solid?
   (*c*) Do part (*b*), if the altitude is 3 yd. and
      the dimensions of the base are 10 ft.
      and 2.5 yd.

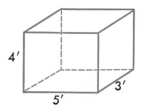

2. What is the total area of the walls and ceiling of a room that is 22 ft. long, 15 ft. wide, and 8 ft. 6 in. high?

3. Prepare a formula for the lateral area, *L*, of a rectangular solid whose altitude is *h*, and whose base has dimensions *a* and *b*.

4. A storage tank has the shape of a right hexagonal prism whose base edges measure 8 ft. If the tank is 15 ft. high, how many square feet of surface are there in the lateral surface and top of the tank?

5. What is the lateral area of a right triangular prism, the edges of whose base are 6 in., 8 in., and 19 in., respectively, altitude 12.5 in.

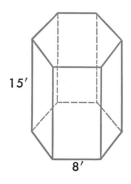

6. How many square yards of surface are there on the walls and ceiling of a room that is 8 ft. high, 8 yd. long, and 5 yd. wide?

7. Prepare a formula for the lateral area, *L*, of a right prism whose base is enclosed by a polygon with perimeter *p* and whose altitude is *h*.

382. To measure the *interior* of any solid:

(1) Select a unit of space, or **cubic unit,** such as the interior of a one-inch cube (cubic inch) or the interior of a one-foot cube (cubic foot).

(2) The **volume** of the solid is the number of cubic units in the interior of the solid.

383. The **length, width,** and **height** of a rectangular solid are the measures of the three edges that meet at a vertex.

1. If the length, width, and height are integers like 7, 5, and 6, the interior will contain 7 × 5 × 6 or 210 cubic units. Why?

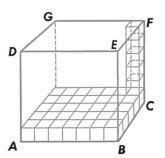

2. What is the volume of a rectangular solid when the three dimensions are:
   (*a*) 7 ft., 5 ft., and 4 ft.?
   (*b*) 10 in., 8 in., and .5 ft.?
   (*c*) 15 cm., 8 cm., and 5 cm.?
   (*d*) 4 yd., 5 yd., and 2 ft.?
   (*e*) 8 m., 3 m., and 9 m.?

SG 61. (Post.) *The volume of a rectangular solid is the product of its length, width, and height, when these are expressed by the same linear unit. The volume, then, is a number of the corresponding cubic units.*

If *l*, *w*, and *h* are its three dimensions, then

$$V = lwh.$$

3. A rectangular bin is 8 ft. long, 6 ft. wide, and 4 ft. high. How many bushels of wheat will it hold if one cubic foot holds .8 bushel?

4. How many gallons of water are needed to fill a swimming pool to the average depth of 5 ft. if the pool is 15 ft. wide and 25 ft. long? *Suggestion.* One cubic foot holds 7.5 gallons.

5. The dimensions of a concrete block are 8 in., 8 in., and 16 in. About how many of such blocks will be needed for a concrete-block wall that is 4 ft. high, 8 in. thick, and 35 ft. long?

6. A concrete drive is to be 8 ft. wide, 9 in. thick, and 51 ft. long. How many cubic yards of concrete will be needed to build it?

7. How many cubic yards of earth must be excavated for a basement that is to be 32 ft. long, 8 yd. wide, and 2 yd. deep?

Do the following exercises. Round off the final results as you are instructed on pages 422 through 424.

1. (*a*) What is the volume of a cube whose edge measures 12 in.?

   (*b*) Prepare a formula for the volume of a cube whose edge measures *e* units.

2. (*a*) How many cubic feet of space are there in a bin that is 15 ft. long, 8 ft. wide, and 6 ft. high?

   (*b*) How many bushels of wheat will this bin hold?

3. What is the weight of a steel plate that is 10 ft. long, 3 ft. wide, and $\frac{1}{2}$ in. thick, if one cubic inch of the steel weighs .28 lb.?

4. What is the volume of the air in a room that is 8.5 ft. high, 14 ft. wide, and 8 yd. long?

5. A concrete floor for a garage is to be 17 ft. wide, 8 in. thick and 8 yd. long. How many cubic yards of concrete will be needed for the floor?

6. The excavation for the basement for a house is to average 6 ft. in depth, 27 ft. in width, and 36 ft. in length. How many cubic yards of earth must be removed?

7. A theoretical board foot is a piece of lumber that is one foot square and one inch thick. How many board feet are there in a timber that is, in the rough, 6 in. wide, 4 in. thick, and 18 ft. in length?

8. How many board feet are there in 120 two-by-fours that are 8 ft. long?

Suggestion. Each two-by-four is considered to be 2 in. thick and 4 in. wide although, actually, it is $1\frac{13}{16}$ in. thick and $3\frac{13}{16}$ in. wide.

9. How deep will one cubic yard of garden soil fill a flower bed that is 4 ft. wide and 12 ft. long?

10. The dimensions of a rectangular solid are 3 ft., 6 ft., and 1.5 ft. What is the total area of the solid and what is the volume of it?

11. How does the total area of the solid in Ex. 10 compare with the total area of a cube of equal volume?

12. (*a*) Prepare a formula for the number of board feet in a piece of lumber that is *l* ft. long, *w* in. wide, and *t* in. thick.

   (*b*) By your formula, find the number of board feet in a timber that is 8 in. thick, 12 in. wide, and 20 ft. long.

13. How many cubic feet of air are there in a schoolroom that is 24 ft. wide, 12 yd. long, and 3 yd. high?

14. How many cubic yards of soil must be bought to cover to a depth of 4 in. two gardens: the first, 1 yd. wide and 100 ft. long and the second 20 ft. by 45 ft.

384. Formulas for computing the volumes of other solids are derived from that for the rectangular solid by means of the theorem that follows. This theorem is suggested by the following illustration.

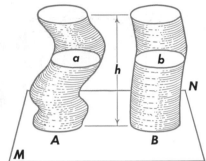

Assume that A and B are two equally high stacks of pieces of thin paper, standing on a plane MN, and that the areas of the two pieces at equal distances from MN are equal, as piece a equals piece b. It appears obvious that the amount of paper in stack A equals that in stack B.

385. Cavalieri's Theorem. Let solids P, Q, R, and S, below, on plane MN, have equal altitudes. Assume that every plane parallel to MN, intersecting the solids, makes equal sections in the solids; that is, assume sections p, q, r, and s have equal areas.

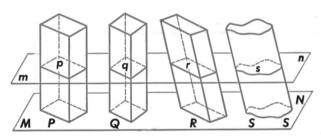

If P and Q are rectangular solids, their bases and altitudes are equal. If h is their common altitude and B their common base, each equals hB, so that their volumes are equal. Although this is not a proof that either R or S equals P and Q, the conditions that have been stated in §385 and the illustration above lead us to accept the following postulate.

SG 62. (Post.) *If two solids stand on the same plane and have the same altitude, and if every plane makes equal sections in them provided the cutting plane is parallel to the base plane, then the solids have equal volumes or are equal.*

The proof of this theorem comes properly in a course in *calculus*. It is introduced at this time because it simplifies the proofs of the formulas for the volumes of certain solids.

SG 63. *The volume of any prism equals the product of the length of its altitude and the area of its base, or* $V = hB$.

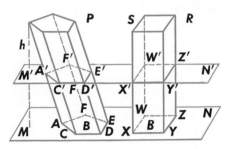

Hypothesis. Prism P has base AE with area B, altitude of length h, and volume V.

Conclusion. $V = hB$

Plan. Use Cavalieri's Theorem.

Proof. 1. Place P on plane MN. Beside it place a rectangular solid R with base XZ of area B, and altitude XS of length h.
2. Let any plane parallel to MN intersect P in section $A'E'$, and R in section $X'Z'$.
3. $\therefore$ $A'E' \cong AE$ and $X'Z' \cong XZ$.   (Prove.)
4. $\therefore$ area of $A'E' = $ area of $AE = B$.
     area of $X'Z' = $ area of $XZ = B$.   (Why?)
5. $\therefore$ area of $A'E' = $ area of $X'Z'$.
6. $\therefore$ volume of $P = $ volume of R.   (SG 62)
7.   Volume of $R = hB$.   (Why?)
8. $\therefore$ the volume of $P = hB$.   (Why?)

1. What is the volume of a cube with edges of length 10 in.?
2. What is the volume of a right regular hexagonal prism whose altitude is 15 in., if the edge of its base is 6 in. and the apothem of its base is $3\sqrt{3}$ in.?
3. What is the volume of a right triangular prism whose altitude is 20 in., if its base edges measure 12 in., 16 in., and 20 in. (See §330.)
4. What is the volume of a right prism with altitude 18 ft., if the base is enclosed by:
   (a) A right triangle with legs measuring 3 ft. and 4 ft.?
   (b) A regular hexagon with 6-in. sides?
   (c) A regular octagon with 5-in. sides?

386. A right circular cylinder is the shape used generally for a coffee can, for cans for fruits and vegetables, for oil tanks, silos, pipes, etc.

Assume: ⊙ ABC has center O, plane $A'B'C'$ ∥ plane ABC, OO' ⊥ plane ABC meets plane $A'B'C'$ at O'. AA', BB', XX', CC', which are all parallel to OO', meet plane $A'B'C'$ at A', B', X', and C' respectively.

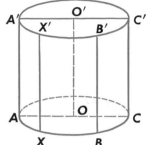

Then: (a) AA', BB', XX', etc. are perpendicular to plane ABC and plane $A'B'C'$. (Why?)

(b) $A'O'$ ∥ AO, $B'O'$ ∥ BO, $X'O'$ ∥ XO, ... (Prove.)

(c) $A'O' = AO$, $B'O' = BO$, $X'O' = XO$, ... (Prove.)

(d) $A'O' = B'O' = X'O'$, ... (Prove.)

(e) $A'B'C'$ is a circle with center O'. (Prove.)

SG 64. (Def.) A **right circular cylinder** is a closed surface that consists of:

(1) Two parallel plane circular **bases** whose line of centers is perpendicular to the bases; and

(2) A lateral surface that consists of the straight-line segments, terminating in the bases, from every point X of the boundary of the lower base perpendicular to the bases.

These segments are the **elements** of the lateral surface. The line of centers of the bases is the **altitude** of the cylinder.

1. Prove that any two elements of a right circular cylinder are opposite sides of a rectangle.

2. If the radius of the base of a right circular cylinder is 6 in., what is the circumference of each base?

3. How long are the elements of a right circular cylinder if the altitude of the cylinder is 18 in.?

4. (a) On somewhat stiff paper, construct a rectangle $ABCD$ having $AB = 5$ in. and $BC = 8$ in.

(b) Cut $ABCD$ from the paper. Roll it until you can attach edge CD to edge AB with gummed paper.

(c) What surface then is formed by $ABCD$?

387. In the lower base of a right circular cylinder with center
O inscribe square $ABCD$. Let O' be the center
of the upper base $A'B'C'D'$ of the cylinder;
and AA', BB', CC', and DD' be elements of
the cylinder.

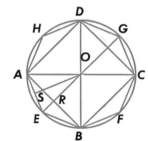

Then:

1. AA', BB', CC', and DD' are parallel, equal,
   and are perpendicular to planes $ABCD$ and
   $A'B'C'D'$.   (Why?)
2. $A'B'BA$, $B'C'CB$, ... are $\boxed{s}$.   (Why?)
3. $A'B'C'D' \parallel ABCD$ (Why?)
4. $\therefore$ solid $A'C$ is a square right prism.   (Why?)
     It is *inscribed in cylinder* $A'C$.

SG 65. (Def.) A right **prism is inscribed in a right circular
cylinder** when its base is inscribed in the base of the cylinder
and its lateral edges are elements of the cylinder. Its altitude is
the same as the altitude of the cylinder.

388. Consider a sequence of regular polygons (§315, p. 278)
inscribed in the base of a right circular cylinder, such as a square,
an octagon, a 16-gon, ...

Let each of these polygons enclose the base of a right prism.
These bases will be the bases of a
sequence of right prisms inscribed
in the right circular cylinder. Since
the bases of the prisms come closer
and closer to the base of the cylinder
(§316, p. 279), the following postulate is suggested:

SG 66. (Post.) *If a sequence of right prisms with bases enclosed
by regular polygons is inscribed in a right circular cylinder, then:*

(a) *Their bases, lateral surfaces, and interiors ultimately differ
    little from or approach as a limit those of the cylinder.*

(b) *Their bases have apothems that ultimately differ little from or
    approach as a limit the radius of the base of the cylinder.*

(c) *The radii of their bases and their altitudes equal those of the
    cylinder.*

389. From SG 66(*a*) it appears that a right circular cylinder is like a right prism that has an infinitely large number of faces. We shall use the following postulate.

SG 67. (**Post.**) *Any theorem about a prism that is independent of the number of faces is true also of a cylinder. In particular:*

(*a*) *The lateral area of a right circular cylinder equals the circumference of its base multiplied by the length of its altitude.*
   Briefly $S = hC$ and $S = 2\pi rh$ where r, h, and C are numbers of the same linear unit, and S is a number of the corresponding surface units.

(*b*) *The volume of a right circular cylinder equals the area of its base multiplied by the length of its altitude. Briefly $V = hB$ and $V = \pi r^2 h$, where V is a number of cubic units corresponding to the units used in measuring h and r.*

1. The radius of the base of a right circular cylinder is 6 in. The altitude of the cylinder is 24 in. A square right prism with base as indicated is inscribed in the base of the cylinder.

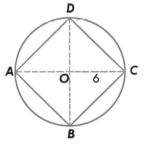

   (*a*) What is the perimeter of the base of the prism and the circumference of the base of the cylinder?
   (*b*) What are the lateral areas of the prism and of the cylinder?
   (*c*) What is the difference between the volumes of the cylinder and the prism?

2. Do all the parts of Ex. 1 if the base of the prism is:
   (*a*) A regular hexagon.
   (*b*) An equilateral triangle. (Use trigonometry if necessary.)

3. (*a*) How much tin is needed for a coffee can that is 6 in. in diameter and 7 in. high?
   (*b*) What is the volume of the coffee can?

4. (*a*) How many square feet of steel are needed for a cylindrical oil tank 50 ft. in diameter and 25 ft. high?
   (*b*) What will the volume of the tank be, if the thickness of the steel is ignored?
   (*c*) How many drums of oil will the tank hold if the capacity of one cubic foot is 7.5 gal. and of one drum is 55 gal.?

1. A hexagonal piece of steel, 8 ft. long, has a cross section that is enclosed by a regular hexagon with 1 in. sides. What is the weight of the piece if one cubic inch of the steel weighs .28 lb.?

2. What will it cost to excavate a cylindrical pit for a well at 75¢ a cubic yard if the diameter of the pit is to be 6 ft. and the depth of it is to be 10 ft., outside measurements?

3. How many cubic feet of concrete will be needed if the pit described in Ex. 2 is floored with concrete 4 in. thick and lined with a wall 6 in. thick?

4. A cylindrical tank is 30 in. in diameter and 10 ft. long. How many gallons of water will the tank hold if one cubic foot holds 7.5 gallons?

5. A cylindrical gas holder is 60 ft. in diameter and 50 ft. high. How many cubic feet of gas will the tank hold?

6. How many square feet of steel were needed to build the tank described in Ex. 5, if the top and bottom are assumed to be flat, and if waste is neglected?

7. How many cubic yards of concrete are needed for one mile (5280 ft.) of road that is to be 24 ft. wide and 9 in. thick?

8. How many cubic yards of concrete are needed for a retaining wall 2.5 ft. thick, that has the shape and dimensions shown in the figure at the right?

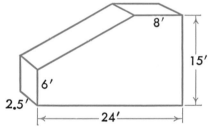

9. What are the lateral area and volume of a right prism with altitude of 8 ft. if the base is enclosed by:
    (a) A square that has 8-in. sides?
    (b) An equilateral triangle that has 8-in. sides?
    (c) A regular hexagon that has 8-in. sides?
    (d) A regular octagon that has 8-in. sides?
    ★ (e) A regular decagon that has 8-in. sides?
    ★ (f) A regular n-gon that has 8-in. sides?

10. A cylindrical silo is 16 ft. in diameter and 40 ft. high, outside measurements. If its floor is 1 ft. thick and its walls are 9 in. thick, what is the volume of its interior?

11. What are the lateral area and volume of the right circular cylinder that circumscribes each of the right prisms described in Ex. 9?

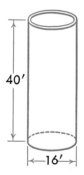

1. What are the total area and the volume of a cube whose edge is 6.3 inches in length?

2. A right prism has a hexagonal base with 8 in. sides. The lateral edges measure 30 in. What is the lateral area of the prism, and what is the volume of the prism?

3. Prepare a formula for the lateral area of a right hexagonal prism with altitude h and base inscribed in a circle of radius r, also a formula for the volume of the prism.

4. What are the lateral area and the volume of a right prism of altitude 24 in., if the base is enclosed by a right triangle whose legs measure 5 in. and 13 in.?

5. (a) What is the lateral area of the right prism with altitude 25 in., if the base is enclosed by a triangle whose sides measure 13 in., 14 in., and 15 in.?
   (b) What is the volume of this prism? (See §330, p. 295.)

6. What are the lateral area and the volume of the right circular cylinder whose radius is 7.5 in. and whose altitude is 27.5 in.?

7. A right circular cylinder and a right hexagonal prism have the same altitude. The prism is circumscribed around the cylinder. If the altitudes are 20 in. and the radius of the base of the cylinder is 3 in.:
   (a) How much more than the lateral area of the cylinder is the lateral area of the prism?
   (b) What is the difference between the volumes of the prism and the cylinder?

8. What is the radius of the base of a right circular cylinder whose lateral area is 150π sq. in. if the altitude is 10 in.?

9. A right circular cylinder is circumscribed about a square right prism whose base has 10 in. diagonals. The altitude of the prism and cylinder is 30 in. Find the lateral areas and the volumes of the prism and the cylinder.

10. In Ex. 2, what are the results if the base of the prism is enclosed by an equilateral triangle inscribed in a circle with radius 6 in.?

11. A regular hexagon, A, with side s, is inscribed in a circle, B. The circle, in turn, is inscribed in a regular hexagon, C. These three figures enclose the bases of a right prism, A', a right cylinder, B', and a right prism, C', respectively, each with height h.
    (a) Find the ratio of the volume of prism A' and cylinder B', and then of cylinder B' and prism C'.
    (b) How does the height, h, enter into these ratios?

390. Review SG 59, p. 280. It will be seen from this section that there are similarities between regular pyramids and right circular cones.

SG 68. (Def.) (*a*) A **right circular cone** is a closed surface that consists of:

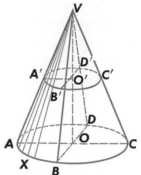

(1) A plane surface, its **base,** enclosed by a circle, as $\odot ABC$ with center $O;$ and

(2) A **lateral surface** that contains the straight-line segments from all points of the boundary of its base to a point, its **vertex,** not on its base, that is in the perpendicular to its base at the center.

(*b*) The **radius** of a right circular cone is the radius of its base. The **altitude** of the cone is the segment from the vertex to the center of the base. An **element** of the cone is the segment from the vertex to any point of the boundary of the base. The **slant height** of the cone is any element of the cone.

1. Prove that any two elements of a right circular cone are equal.

2. Prove that two elements of a right circular cone make equal angles with the altitude of the cone.

3. If a plane that is parallel to the base of right circular cone V–$ABCD$ above intersects the altitude VO at O':
   (*a*) Prove that $O'A' : OA = O'B' : OB, \ldots$.
   (*b*) Prove $A'B'C'D'$ is a circle with center O'.
   (*c*) Prove that cone V–$A'B'C'D'$ is a right circular cone.
   (*d*) Prove that $O'A' : OA = VO' : VO$.
   (*e*) Prove that the circumference of $\odot O'$ has the same ratio to the circumference of $\odot O$ as VO' has to VO.
   (*f*) Prove that the area of $\odot A'B'C'D'$ has the same ratio to the area of $\odot ABCD$ as VO'^2 has to VO^2.

4. If a right circular cone with diameter 10 in. and altitude 25 in. is cut by a plane that is parallel to the base at a point 5 in. below its vertex, find:
   (*a*) The slant height of the cone above the plane.
   (*b*) The circumference of the base of the cone and of the section.

391. Let $V–ABCD$ be a right circular cone with altitude VO and base $ABCD$. Let points A, B, C, and D be the vertices of a square inscribed in $ABCD$. Then the planes AVB, BVC, CVD, and DVA are the lateral faces of a pyramid that is inscribed in cone $V–ABCD$. It is a regular pyramid because its base is enclosed by a square and its vertex is in the perpendicular to its base at the center of the base.

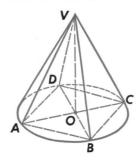 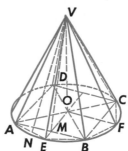

If, successively, regular pyramids that have four, eight, sixteen, . . . , faces are inscribed in a right circular cone, by doubling the number of sides of the base by the method described in §292, p. 263, you see that the pyramids:

(a) All have the same altitude as the cone.

(b) All have the same radius as the cone.

(c) All have the same point as the center of their bases.

(d) Have slant heights that come closer and closer to the slant height of the cone.

   Thus: The slant height of pyramid $V–ABCD$ is VM; that of pyramid $V–AEBFC$ is VN, where $VN \perp AE$. $VN > VM$. The slant height of the 16-faced pyramid will be longer than VN.

(e) Have lateral surfaces that come closer and closer to the lateral surface of the cone.

   Thus: That of the 16-faced pyramid is greater than that of the 8-faced pyramid; in fact, it would be difficult to distinguish between the lateral area of the former and that of the cone.

(f) Have interiors that come closer and closer to the interior of the cone. These observations suggest:

SG 69. (Post.) *Any theorem about a regular pyramid that is independent of the number of faces of the pyramid is equally true of a right circular cone.*

1. If *V–ABCDE* is a regular pentagonal pyramid and *VM* is its slant height on face *AVB* and if *VM* = 11.5 in. and *AB* = 12 in.:

   (*a*) What is the slant height on faces *BVC*, *CVD*, *DVE*, and *EVA?*

   (*b*) What are the areas of △*AVB*, △*BVC*, △*CVD*, △*DVE*, and △*EVA?*

   (*c*) Express by an equation the lateral area, *S*, of *V–ABCDE*, using your results from part (*b*).

   (*d*) Simplify the right side of the result you obtain for part (*c*).

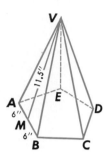

2. In like manner, find the lateral area, *S*, of a regular hexagonal pyramid whose slant height is 24 in. and whose base is enclosed by sides of length 5 in.

   Exercises 1 and 2 suggest the following theorem.

SG 70. *The lateral area of a regular pyramid equals the product of half the length of its slant height and the perimeter of its base.*

Briefly, $S = \frac{1}{2}sp$, where *s* and *p* are the measures of the slant height and the perimeter of the base in terms of the same linear unit, and *S* is the measure of the area in terms of the corresponding surface unit.

3. The base of a regular pyramid is enclosed by a square with 8-in. sides, and the slant height of the pyramid is 2 ft. 6 in. What is the lateral area of the pyramid?

4. Do Ex. 3 if the pyramid is a regular pentagonal pyramid whose lateral edges are 18 in. long and the angle between two adjacent edges is 60°.

When we apply SG 69, we have the following theorem:

SG 71. *The lateral area of a right circular cone equals the product of half the length of its slant height and the circumference of its base.* Briefly $S = \frac{1}{2}sC$, or $S = \pi rs$.

5. The radius of the base of a right circular cone is 6 in. and the altitude of the cone is 20 in.

   (*a*) What is the slant height of the cone?

   (*b*) What is the lateral area of the cone?

6. In Ex. 5, what is the lateral area of the regular square pyramid that is inscribed in the cone?

7. Using a figure like that for Ex. 1, but without specific measures, prove SG 70.

1. A regular pyramid has an altitude of 20 in. Its base is enclosed by a square that is inscribed in a circle with 4 in. radius.
   (a) How long are the lateral edges of the pyramid?
   (b) How long is the edge of the base?
   (c) How long is the slant height of the pyramid?
   (d) What is the lateral area of the pyramid?

2. In Ex. 1, if a plane parallel to the base passes through the point on the altitude that is 15 in. from the vertex:
   (a) What is the slant height of the frustum formed?
   (b) What is the perimeter of the upper base?
   (c) What is the lateral area of the frustum?

3. (a) How long are the elements of a right circular cone when the altitude is 25 in. and the radius of the base is 15 in.?
   (b) What is the lateral area of the cone?

4. In Ex. 3, if a plane that is parallel to the base of the cone passes through the point on the altitude that is 10 in. from the vertex of the cone, what is the lateral area of the frustum that is formed?

5. A right triangle ABC having $\angle B = 90°$, $\angle A = 30°$, and $AC = 18$ in. revolves around the side AB.
   (a) What kind of surface is generated by ACB?
   (b) What is the lateral area of the surface?
   (c) What is the lateral area of the surface generated by broken line CAB when it revolves around BC?

6. What is the lateral area of a regular hexagonal pyramid whose base is inscribed in a circle with radius 6 in. if the lateral edges of the pyramid are 20 in.?

7. What is the lateral area of the regular hexagonal pyramid whose base is inscribed in a circle with radius 8 in. if the altitude of the pyramid is 20 in.?

8. In the figure for Ex. 7, what is the lateral area of the right circular cone that circumscribes the pyramid?

9. A circular cylindrical tent with vertical walls that are 10 ft. high is surmounted by a right circular cone. The diameter of the cylinder is 40 ft. The height of the cone above the ground is 15 ft. How many square yards of canvas were needed to make this tent?

10. A regular square pyramid is inscribed in, and another is circumscribed about, a right circular cone that has a 6-in. radius and a 15-in. altitude.
    (a) Find the difference in the lateral areas of the two pyramids.
    (b) Find the ratio of the lateral area of the inside pyramid and the cone, then of the cone and the outside pyramid.

392. As in the case of the lateral areas, we find first the formula for the volume of a regular pyramid and then apply SG 69, p. 359, to obtain the formula for the volume of a right circular cone. Before reading the rest of this page, review §346, p. 314.

SG 72. *If two pyramids have equal bases and altitudes, they are equal.*

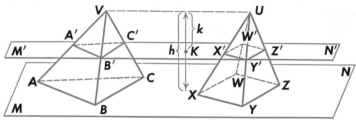

Hypothesis. $V-ABC$ and $U-XYZW$ have equal bases and equal altitudes, h.

Conclusion. $V-ABC = U-XYZW$

Plan. Use Cavalieri's Theorem.

Proof. 1. Place the two pyramids on plane MN. Let a plane that is parallel to plane MN cut their common altitude h in K, cut $V-ABC$ in $A'B'C'$ and $U-XYZW$ in $X'Y'Z'W'$.

2. $\triangle A'B'C' \backsim \triangle ABC$, $X'Y'X'W' \backsim XYZW$ (Prove.)

Suggestions. $A'B' \parallel AB$, $B'C' \parallel BC$, . . .   (Why?)

$\angle A'B'C' = \angle ABC$, $\angle B'C'A' = \angle BCA$, . . . (Why?)

3. $\therefore$ $\dfrac{\triangle A'B'C'}{\triangle ABC} = \dfrac{A'B'^2}{AB^2} = \dfrac{VA'^2}{VA^2} = \dfrac{k^2}{h^2}$ (§345, p. 313)
(§244, p. 213)

4.   Also $\dfrac{X'Y'Z'W'}{XYZW} = \dfrac{X'Y'^2}{XY^2} = \dfrac{UX'^2}{UX^2} = \dfrac{k^2}{h^2}$ (§346, p. 314)

5. $\therefore$ $\dfrac{\triangle A'B'C'}{\triangle ABC} = \dfrac{X'Y'Z'W'}{XYZW}$ (Why?)

6. $\therefore$ $\triangle A'B'C' = X'Y'Z'W'$ (Why?)

7. $\therefore$ volume of $V-ABC$ = volume of $U-XYZW$

Note. You can visualize this theorem by thinking of the pyramids as being stacks of cards or thin slips of paper such that the stacks are equally high and the slips at equal distances from the tops are equal in area. The volumes then must be equal.

SG 73. *The volume of a triangular pyramid equals one third the product of the length of its altitude and the area of its base.* Briefly $V = \frac{1}{3}hB$.

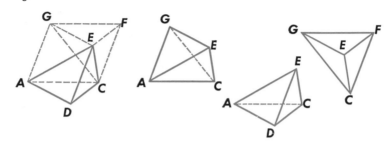

Hypothesis. Pyramid $E{-}ADC$ has base with area B and altitude of length h.

Conclusion. $E{-}ADC = \frac{1}{3}hB$

Plan. Prove $E{-}ADC$ equal to one third of a prism that has the same base and altitude.

Proof. 1. Form prism $EFG{-}ADC$ by plane $ADEG$ through AD and DE, plane $DCFE$ through DC and DE, plane $ACFG$ through AC parallel to DE, and plane EFG through E parallel to ADC.

2. Planes EAC and ECG separate the prism $EFG{-}ADC$ into the three triangular pyramids $E{-}ADC$, $E{-}ACG$, and $E{\ } GCF$. These pyramids will be proved equal.

3. (a) $E{-}ADC$ is the same as $C{-}ADE$.
              $E{-}ACG$ is the same as $C{-}AGE$.
                  In $C{-}ADE$ and $C{-}AGE$:
                  base ADE = base AGE;   (Why?)
    the altitude of each is the $\perp$ from C to $ADEG$.   (Why?)
                      $\therefore$ $C{-}ADE = C{-}AGE$ (Why?)
                  or $E{-}ADC = E{-}ACG$

   (b) In $E{-}ACG$ and $E{-}GFC$:
                  base ACG = base GFC;   (Why?)
                  the altitudes are equal.
                      $\therefore$ $E{-}ACG = E{-}GFC$

4. $\therefore$ $E{-}ACG = E{-}GFC = E{-}ADC$ (Steps $3(a),(b)$)
5. $\therefore$ $E{-}ADC = \frac{1}{3}$ prism $EFG{-}ADC$
6.   Prism $EFG{-}ADC = hB$ (Why?)
7. $\therefore$ $E{-}ADC$ $= \frac{1}{3}hB$ (Why?)

SG 74. *The volume of any pyramid equals one third the product of the length of the altitude and the area of the base.* Briefly $V = \frac{1}{3}hB$.

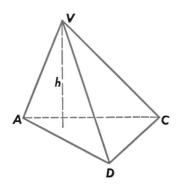
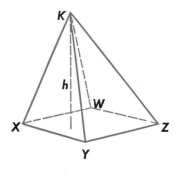

Hypothesis. $K\text{--}XYZW$ is a pyramid with base having area B and altitude having length h.

Conclusion. $K\text{--}XYZW = \frac{1}{3}hB$

Plan. Use SG 72 and SG 73.

Proof. 1. Construct a triangular pyramid $V\text{--}ADC$ whose base equals base $XYZW$ and whose altitude has length h.

2.   Then $V\text{--}ADC = K\text{--}XYZW$.   (SG 72)
3.   Vol. $V\text{--}ADC = \frac{1}{3}hB$ (Why?)
4. $\therefore$ vol. $K\text{--}XYZW = \frac{1}{3}hB$ (Why?)

SG 75. *The volume of any cone equals one third the product of the length of its altitude and the area of its base.* $V = \frac{1}{3}hB$, or $V = \frac{1}{3}\pi r^2 h$.

In SG 74 and SG 75, as usual, h and r are numbers of the same linear unit, B is a number of the corresponding surface units, and V is a number of the corresponding space units.

1. What is the volume of a square pyramid whose base edge is 10 in. and whose altitude is 25 in.?
2. Find the volume of a regular hexagonal pyramid whose altitude is 24 in. and whose base is inscribed in a circle with radius 6 in.
3. In Ex. 2, how much larger than the pyramid is the right circular cone that circumscribes the pyramid that is described?
4. What is the volume of the regular square pyramid whose base edges measure 8 in. and whose lateral edges measure 24 in.

393. Review or study p. 281 before studying this page.

1. Assume that V–$ABCDE$ is a regular pyramid with plane $A'D'$ parallel to AD, bisecting VA. Let VM be perpendicular to AB. Prove:

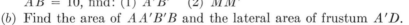

    (a) $VM \perp A'B'$ (b) $VB' = \frac{1}{2}VB$
    (c) $A'B' = \frac{1}{2}AB$ (d) $VM' = \frac{1}{2}VM$
    (e) $A'B'BA$ is an isosceles trapezoid.
    (f) The faces of frustum $A'D$ are bounded by congruent trapezoids.
    (g) $A'B'C'D'E' \backsim ABCDE$.

2. (a) Using the hypothesis of Ex. 1 and the additional facts that $VA = 13$ and $AB = 10$, find: (1) $A'B'$ (2) MM'
    (b) Find the area of $AA'B'B$ and the lateral area of frustum $A'D$.

3. What is the lateral area of a frustum of a regular pentagonal pyramid (see Ex. 1) if $AB = 12$ in., $A'B' = 8$ in., and $MM' = 5$ in.?

Exercises 1 to 3 prepare you for the following theorem.

SG 76. *The lateral area of a frustum of a regular pyramid equals half the length of the slant height of the frustum multiplied by the sum of the perimeters of the bases of the frustum.*

        Informal proof. 1. If $A'D$ is a frustum of a regular pyramid, its lateral faces are enclosed by congruent isosceles trapezoids, whose altitudes equal the slant height of the frustum. Let $s =$ the slant height, p and p' the perimeters of the bases, and S the lateral area.

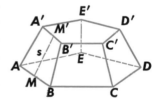

2.   Area of $AA'B'B = \frac{1}{2}s(A'B' + AB)$ (§331, p. 296)
           Area $B'C'CB = \frac{1}{2}s(B'C' + BC)$, etc.

3. $\therefore$ $S = \frac{1}{2}s(A'B' + AB) + \frac{1}{2}s(B'C' + BC) +$
                                  $\frac{1}{2}s(C'D' + CD) + \ldots$

4. $\therefore$ $S = \frac{1}{2}s(A'B' + AB + B'C' + BC + C'D' + CD + \ldots)$
                                             (Note 1)

5. $\therefore$ $S = \frac{1}{2}s[(A'B' + B'C' + C'D' + \ldots) +$
                    $(AB + BC + CD + \ldots)]$ (Note 2)

6. $\therefore$ $S = \frac{1}{2}s(p' + p)$

Note 1. By the distributive law of multiplication.
Note 2. By the commutative and associative laws of addition.

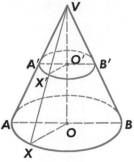

1. Let $V–AXB$ be a right circular cone with altitude VO, $A'X'B'$ be the section by a plane that is parallel to AXB. Prove:
   (a) $VO \perp$ plane $A'X'B'$ at O'.
   (b) $O'A' \parallel OA$, $O'X' \parallel OX$, etc.
   (c) $O'A':OA = O'X':OX = O'B':OB, \ldots$
   (d) $O'A' = O'X' = O'B', \ldots$
   (e) $A'X'B'$ is a circle with center O'.
   (f) $A'A = X'X = B'B, \ldots$

SG 77. (**Def.**) (a) If a right circular cone is cut by a plane that is parallel to its base, the section, its interior, and the part of the cone below the cutting plane form a **frustum of the cone.**

(b) The cutting plane is the **upper base** of the frustum, and the base of the cone is the **lower base** of the frustum. *The upper base is enclosed by a circle.* The **altitude** of the frustum is the distance between the bases. The **elements** of the frustum are the parts of the elements of the cone between the bases of the frustum. *The elements are equal.* Any element is the **slant height** of the frustum.

SG 78. *The lateral area of a frustum of a right circular cone equals one half the length of its slant height times the sum of the circumference of the bases.* Briefly
$$S = \tfrac{1}{2}s(C + C'), \quad \text{or} \quad S = \pi s(r + r').$$
This is a consequence of SG 69, p. 359.

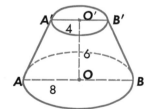

2. (a) $AA'O'O$ is a trapezoid having $A'O'$ and AO both perpendicular to $O'O$. If AA' and OO' are extended to meet at V, and $\triangle VOA$ is revolved around VO, prove that $\triangle VOA$ generates a right circular cone.
   (b) Find the lateral area of this cone, if $A'O' = 4$ in., $O'O = 6$ in., and $AO = 8$ in.

3. (a) In Ex. 2, prove that $AA'O'O$ generates a frustum of a right circular cone.
   (b) Find the lateral area of the frustum.

4. Give the algebraic demonstration of the second formula that appears in SG 78.

1. What is the volume of a right circular cone whose radius is 8 in. and whose altitude is 24 in.?

2. What is the volume of the square pyramid that is inscribed in the cone described in Ex. 1?

3. What is the volume of the right circular cone with radius 8 in. that has slant height of 30 in.?

4. What is the volume of the regular hexagonal pyramid that is inscribed in the cone described in Ex. 3?

5. Assume that a plane that is parallel to the base of the cone in Ex. 3 passes through the point on an element of the cone that is 10 in. from the vertex of the cone forming a frustum of the cone in Ex. 3, and of the pyramid inscribed in it in Ex. 4.
   (a) Find the volume of the frustum of the cone.
   (b) How much less than the result in part (a) is the volume of the frustum of the pyramid?

6. What are the volume and the lateral area of the right circular cone whose elements are 18 in. long and whose radius is 4 in. in length?

7. What are the lateral area and the volume of the right hexagonal pyramid that is inscribed in the cone described in Ex. 6?

8. What are the lateral area and the volume of the right circular cone whose altitude is 20 in. and whose radius of the base is 15 in.?

9. What are the lateral area and the volume of the regular triangular pyramid that is inscribed in the cone in Ex. 8?

10. The center of a cube whose edges are 12 in. in length is joined to each of the vertices of the cube.
    (a) Prove that the pyramid formed by one face and the planes determined by its edges and the center of the cube is regular.
    (b) What is the volume of this pyramid?
    (c) What part of the cube is the pyramid?

11. $\triangle XYZ$, having $\angle Z = 30°$, $\angle Y = 90°$ and $XZ = 30$ in., revolves around leg XY.
    (a) Find the volume of the solid that is generated.
    (b) Find the lateral area of the solid.
    (c) Do parts (a) and (b) if the triangle is revolved around YZ.

12. A right $\triangle ABC$ has BC of length a, AC of length b, and hypotenuse AB of length c. What are the lateral area and the volume of the cone of revolution generated by revolving $\triangle ABC$ about leg CA?

SG 79. The formula for the area of a sphere is $S = 4\pi r^2$.

Informal proof. (*a*) 1. Review SG 62, p. 351.

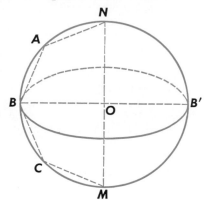

2. Let $NABCM$ be half of a regular octagon inscribed in semicircle NBM of a great circle O of the sphere.

3. Revolve $\overset{\frown}{NBM}$ around NM through 360°. It passes over or generates the sphere. NA and CM generate the lateral surfaces of right circular cones. AB and BC generate lateral surfaces of frustums of right circular cones. $NABCM$ generates a surface that is less than the sphere.

4. We must find a formula for the area of this surface.

(*b*) 1. The adjoining figure is a section of the figure above made by plane NBM. Let XY be any chord of $\overset{\frown}{NBM}$, and let Z bisect XY. Then $ZO \perp XY$.

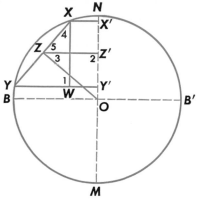

2. Let S_{XY} represent the area of the surface generated by XY when $\overset{\frown}{NBM}$ revolves around NOM. This surface is the lateral surface of a frustum of a right circular cone.

3. $\therefore$ $S_{XY} = XY \times 2\pi ZZ'$ (SG 78, p. 366)

4.   In $\triangle YWX$ and $\triangle OZZ'$: $\angle 1 = \angle 2$,   (Why?)
   $\angle 4 + \angle 5 = 90°$, $\angle 3 + \angle 5 = 90°$, $\therefore$ $\angle 4 = \angle 3$ (Why?)

5. $\therefore$ $\triangle YWX \backsim \triangle OZZ'$ (Why?)

6. $\therefore$ $XY : ZO = XW : ZZ'$ (Why?)

7. $\therefore$ $XY \times ZZ' = ZO \times XW = ZO \times X'Y'$ (Prove.)

8. From Step 3: $S_{XY} = 2\pi \times ZO \times X'Y'$ (Why?)

This formula will help us to derive the formula for the surface generated by $NABCM$ when line $NABCM$ is revolved around NOM.

(c) 1. Let broken line $NABCM$ be half of a regular 8-gon inscribed in $\overset{\frown}{NBM}$. Let $\overset{\frown}{NBM}$ and $NABCM$ revolve through 360° around NOM.

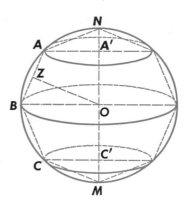

2. Since NA, AB, BC, and CM are equal chords, they are equidistant from O. That distance is ZO, the apothem a_8 of the 8-gon.

3. By Step 8 of (b),
$$S_{NA} = 2\pi a_8 \times NA'$$
$$S_{AB} = 2\pi a_8 \times A'O$$
$$S_{BC} = 2\pi a_8 \times OC'$$
$$S_{C'M} = 2\pi a_8 \times C'M$$

4. Adding the results in Step 3,
$$S_{NABCM} = 2\pi a_8(NA' + A'O + OC' + C'M)$$

5. $\therefore$ $S_{NABCM} = 2\pi a_8 \times 2r$, or $4\pi r a_8$ (Prove.)

Note. This means that the surface generated by half an 8-gon is $4\pi r$ times the apothem of the 8-gon.

6. If a sequence of regular polygons having 16, 32, . . . sides is inscribed and revolved, the result in Step 5 gives us:
$$S_{\frac{1}{2}p_8} = 4\pi r a_8, \; S_{\frac{1}{2}p_{16}} = 4\pi r a_{16}, \; S_{\frac{1}{2}p_{32}} = 4\pi r a_{32}$$

7. It is obvious that the resulting surfaces come closer and closer to the surface of the sphere, and, ultimately, differ little from it; also that the apothems, ultimately, differ little from the radius of the sphere.
$$S_{NBM} = 4\pi r \times r, \text{ or } \mathbf{S = 4\pi r^2}$$

Remark. Proofs such as this give a mathematician a thrill, and we hope that this proof gives you one.

1. What is the area of a sphere whose radius is 10 in.?

2. What is the area of a sphere whose diameter is 15 in.?

3. Prepare a formula for the area of a sphere whose diameter is d.

4. How does the area of a sphere compare with the area of one of the great circles of the sphere?

5. How does the area of a sphere compare with the lateral area of a right circular cylinder whose altitude equals the diameter of the sphere and whose diameter equals the diameter of the sphere?

SG 80. *The formula for the volume of a sphere of radius* r *is*
$$V = \tfrac{4}{3}\pi r^3.$$

Plan. Prove that a sphere equals the difference between a right circular cylinder circumscribed around the sphere and two right circular cones inscribed in the sphere.

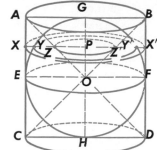

Proof. 1. Around sphere O with diameters EF and GH of length $2r$, circumscribe right circular cylinder AD whose bases are tangent to the sphere at G and H, and parallel to the section EF made by a plane through O.

2. Right circular cones $O–AB$ and $O–CD$ have diameters AB and CD, equal to EF, and altitudes OG and OH equal to r.

3. Pass a plane parallel to the plane of circle EF through a point P at distance d from O. This plane cuts the cylinder in $\odot XX'$, the sphere in $\odot YY'$, and the upper cone in $\odot ZZ'$.
We shall prove that $\odot YY' = \odot XX' - \odot ZZ'$.
Use the following section of the sphere determined by AGB and GOH.

4. Area of $\odot XX' = \pi XP^2 = \pi r^2$
5. $\qquad ZP = OP = d \qquad$ (Why?)
6. $\qquad \therefore \quad$ area of $\odot ZZ' = \pi d^2$
7. $\quad \therefore \quad \odot XX' - \odot ZZ' = \pi(r^2 - d^2)$
8. $\qquad YP^2 = OY^2 - OP^2,$
   or $YP^2 = r^2 - d^2$
9. $\therefore \quad$ area of $\odot YY' = \pi(r^2 - d^2)$
10. $\therefore \quad \odot YY' = \odot XX' - \odot ZZ'$
11. Hemisphere above $\odot EF$ = cylinder AF - cone $O–AB$.
    (SG 62, p. 351)
12. $\therefore \quad$ vol. of the sphere = cylinder AD - 2 × cone $O–AB$
13. $\qquad$ Volume of cylinder $AD = 2r \times \pi r^2$, or $2\pi r^3$
    $\qquad$ Volume of cone $O–AB = \tfrac{1}{3}r \times \pi r^2$, or $\tfrac{1}{3}\pi r^3$
14. $\therefore \quad$ the volume of the sphere $= 2\pi r^3 - \tfrac{2}{3}\pi r^3$, or $\tfrac{4}{3}\pi r^3$

Remark. This elegant mathematical proof involves only facts that you have learned during your course in geometry. It is a fitting climax to the course.

1. What are the area and the volume of the sphere whose radius is 7 in.? (Let $\pi = 3\frac{1}{7}$.)

2. What are the area and the volume of the sphere whose diameter is 20 in.? (Now use $\pi = 3.14$.)

3. What are the area and the volume of the sphere when the area of one of its great circles is 85 sq. in.?

4. Prove that the area of a sphere is four times the area of one of the great circles of the sphere.

5. The radius of the earth is approximately 4000 miles. About 30% of the surface of the earth is covered by land. About how many square miles of land are there on the earth?

6. A hollow float has the shape and dimensions shown in the figure at the right.
   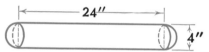
   (a) How many square inches of metal were needed to make this float?
   (b) How many cubic inches of air are in the interior of the float?

7. (a) Prove that a sphere can be passed through the vertices of a cube.
   (b) Compare the area of this sphere with the total area of the cube.
   (c) Compare the volume of the sphere with the volume of the cube.

8. A storage tank for oil has the form of a sphere with diameter 40 ft.
   (a) How much metal is there in the tank?
   (b) What is the capacity of the tank in gallons if one cubic foot contains 7.5 gallons?

9. A cylindrical tank with 10 in. diameter was filled with water. A spherical ball, immersed wholly in it, caused the water to overflow. When the ball was removed, the depth of the water remaining in the tank was decreased by 2.5 in. What was the diameter of the ball?

10. What is the weight of a spherical ball made of material that is .5 in. thick if the outside diameter of the ball is 12 in., and one cubic inch of the material weighs .25 lb.?

11. How does the volume of a sphere change when the radius of the sphere is doubled?

12. The radius of one sphere is three times that of another sphere. Compare the area of it with that of the second sphere.

1. How many square yards of canvas are needed for a vertical wall of an enclosure that has the form of a right circular cylinder with diameter 250 feet and height 10 feet?

2. A rectangular athletic field that is 300 feet long and 100 feet wide is to be enclosed by a canvas wall 8 feet high. How many square yards of canvas will be needed?

3. A swimming tank is 45 feet long and 30 feet wide. At one end it is 4 feet deep, at the other it is 8 ft. deep. The bottom of the tank is a plane surface. How many gallons of water are needed to fill the tank to the depth of 3 feet at the shallow end?

4. (a) Prove that all the diagonals of a rectangular parallelepiped pass through a point that bisects each of them.
   (b) Prove that a sphere can be passed through all the vertices of a rectangular parallelepiped.
   (c) What is the radius of the sphere in part (b) if the lengths of the edges are 5 in., 6 in., and 13 in. respectively?
   (d) In part (c), how much more than the total area of the parallelepiped is the area of the sphere?
   (e) In part (c), how much more than the volume of the parallelepiped is the volume of the sphere?

5. (a) Find the volume generated when rectangle $ABCD$ in which AB equals h units and BC equals k units:
      (1) Revolves around AB (2) Revolves around BC
   (b) What is the ratio of the volume generated in part (1) of (a) to that generated in part (2)?

6. If diameter NOS of sphere O is perpendicular to great circle AXB, then N and S are the poles of $\odot AXB$ and NOS is the axis of $\odot AXB$.

   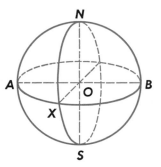

   (a) Prove that great circle arc NX is a quadrant of a great circle of sphere O.
   (b) $\widehat{NX}$ is called the polar distance of circle AXB. Prove that the polar distances of all points on $\odot AXB$ are equal.

7. In the figure for Ex. 6, let a plane that is parallel to $\odot AXB$ intersect the sphere in section CYD, the arc NX at point Y, and NOS at point Z.
   (a) What kind of line is section $CYD?$
   (b) Prove $\widehat{NC} = \widehat{NY} = \widehat{ND}$.

CHAPTER 13

REASONING

Ability to reason is a characteristic of human beings. Because we can reason we have the capacity to live a good life in material comfort and safety, in our mutual relationships with others, and in our intellectual activity. Without reasoning we would be reduced to living by instincts and habits only.

Much of our reasoning we do without realizing how we reach our conclusions. Thus, when we see people go by with umbrellas up, we immediately think, "It is raining," without consciously going through the steps that lead to that idea.

If, however, we become aware of how we reason, we may learn to reason more effectively. The study of geometry, because of the clearcut nature of the subject matter, offers an excellent opportunity to learn *how* we reason.

From time to time in your study of geometry this year you will be referred to this chapter, in which more about some of the concepts of reasoning is presented.

Guided by the three characteristics of a definition as stated on page 33,
define:

1. Footpath   2. Bicycle path   3. Path of a bullet

4. Flag   5. Bicycle   6. School

7. Headlight   8. Elevator   9. Semester

10. "Holding" in the game of football

11. "Touchdown" in football

12. "Personal foul" in basketball

13. "Home run" in baseball

14. (*a*) The words *men, free,* and *equal* in:
    "All men are created free and equal."
    (*b*) According to your definitions:
    (1) Is Mary Jones free?
    (2) Is Mary Jones equal to Sally Smith?
    (3) Is Tom Jones free to take bread from a bakery without
        paying for it?
    (4) Is Tom Jones equal in height to Sam Smith?

15. What words need definition to make the following sentences mean-
    ingful?
    (*a*) Every head of a family may deduct from his gross income the
          amount of $600 for each dependent.
    (*b*) This insurance policy furnishes comprehensive public liability
          insurance.
    (*c*) He is a qualified voter in a local election.
    (*d*) He became a citizen of the United States.
    (*e*) He is a member of the Science Club.
    (*f*) Motorcycles must not be parked in the bicycle shed.
    (*g*) Children are admitted free.
    (*h*) Residents of the village may use the facilities of the beach if
          they buy a season permit.
    (*i*) A student must have fifteen units to be admitted to X college.
    (*j*) Three majors or two majors and two minors are required for
          admission to Z University.

16. Which word in the following pairs of words must be defined before
    the other?
    (*a*) Tree or oak?   (*b*) Dictionary or book?
    (*c*) Store or grocery?   (*d*) Boat or canoe?

You have seen (page 31) that assumptions (axioms and postulates) and a few undefined concepts are necessary in geometry to start the chain of reasoning which we call proof.

We constantly make assumptions in our thinking and talking. Thus we say, "Since father will be late tonight, we'll keep his dinner warm in the oven and go ahead without him." The assumption that father will be late is stated explicitly.

Many of our assumptions are left unsaid and often we do not even think what they are, so we may be making assumptions which we really do not believe or which are not true.

Thus: When Johnny says, "Betty did her homework in twenty minutes, so I need to allow only twenty minutes to do mine," there is a hidden assumption. Johnny is assuming that if Betty can finish her homework in twenty minutes, he can too. This assumption may not be true.

For each of the following statements give what you think is the hidden assumption and tell whether you think the assumption is usually true, usually false, or neither.

1. Since Martha is good looking and friendly, she will be popular with her classmates.

2. To help obtain the acquittal of his client, a lawyer used the fact that his client attended church regularly.

3. When a college boy ran out of money, he wrote home to his parents for more.

4. Mary became sick from eating mince pie, so I'm never going to eat mince pie again.

5. I've finished all my book reports for this year, so I am not going to read any more books.

6. Since Mr. Simpson's hair is gray, he must be quite old.

7. Since there are severe thunderstorms between here and Detroit, I won't try to fly my plane to Detroit this afternoon.

8. Miss Smith graduated from X college, so she will be a good teacher.

9. Plentysoft Hand Lotion must be good because more of it than any other hand lotion is sold.

10. Bill will make a good president of his class because he is the most popular boy in school.

394. Inductive reasoning produces a general conclusion that is suggested by special cases.

1. (a) Draw $\triangle ABC$ having $\angle B = 60°$, $BC = 2$ in., and $\angle C = 40°$. Measure and compare AC and AB.

   (b) Do part (a) when $\angle B = 70°$ and $\angle C = 45°$; also when $\angle B = 80°$ and $\angle C = 50°$.

   (c) What general conclusion is suggested by parts (a) and (b)?

   (d) Test your conclusion by drawing another triangle in which $\angle B$ is greater than $\angle C$.

   (e) Do you think your conclusion is always true?

2. (a) A visitor to a certain city rode on five buses and noticed that in each case the bus driver was very courteous.

   (b) What general conclusion would he be likely to make?

   (c) Do you think this conclusion is always true?

3. (a) For the last seven years the president of the Student Council has been a boy.

   (b) Does this fact prove that the president of the Student Council must always be a boy?

4. (a) Fifty samples taken from different parts of a shipment of tea are tested and found to be of high quality.

   (b) What general conclusion could be reached about the whole shipment of tea?

   (c) Could a merchant safely use this conclusion in determining the price he would pay for the shipment?

The above examples illustrate the fact that, while it is frequently possible to make a sound generalization from observation of several cases, the generalization is not always true.

Often the evidence is strong enough to justify calling the generalization a *probable conclusion*. This would be the case in Examples 1 and 4 above.

Sometimes such a probable conclusion can be proved *by other* methods to be a true conclusion. The conclusion in Example 1 is proved by deductive reasoning on page 145.

If the evidence is insufficient or poorly chosen, a conclusion reached by inductive reasoning may be far from true. Examples 2 and 3 illustrate this possibility.

In Exercises 1 to 9:

(a) *To what conclusion does inductive reasoning lead?*

(b) *Do you think this conclusion is a* probable *conclusion?*

(c) *If you can prove your conclusion in (a) is true, do so.*

1. A biology student observed that twenty samples of leaves from beech trees had the leaves in groups of five.

2. A stranger in a certain city noticed several times that cars turned right on a red traffic light after stopping.

3. In the same city the stranger saw a car parked next to a fire hydrant.

4. In ten different isosceles triangles, the base angles were measured and found to be equal.

5. It rained every day of our recent vacation that we spent in Pleasant-town.

6. Twenty times I added an even number to an odd number, and found an odd number for the sum.

7. On four successive mornings, Mr. A. left his home at 7:30 A.M.

8. Every fire engine which I have ever seen has been painted red.

9. Our football team won the first five games of the season.

10. A reporter, inquiring in twelve city high schools, found that all the schools offered a course in trigonometry. He reported that trigonometry is offered in all high schools. What is wrong with his reasoning?

11. Mrs. W. bought a dozen eggs at a neighborhood store and later found that one of the eggs was bad. She never went back to that store. What faulty generalization may she have made?

12. A prime number is an integer which is not divisible by any integer except itself and one. Thus, 2, 7, 13, 29 are examples of prime numbers.

    (a) If we substitute $x = 1$ in the expression $x^2 - x + 41$, is the result a prime number?

    (b) Do part (a) for $x = 2$, $x = 3$, $x = 4$, and $x = 5$.

    (c) What general statement do parts (a) and (b) suggest?

    (d) If (as can be shown) $x^2 - x + 41$ continues to give a prime number for every integral value of x up to $x = 40$, would you be fairly well convinced that $x^2 - x + 41$ is a prime number for all integral values of x?

    (e) Is $x^2 - x + 41$ a prime number when $x = 41$?

395. **Deductive reasoning** can be used when no mathematics is involved.

Thus: John said, "Mary has a geometry book." His reasoning was:

1. Every student in Mr. Greene's geometry class has a geometry book.
2. Mary is a student in Mr. Greene's geometry class.
3. Mary has a geometry book.

In logic the three steps of John's reasoning form a **syllogism.**

Step 1 is a general statement, called the *major premise.*

Step 2 is a particular statement, called the *minor premise,* in which the hypothesis of the major premise is fully satisfied.

Step 3 is a particular statement, called the *conclusion,* which follows from Steps 1 and 2.

396. **Valid Conclusions.** A conclusion reached by correct use of a syllogism is a *valid* conclusion from the given major premise. We call the major premise the *authority* for the conclusion. Above, "Mary has a geometry book," is a valid conclusion.

If the major premise is true, a valid conclusion from it is true. If, however, the major premise is false, a valid conclusion from it may or may not be true.

Thus: If we reason from the general statement "all four-footed animals are horses," we are using a false major premise. If the minor premise is "This mare is a four-footed animal," the conclusion, "This mare is a horse," is *valid* and it is *true*. If the minor premise is "This dog is a four-footed animal," the conclusion, "This dog is a horse," is *valid*, but *false*.

397. **Acceptable authorities.** In mathematics, the initial major premises are the *definitions*, *axioms*, and *postulates*. The conclusions reached from these authorities by deductive reasoning are *theorems*, which, in turn, may be used as authorities for more deductive reasoning.

Generally, only those conclusions which appear in numbered sections of the textbook are used as authorities.

398. Non-Euclidean Geometry. In pure mathematics we are concerned with reaching valid conclusions. Some of our major premises are postulated. While it is convenient for most purposes to have the postulates agree with our experience, we are not concerned primarily with the "truth" or "falsity" of our postulates.

The mathematicians Nicholas Lobachevsky (1793–1856) and Johann Bolyai (1802–1860) accepted the postulate that through a given point it is possible to draw in a plane any number of lines parallel to a given line, instead of our Postulate 23, which says that only one such line can be drawn. Lobachevsky and Bolyai were able to draw valid conclusions from this postulate. In fact, they built up a whole new geometry, part of what is now called "non-Euclidean geometry." The fact that some of their conclusions do not agree with what we see, does not prevent them from being logically sound.

399. Conclusions which are not valid. It is possible to start with an acceptable authority and reach a conclusion which is not valid, if Step 2 or Step 3 of a syllogism is not done correctly.

(a) If the minor premise does not satisfy all the conditions of the hypothesis of the major premise, the conclusion will be invalid.

Thus: If a man is over 20 years old and has had experience as a tinsmith, he may apply for employment in the X Manufacturing Company. Harry Smith is 27 years old. Therefore Harry Smith may apply for employment in the X Manufacturing Company. The conclusion is not valid because there is no statement that Harry is experienced as a tinsmith.

(b) If the conclusion is not an application of the conclusion of the major premise (Step 3 in the syllogism), it will not be valid.

Thus: If a man is over 20 years old and has had experience as a tinsmith, he may apply for employment in the X Manufacturing Company. John Jones is 30 years old and has had experience as a tinsmith. Therefore John Jones may apply for employment in the Y Manufacturing Company. Since the conclusion of the major premise has not been applied correctly, the final statement is invalid.

In Exercises 1–5 the conclusions are invalid. Tell why in each case.

1. If the cost of fuel oil increases, the school budget will be higher. The school budget is higher this year. Therefore the cost of fuel oil has increased.

2. All members of the Engineering Club are boys. Sam Smith is a member of the Engineering Club. Therefore he is planning to be an engineer.

3. A student who has not had disciplinary trouble and has not been tardy will be admitted to the Honor Study Hall. Sarah Williams has never been tardy. Therefore she will be admitted to the Honor Study Hall.

4. Passengers on train #20 to New Orleans must have seat reservations. Mr. Wilson is going to New Orleans. Therefore he must have a seat reservation.

5. If it rains, the grass will grow. The temperature has been over 80° for the last week. Therefore my grass is full of weeds.

In Exercises 6–8, the conclusions are all valid, but some are true and some are false. Tell for each whether it is true or false and discuss your answer.

6. If a library book is overdue, the borrower must pay a fine. Billy Brown borrowed a library book which is now overdue. Billy must pay a fine.

7. If you plant radish seeds, you will have a big crop of sunflowers. Farmer Brown planted radish seeds. Therefore he will have a big crop of sunflowers.

8. Every student graduating from high school in the United States is a girl. Mary Morrison graduated from a high school in the United States. Therefore Mary Morrison is a girl.

In Examples 9–13, write a conclusion and discuss its truth or falsity.

9. If a customer buys three cans of soup, she receives a fourth one free. Mrs. White bought three cans of soup. Therefore. . . .

10. If a customer buys three cans of soup, she will be thrown out of the store. Mrs. White bought three cans of soup. Therefore. . . .

11. If a man has yellow hair, he lives in the United States. Mr. Johnson, who is a resident of Arizona, has yellow hair. Therefore. . . .

12. If a student is to study physics, he should have at least three years of mathematics. Joe is going to study physics. Therefore. . . .

13. All vehicles with at least four wheels are automobiles. This locomotive has twelve wheels. Therefore. . . .

400. Often **indirect reasoning** can be used when one of two or more possible conclusions must be correct.

Example 1. An electric light bulb will not light. What is the cause if other light bulbs do light up?

Solution. 1. An inspection shows that there are three points, A, B, and C at which the connection might be broken or the light bulb itself might be burned out.

2. Assume that the bulb is not burned out. Then try the other possibilities.

3. Is connection A broken? Investigation shows that current passes through connection A.

4. Similarly investigation shows that current passes through connections B and C.

5. ∴   the bulb must be burned out because that is the only remaining possibility.

(*a*) In mathematics, start by assuming that the desired conclusion is false. This is equivalent to assuming that at least one of the other possible conclusions is true.

(*b*) In turn, assume and follow up each of the other possible conclusions. If a contradiction is found, the assumed conclusion must be false.

(*c*) If each possible conclusion except the desired conclusion is false, we know that the desired conclusion must be true.

Example 2. At a point B on DC, there can be only one perpendicular to DC.

Hyp. $AB \perp CD$

Con. AB is the only perpendicular to DC at B.

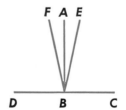

Proof. 1. Assume that AB is not the only perpendicular to DC at B. Assume BE at the right (or BF at the left) of BA is $\perp DC$ at B.

2.   ∴ $\angle CBE$ = a rt. $\angle$

3.   But $\angle CBA$ = a rt. $\angle$.
          $\angle CBE = \angle CBA$

4. But $\angle CBE$ is less than $\angle CBA$.

5. ∴ BE cannot be $\perp DC$ at B. Similarly $BF \not\perp DC$.

6.   ∴ BA is the only $\perp DC$ at B.

In the following exercises, what conclusion follows by indirect proof from the information given?

1. On a key ring there are keys 1, 2, 3, and 4, one of which is known to fit a certain lock. You have tried keys 1, 3, and 4 and found that they do not fit the lock.

2. A bank robbery probably was committed by one of four persons: X, Y, Z, and W. X has proof that he was in a city far removed from the scene of the crime. Y has proof that he was in a restaurant at the time of the crime. W is known to have been in the hospital with pneumonia at the time.

3. Mr. Q is known to have one of three diseases, A, B, or C. With disease A the patient always has a fever, and Mr. Q has no fever. A chest X-ray indicates that Mr. Q does not have disease C.

4. The supervisor of ushers knew that either Jack or Bob had been assigned to the center door at the concert, but could not remember which. He found that Bob was assigned to the left aisle.

5. Mr. Turner, to reach a business appointment, can go by train, by auto, or by airplane. It is now one o'clock, and he must be there by six o'clock. The weather forecast indicates severe thunderstorms over the area. The first possible train leaves at three o'clock, and requires three and one half hours.

6. There are six problems on a page from which a study assignment has been made. Ruth knows that four problems have been assigned for homework. She is sure that number 5 was not assigned and number 1 was assigned for a previous lesson.

7. One of three men, A, B, and C, is to be hired as foreman. Both A and B have had experience, while C has never done this kind of work before. B is known to have trouble getting along with the people with whom he works.

8. There are four geometry teachers in Central High School. Susan is in Mr. Smith's class and Mary is not in that class with her. Susan knows that Mr. Black's class is in the third period and Miss Johnson's class is in the fifth period. Only boys are in Mr. Bing's class. Susan and Mary both have English in the third period. Who is Mary's geometry teacher?

9. The coach had only five boys who could play quarterback in the football game: Bill, John, Joe, Austin, and Jacob. John has a broken leg. Joe and Jacob have become ineligible because of low grades. Austin cannot play because of a death in his family. Which boy must the coach use for the game?

401. Converses must be understood and used in reasoning. Recall that definitions *should be reversible*. (See §35 and §36.) This means that the converse of a definition is true. For example:

(*a*) Two lines are perpendicular if they form a right angle. *Conversely*. If two lines are perpendicular, they form a right angle.

(*b*) A pupil is intelligent if he has a high I.Q. *Conversely*. If a pupil is intelligent, he has a high I.Q.

1. (*a*) Write the converse of:
    An equilateral triangle is a triangle with three equal sides.
    (*b*) Is the converse true?

2. (*a*) Write the converse of:
    If a smaller body is revolving around a larger one, it is a satellite.
    (*b*) Is the converse true?

3. Do the following sentences satisfy the requirement that a good definition must be reversible?
    (*a*) If two angles coincide, they are equal angles.
    (*b*) A pencil is an instrument used for writing.
    (*c*) If a line segment is bisected, it is divided into two equal parts.
    (*d*) A rumor is an unverified report passing from person to person.

4. (*a*) In a dictionary, find definitions of *rug, putty, pedestrian*, and *broom*.
    (*b*) Test each definition to see whether it is reversible.

5. In each of the following supply the missing word or words which will make the statement reversible and a good definition.
    (*a*) If a line is perpendicular to another line, it makes equal angles with the other line.
    (*b*) If a figure is a trapezoid, it has two parallel sides.
    (*c*) If an angle is bisected, it is divided into two parts.

402. *The converse of a postulate, or theorem, or of a nonmathematical statement may or may not be true.* For example:

(*a*) Postulate 18, p. 35, the converse of Postulate 16, is true.

(*b*) The converses of Postulates 8 and 10 are false.

(*c*) If a car driver is speeding, he is violating a traffic law.
    Conversely. If a car driver is violating a traffic law, he is speeding. False.

In Exercises 1 *through* 4, *write the converse and tell whether it is true.*

1. The diagonals of a square are perpendicular to each other.

2. If two points are each equidistant from the ends of a line segment, the line through the two points is the perpendicular bisector of the line segment.

3. Crops die when there is no rain.

4. If a majority of the club members vote for Tom Taylor, he becomes the new president of the club.

403. *Often a conclusion may be false because it is supported by the converse of an accepted statement, when in fact the converse is not true.* For example:

An intelligent and studious person will master algebra if he has a good teacher. John, who is both intelligent and studious, has mastered algebra.

Someone may infer that John has had a good teacher. Actually John may not have had a teacher. He may be self-taught.

The conclusion is wrong because it is based on the converse statement, "If a person has mastered algebra, he has had a good teacher," which is not necessarily true.

5. Automobiles with defective steering apparatus are unsafe. Tom's car did not pass the safety test.
   Conclusion. Tom's car has defective steering apparatus.
   Is this conclusion justified by the premises?
   May this have been the reason why Tom's car failed to pass the safety test?

6. If people receive high wages, they can live well. The family of Mr. Bryant lives well.
   Conclusion. Mr. Bryant receives high wages.
   Is this conclusion necessarily true?

7. If a nation is aggressive, it has a large military force. Nation X has a large military force.
   Conclusion. Nation X is aggressive.
   Is this conclusion necessarily true?

8. If a member of the Y Party is elected, taxes will increase. Taxes did increase.
   Conclusion. A member of the Y Party was elected.
   Is this conclusion necessarily true?

404. Related theorems such as those in §360, p. 330, occur also when mathematics is not involved. An understanding of the following four related statements is helpful in clear thinking.

   I. *Original statement.* If it is raining, we postpone the game.
  II. *Converse.* If we postpone the game, it is raining.
 III. *Inverse.* If it is not raining, we do not postpone the game.
 IV. *Contrapositive.* If we do not postpone the game, it is not raining.

To talk in general about compound sentences such as these, it is convenient to let p and q represent simple sentences, as "It is raining," "A boy runs," or "The triangles are congruent." In this case, if p represents "It is raining," and q represents "We postpone the game," then the above sentences become:

	Hypothesis	Conclusion
I. *Original statement*	If p,	then q.
II. *Converse*	If q,	then p.
III. *Inverse*	If *not p*,	then *not q*.
IV. *Contrapositive*	If *not q*,	then *not p*.

We see from this: to form the converse of a statement, we interchange the hypothesis and the conclusion; to form the inverse, negate the hypothesis and the conclusion; to form the contrapositive, negate the hypothesis and the conclusion and interchange them. Observe that the contrapositive is the converse of the inverse. It is also the inverse of the converse.

If I (the original statement) is true, then IV (the contrapositive) is true, and conversely. We use the indirect method.

Hypothesis. "If p, then q," is true.

Conclusion. "If *not q*, then *not p*," is true.

Proof. If the conclusion were false, then "If not q, then p" would be true. But "If p, then q" is true by hypothesis. These two statements lead to the contradiction "If not q, then q." ∴ the conclusion "If not q, then not p" is true by §86.

Prove in a similar manner.

1. If IV is true, then I is true.   **2.** If II is true, then III is true.
3. If III is true, then II is true.

The relations proved on page 385 lead us to the conclusion that a statement and its contrapositive are either both true or both false. If one of them is proved, the other automatically is true. The same is true for the converse and the inverse.

Statement   Converse

Inverse   Contrapositive

In particular, where the proof of a locus theorem calls for proving a statement and its inverse, it is equally correct to prove the statement and its converse.

In Exercises 1 through 7, write in if—then form the four statements described on page 385, if p and q are the sentences given. Tell which of the four resulting statements are true.

1. *p:* Two sides of a triangle are equal.
   q: The angles opposite these sides are equal.

2. *p:* A point is equidistant from the sides of an angle.
   q: The point is on the bisector of the angle.

3. *p:* Two triangles are congruent.
   q: The three angles of one triangle are equal respectively to the three angles of the other triangle.

4. *p:* Two angles are equal.
   q: They are vertical angles.

5. *p:* The diagonals of a quadrilateral bisect each other.
   q: The quadrilateral is a parallelogram.

6. *p:* The diagonals of a quadrilateral are equal.
   q: The quadrilateral is a rectangle.

7. *p:* Two triangles are similar.
   q: The triangles are equal in area.

In Exercises 8 through 14,
(a) Write the converse, the inverse, and the contrapositive.
(b) Tell which of the four statements are true, or probably true.

8. If a lawn is fertilized, the grass will be green.

9. If a tree has acorns, it is a maple tree.

10. If a person does not have enough rest, he cannot study well.

11. If a person is a student in the school, he has a registration card in the office.

12. If a boy is a good swimmer, he is not likely to drown.

13. If there is a heavy snowstorm, plane flights are canceled.

14. If you live in southern Florida, you do not need a fur coat.

ADDITIONAL EXERCISES

Note to the Teacher. Cross references to the following exercises appear in the textbook, as the note on page 62. This footnote means that all theorems needed in the proofs of the listed exercises, and of all exercises in this set that precede them, have been studied.

The exercises on pages 387 through 410 marked with a star are more difficult than the rest.

1. If $AO \perp CE$, $AO = OE$, and $BO = OH$, prove $AB = HE$.

2. If AD bisects BG, and $AO = OD$, prove $AB = DG$.

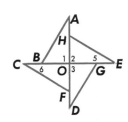

3. If $AOD \perp COE$ and bisects COE, and $\angle 6 = \angle 5$, prove $CF = HE$.

4. Let $AB \perp DF$, $\angle 1 = \angle 2$, $BC = BE$, and B bisect DF.
   (a) Then $CD = EF$.
   (b) What angle equals $\angle C$?

5. Let $AB = CD$, E bisect CD, F bisect AB, $AB \perp BC$, and $DC \perp BC$.
   (a) Prove $CF = BE$.
   (b) Prove $\angle 1 = \angle 2$.
   (c) Prove $\angle 3 = \angle 4$.

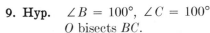

6. If two opposite angles of a quadrilateral are bisected by the line joining their vertices, then two congruent triangles are formed.

7. If $AE \perp AC$, $CD \perp AC$, B bisects AC and $\angle 1 = \angle 2$, then $BE = BD$.

8. If BX bisects $\angle DBE$, $BE = BD$, $BX \perp AC$, and B bisects AC, then $AE = CD$.

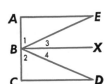

9. **Hyp.** $\angle B = 100°$, $\angle C = 100°$
   O bisects BC.

   Con. (a) $\triangle ACO \cong \triangle BDO$
   (b) $\angle A = \angle D$

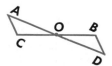

10. Hyp. $\angle 1 = \angle 2$, $\angle 3 = \angle 4$
   Con. $AB = CD$, $\angle A = \angle C$

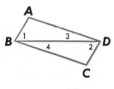

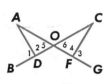

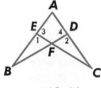

EX. 10   EX. 11   EX. 12–14

11. Hyp. $OD = OF$ **Con.** (a) $\angle A = \angle C$
          $\angle 1 = \angle 3$ (b) $AO = OC$

12. If $AB = AC$ and $\angle B = \angle C$, prove that $BD = EC$.

13. If $AE = AD$, $CE \perp AB$, and $BD \perp AC$, prove $\angle B = \angle C$.

14. If $AD = AE$ and $\angle 3 = \angle 4$, then $DB = EC$.

15. Draw $\triangle ABC$ having $AB \perp BC$, and $\triangle XYZ$ having $XY \perp YZ$. Make $AB = XY$ and $BC = YZ$. Prove $\triangle ABC \cong \triangle XYZ$.

16. If $\angle ABC = \angle DCB$ and $\angle 2$ equals $\angle 4$, then $AB = CD$.

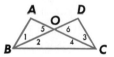

17. After proving Ex. 16, prove that $AO = OD$.

18. If $AB = AC$, $AD \perp AB$, $AE \perp AC$, and $\angle 1 = \angle 2$, then $CE = BD$.

19. If $AB = AC$, $AD = AE$, $AD \perp AB$, and $AE \perp AC$, then $BD = EC$.

20. If $AB = AC$, $\angle 3 = \angle 4$ and $AD = AE$, then $BD = EC$.

21. If isosceles triangles ABC and BDC are on opposite sides of their common base BC, then $\angle ABD = \angle ACD$.

22. If the base of an isosceles triangle be trisected, the segments joining the points of division to the vertex of the triangle are equal.

Suggestion. Trisected means divided into three equal parts.

23. If $AB = AC$, $\angle DBC = \angle ECB$, and $BD = CE$, then $AD = AE$.

24. In isosceles $\triangle ABC$, BS and CR are drawn so that $\angle 1 = \angle 3$. Prove that $BS = CR$.

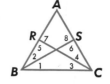

25. If $AB = AC$ and $\angle 2 = \angle 4$, then $\angle 5 = \angle 6$.

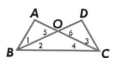

26. If $AB = DC$ and $AC = BD$, prove $\triangle AOB \cong \triangle OCD$.

27. If $AB = DC$ and $AC = BD$, then $\triangle BOC$ is isosceles.

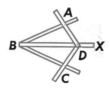

28. AB, BC, and BX are attached at B but can be moved around B. $AB = BC$; AD and DC can move around points A and C respectively; $AD = DC$. At D, AD and DC are attached to BX so that they can slide together along BX. If AB and CB are placed on the sides of an angle, prove that BX bisects the angle.

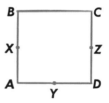

29. As you know, the sides of a square are equal and the angles are all right angles. In the adjoining square, assume that X bisects AB, Y bisects AD, Z bisects CD.
   Prove: (a) $XY = YZ$ (b) $XD = AZ$
          (c) $CX = BY$ (d) $BZ = CY$

30. Hyp. $AB = BC$
             $AD = DC$
     Con. $AX = CX$

31. Hyp. $AD = DC$
             $\angle 1 = \angle 2$
     Con. $AB = BC$
             $AX = XC$

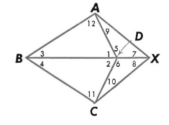

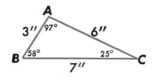

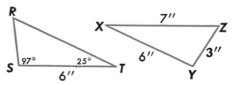

32. (a) Prove $\triangle ABC \cong \triangle RST$, also $\triangle ABC \cong \triangle XYZ$.
   (b) How long is: RS? RT?
   (c) How large is: $\angle X$? $\angle Y$? $\angle Z$?
   (d) Prove $\triangle RST \cong \triangle XYZ$.

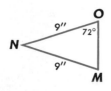 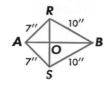

33. How large is ∠M? What is *the* base of △MNO?

34. If RO = 4 in., how long is OS? How large is ∠AOR?

35. How do ∠X, ∠Y, and ∠Z compare?

36. How does ∠2 compare with ∠1?

37. If AB ∥ CD and ∠1 = ∠4:
(a) Prove ∠3 = ∠7.
(b) Prove ∠6 = ∠13.
(c) Prove ∠4 = ∠12.
(d) Prove ∠4 is supp. of ∠11.
(e) Prove ∠3 is supp. of ∠14.
(f) Prove ∠1 = ∠12.

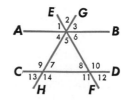

38. If AB = AC, BD = DC, XY ∥ BC,
and ZW ∥ BC:
(a) Prove ∠1 + ∠4 = ∠ABD.
(b) Prove ∠8 = ∠2.
(c) Prove ∠7 = ∠5.
(d) Prove ∠4 = ∠5.
(e) Prove ∠ACD = ∠4 + ∠8.

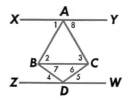

39. In ABCD, BC ∥ AD.
(a) Prove ∠A + ∠B = 180°.
(b) If ∠A = ∠D,
prove ∠B = ∠C.

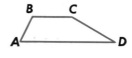

40. Hyp. AB = XZ, AC = YZ
BY = CX
Con. AB ∥ XZ

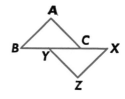

41. Hyp. AB ∥ XZ, AB = XZ
BY = CX
Con. AC ∥ YZ

42. △ABC is isosceles having AB = AC. From B, line BD is drawn below BC, parallel to AC. Prove that BC bisects ∠ABD.

43. If a line a is perpendicular to a line x, a line b is perpendicular to a line y, and x is parallel to y, prove that a must be parallel to b.

44. How large is the second acute angle of a right triangle if the first acute angle of the triangle is:
(a) 40°?   (b) 75°?   (c) 35°?   (d) 40°30′?

45. The vertex angle of an isosceles triangle contains 50°. How large is:
(a) Each base angle?
(b) The exterior angle at each end of the base?

46. The exterior angle at the vertex of an isosceles triangle contains 100°. How large is each base angle of the triangle?

47. In $\triangle ABC$, $\angle B = 90°$, $BD \perp AC$ at D, and $\angle A = 35°$.
Find: (a) $\angle C$ (b) $\angle ABD$ (c) $\angle DBC$

48. In $\triangle XYZ$, $XY = XZ$, $\angle X = 50°$, and $YW \perp XZ$.
Find: (a) $\angle Z$ (b) $\angle XYW$ (c) $\angle ZYW$

49. If $\angle A$ of $\triangle ABC$ contains 40° and $\angle B$ contains 80°, how many degrees are there in the angle between the bisectors of $\angle A$ and $\angle B$?

50. In $\triangle ABC$, $AB = AC$, RC bisects $\angle C$ meeting AB at R, BS bisects $\angle B$ meeting AC at S, and $\angle A = 50°$.
Find: (a) $\angle CBS$ (b) $\angle SCR$ (c) $\angle ASB$

51. In $\triangle ABC$, $AB = AC$, $CR \perp AB$ at R, $BS \perp AC$ at S, and $\angle CBA = 50°$.
Find: (a) $\angle BCR$ (b) $\angle BRC$ (c) $\angle A$

52. If two opposite angles of a quadrilateral are equal, and the diagonal joining the other two angles bisects one of them, then it bisects the other also.

53. The exterior angle at the vertex of an isosceles triangle is double either of the base angles of the triangle.

54. The perpendiculars drawn from any point in the base of an isosceles triangle to the equal sides of the triangle make equal angles with the base of the triangle.

55. Prove that the altitude drawn to the hypotenuse of a right triangle separates the right angle into two parts that are equal respectively to the acute angles of the triangle.

56. Hyp. $AB \parallel CD$, AD bisects $\angle CAB$.
          CB bisects $\angle ACD$.
   Con.   (a) $AD \perp CB$ at E
          (b) $CE = EB$
          (c) $AE = ED$

57. Find the three angles of a triangle if the second is equal to four times the first, and the third is seven times the first. (Use algebra.)

58. If the sum of two angles of a triangle equals the third angle, the triangle is a right triangle.

59. Prove that the angle formed by the bisectors of two angles of a triangle always is an obtuse angle.

60. Prove that the exterior angle at the base of an isosceles triangle equals the angle between the bisectors of the base angles.

61. In $\triangle ABC$, $AB = AC$; D bisects AB; E bisects AC; $DY \perp AB$, meeting BC at Y; $EX \perp AC$, meeting BC at X. Prove that $DY = EX$.

62. In $\triangle ABC$, $\angle A = 90°$; BD the bisector of $\angle B$ meets AC at D; $DE \perp BC$ at E. Prove that $AB = BE$.

63. In $\triangle ABC$, $AB = BC$; AB is extended through B to K, and CB through B to L, so that $BL = BK$. Prove that $KL \parallel AC$.

64. If equal oblique segments are drawn to a line from a point on a perpendicular to the line, they cut off equal segments from the foot of the perpendicular, and make equal angles with the perpendicular.

65. If $\angle A$ of $\triangle ABC$ equals $90°$; if E is on BC so that $BE = BA$; if $ED \perp BC$, meeting AC at D; then BD bisects $\angle ABC$.

66. Prove that the altitudes drawn to two corresponding sides of two congruent triangles are equal.

67. If a line through one vertex of a triangle, parallel to the opposite side, makes equal angles with the two sides that meet at the vertex, then the two sides are equal.

68. In $\triangle ABC$, $AB = AC$. From X on AB, XY is drawn parallel to AC, meeting BC at Y. Prove $\triangle BXY$ is isosceles.

69. D is any point in the base BC of isosceles $\triangle ABC$. The side AC is extended from C to E so that CE equals CD, and ED is drawn, meeting AB at F. Prove that $\angle AFE = 3\angle AEF$.

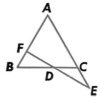

Suggestions. $\angle AFE$ is exterior to $\triangle DBF$.

$\angle B = \angle ACD$, which is exterior to $\triangle CDE$.

70. By means of straightedge and compasses, trisect:
(*a*) A right angle.   (*b*) A straight angle.   (*c*) A 45° angle.

71. A line parallel to any side of an equilateral triangle, cutting the other two sides, forms with the latter another equilateral triangle.

72. In $\triangle BCD$, $BC = BD$; CB is extended through B to A; $\angle ABD = 120°$. Prove that $\triangle BCD$ is equilateral.

73. Hyp. $AB = AC$, $AS = SC$,
$$AR = RB$$
     Con. $\triangle BOC$ is isosceles.

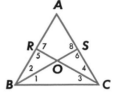

74. Hyp. $AB = AC$, BS bisects $\angle ABC$.
          CR bisects $\angle ACB$.
     Con. $\triangle BOC$ is isosceles.

75. Hyp. $AB = AC$, $BS \perp AC$
$$CR \perp AB.$$
     Con. $\triangle BOC$ is isosceles.

76. In $\triangle ABC$, $AB = BC$. E is taken on AB; BC is extended through C to D so that $CD = AE$; ED is drawn cutting AC at O. Prove that O bisects ED.

Suggestion. Draw $EX \parallel BD$, meeting AC at X.

77. In $\square ABCD$, having $\angle B = 30°$ and $AB = 12$ in., altitude AE is drawn to BC. How long is AE?

78. In $\square ABCD$, CD and AB are both perpendicular to diagonal AC, and $AC = DC$.
    Find: (*a*) The size of $\angle D$.   (*b*) The size of $\angle DAB$.

79. Hyp. $XYZW$ is a $\square$.
           $YR \perp XZ$, at R.
           $WS \perp XZ$, at S.
     Con. $RYSW$ is a $\square$.

80. Hyp. $XYZW$ is a $\square$; YR bisects $\angle Y$, meeting XZ at R.
           WS bisects $\angle W$, meeting XZ at S.
     Con. $RYSW$ is a $\square$.

81. Hyp. $ABCD$ is a $\square$.
           $AX = CZ$
           $BY = DW$
     Con. (*a*) $XY \parallel WZ$
              (*b*) $XW \parallel YZ$

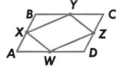

★**82.** Prove that the line joining the mid-points of the diagonals of a trapezoid is parallel to the bases and equal to half their difference.

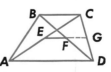

Suggestions. 1. Draw $EG \parallel AD$, meeting CD at G.
       2. Prove EG passes through point F.
       3. Compare EG with AD, and FG with BC.

83. Hyp. $ABCD$ is a $\square$.
          BA is extended to X,
          and DC to Y so that
          $AX = CY$.
          Similarly, $AZ = CW$.

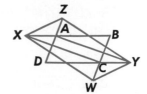

    Con.   (a) $XAYC$ is a $\square$.
          (b) $XZYW$ is a $\square$.
          (c) AC, BD, XY, and ZW
                 bisect each other.

★**84.** Given a point P inside $\angle ABC$. Through P construct a segment ending on AB and CB that is bisected by point P.

Suggestion. Draw BP and extend it to D so that $DP = BP$. The required line is the other diagonal of a parallelogram of which BD is one diagonal.

★**85.** Prove that the bisectors of the interior angles of a parallelogram form a rectangle unless they meet at a point.

★**86.** Prove that the bisectors of the angles of a rectangle form a square unless they meet at a point.

87. What construction must you do at the center of a circle if you wish to divide the circle into:
(a) 10 equal parts?   (b) 6 equal parts?   (c) 5 equal parts?

88. If a circle circumscribes an isosceles triangle having $AB = AC = 2$ in., and $BC = 1.5$ in., prove that $\overset{\frown}{AB}$ equal $\overset{\frown}{AC}$.

89. If the perpendiculars from a point of an arc to the radii drawn to the ends of the arc are equal, then the point bisects the arc.

90. Assume that a circle O is divided into six equal arcs. Prove that the chords of these arcs and the radii drawn to the ends of the arcs form six congruent equilateral triangles.

91. In Ex. 90 how many degrees are there in the central angle formed by two consecutive radii?

92. AOB and COD are chords. If $AO = OC$ and $BO - OD$, prove that $\overset{\frown}{AD} - \overset{\frown}{BC}$.

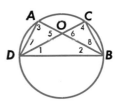

93. If $AB = DC$, prove that $AO = OC$ and $DO = OB$.

Suggestion. Draw BD. Prove $\angle 1$ equals $\angle 2$ by proving $\triangle ADB \cong \triangle DCB$.

94. Chord XY is parallel to diameter ZW. Prove $\overset{\frown}{XZ} = \overset{\frown}{YW}$.

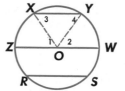

95. Chord XY is parallel to chord RS. Prove $\overset{\frown}{XR} = \overset{\frown}{YS}$.

★ 96. From point A of a circle O, chords AB and AC are drawn on opposite sides of diameter AOD. Prove that $\angle BOD$ plus $\angle DOC$ equals twice $\angle BAC$.

★ 97. A, B, C, D, and E in order on a circle divide the circle into five equal arcs.
   (a) Prove that polygon $ABCDE$ is equilateral.
   (b) Prove that any two diagonals of $ABCDE$ are equal.
   (c) Prove that $\angle A = \angle C$, and also $\angle A = \angle B$.

98. Prove that the perpendiculars from the center of a circle to the sides of an inscribed equilateral polygon are equal.

99. In a circle construct a chord that is equal to a given chord.

100. In a circle construct a chord that is equal and parallel to a given chord.

101. A chord is parallel to a tangent. Prove that the diameter of the circle that is drawn to the point of contact of the tangent is perpendicular to the chord.

102. If two circles are concentric, any chord of the larger that is tangent to the smaller is bisected by its point of contact with the smaller circle.

103. Prove that the angle formed by two tangents is supplementary to the angle formed by the radii drawn to their points of contact.

★ 104. Draw any chord AB of a circle O and find its mid-point C. Prove that AB is tangent to the circle drawn with center O and radius OC.

★ 105. Prove that a parallelogram circumscribed about a circle must be a rhombus or a square.
Suggestion. Use Ex. 10, p. 174.

★ 106. (a) If tangents are drawn to a circle at the extremities of any pair of diameters that are not perpendicular to each other, they form a rhombus.
   (b) Can they ever form a square?

★**107.** *AB* and *AC* are tangents to a circle from *A*, and *D* is any point in the smaller of the arcs subtended by the chord *BC*. If a tangent to the circle at *D* meets *AB* at *E* and *AC* at *F*, prove that the perimeter of △*AEF* = *AB* + *AC*.

★**108.** If *ABCD* is a quadrilateral circumscribed about a circle whose center is *O*, prove that
∠*AOB* + ∠*COD* = 180°.

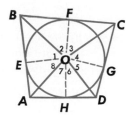

Suggestion. Compare ∠*EOB* and ∠*BOF;* also ∠*EOA* and ∠*AOH;* etc.

109. The base of an inscribed isosceles triangle is a diameter of a circle. How large is each angle of the triangle?

110. Points *R*, *S*, *T*, *W*, and *X*, in order, divide a circle into five equal arcs. Prove that ∠*RXS* = ∠*SWT* = ∠*XSW*.

111. The angles of an inscribed triangle measure 30°, 70°, and 80°, respectively. How large are the arcs of which the sides of the triangle are chords?

112. Prove that the chords joining in order the four points that divide a circle into four equal arcs form a square.

113. *AC* and *DE* are perpendicular diameters of a circle *O*. *B* is any point of $\overset{\frown}{AEC}$. How large is ∠*ABC?* ∠*ABD?* ∠*DBC?*

114. If equal chords are drawn from opposite ends of a diameter and on opposite sides of it, they must be parallel.

115. Chords *AB* and *CD* are equal. When they are extended through *B* and *D*, respectively, they meet at *E*. Prove △*ACE* is isosceles.

116. If *A*, *B*, *C*, and *D* are four points in order on a circle, and if $\overset{\frown}{AB} = \overset{\frown}{BC} = \overset{\frown}{CD}$, then *ABCD* is an isosceles trapezoid whose diagonal *AC* bisects ∠*A*.

117. Two opposite sides of an inscribed quadrilateral are equal. Prove that the figure is an isosceles trapezoid or a rectangle.
Suggestion. Draw a diagonal.

118. Draw any △*ABC*. Construct the circle that has *AB* as diameter, cutting *AC* at *Y* and *BC* at *X*. Prove that *AX* and *BY* are the altitudes to *BC* and *AC*, respectively.

119. Two chords that are perpendicular to a third chord at its extremities are equal.
Suggestion. Prove that their arcs are equal.

120. AB is the common chord of two circles that intersect. AC and AD are diameters. Prove CBD is a straight line.

121. Chord AC is parallel to diameter XOY. AOB is the diameter from A. Prove that $\overarc{CY} = \overarc{YB}$.

★**122.** AOB is a diameter of circle O, and C is any point of semicircle AB. AC is extended its own length to D, and D is joined to B. Prove that $\triangle ABD$ is isosceles.

★**123.** AB and CD are equal chords of circle O. If AB, extended through B, and CD, extended through D, meet at E, prove that $AE = CE$ and $BE = DE$, without using §182.

★**124.** The circle drawn on one side of an equilateral triangle as diameter bisects each of the other sides of the triangle.

★**125.** Chords AB and BC are drawn from point B on a circle. CB is extended through B to D. Prove that $\angle ABD \overset{m}{=} \tfrac{1}{2}\overarc{ABC}$.

★**126.** $\triangle ABC$ is inscribed in circle O. $AD \perp BC$ at D. AOE is a diameter. CE is drawn. Prove that $\triangle ABD$ and $\triangle ACE$ are mutually equiangular.

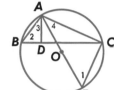

★**127.** If a quadrilateral is inscribed in a circle, the exterior angle formed at any vertex by extending one of the sides equals the interior angle at the opposite vertex.

128. $ABCD$ is a square inscribed in circle O. XY is tangent to circle O at A. Prove XY is parallel to BD.

129. BE is tangent to a circle at B; EDC is a secant cutting the circle at D and C. Prove $\triangle BDE$ and $\triangle BEC$ mutually equiangular.

130. From point B tangents are drawn to circle O, meeting it at A and C, respectively; AC, OA, and OC are drawn. Prove that $\angle AOC = 2\angle BAC$.

★**131.** Quadrilateral $ABCD$ is inscribed in a circle. Prove that $\angle ADC$ equals the angle formed with AB by the tangent at B, increased by the angle the tangent makes with BC.

★**132.** $ABCD$ is inscribed in a circle. AD and BC extended meet at P. A circle is circumscribed about $\triangle ABP$ and XY is drawn tangent to it at P. Prove $XY \parallel CD$.

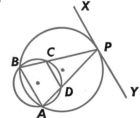

Suggestion. Compare $\angle DCP$ and $\angle XPC$ each with $\angle BAD$.

133. AOB is a diameter of a circle. AC and DB are two chords that intersect at E. If $\angle AEB = 120°$, how many degrees are there in $\overset{\frown}{DC}$?

134. $\triangle ABC$ is inscribed in a circle. D and E bisect $\overset{\frown}{AB}$ and $\overset{\frown}{AC}$, respectively. DE cuts AB at F and AC at G. Prove that $AF = AG$.

★135. If sides AB and BC of inscribed quadrilateral $ABCD$ have arcs of 69° and 112°, respectively, and $\angle AED$ between the diagonals is 87°, how many degrees are there in each angle of the quadrilateral?

Suggestion. Let $x = \overset{\frown}{AD}$ and $y = \overset{\frown}{CD}$.

136. Two tangents are drawn to a circle from point X. They form an angle of 45°. How large are the minor and the major arcs made by their points of contact?

137. Let OB be any ray from O, inside $\angle AOC$. Take Y and Y' on OB. Draw YX and $Y'X' \perp OA$; draw YZ and $Y'Z' \perp OC$. Prove $OX : OX' = OZ : OZ'$.

138. $XY \parallel WZ$, and $YR \parallel WS$.
(a) Prove $BX : XZ = BR : RS$.
(b) Prove $BX : BZ = BR : BS$.
(c) Prove $XZ : BZ = RS : BS$.

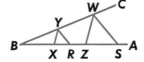

139. From points X, Y, and Z on side OB of $\angle AOB$ perpendiculars are drawn to OA, meeting OA at R, S, and T respectively.

Prove that $\dfrac{OX}{OR} = \dfrac{OY}{OS} = \dfrac{OZ}{OT}$.

140. Point O lies inside and is joined to the vertices of pentagon $ABCDE$. Point X is placed on OA one third the way from O to A; Y on OB, one third the way from O to B; and Z, W, and K are placed similarly on OC, OD, and OE. Prove that $ABCDE$ and $XYZWK$ are mutually equiangular.

Suggestion. Prove that the corresponding sides are parallel and then use §101.

141. One of two similar triangles has angles that measure 37°, 83°, and 60°, respectively. How large are the angles of the other triangle?

142. The sides of one pentagon are 5, 7, 8, 10, and 11 in., respectively. The shortest side of a similar pentagon is 15 in. What is the perimeter of the second pentagon?

143. Prove that any two isosceles right triangles are similar.

144. In the figure at the right, prove $\triangle ADE \backsim \triangle CBE$.

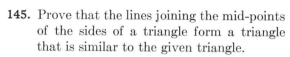

145. Prove that the lines joining the mid-points of the sides of a triangle form a triangle that is similar to the given triangle.

146. $\triangle ABC \backsim \triangle XYZ$. BD bisects $\angle B$, meeting AC at D; YW bisects $\angle Y$, meeting XZ at W. Prove $\triangle BDC \backsim \triangle YWZ$ and $\triangle ABD \backsim \triangle XYW$.

147. In similar triangles ABC and XYZ, corresponding altitudes BD and YW are drawn. Prove that two pairs of similar triangles are formed.

★**148.** In the adjoining figure, prove that $\triangle WPZ \backsim \triangle RPS$.

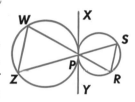

149. Let AC be the hypotenuse of right $\triangle ABC$, and E and F be any points of AB and BC, respectively; let ED and FG be perpendicular to AC, meeting AC at D and G, respectively. Prove $\triangle AED \backsim \triangle FGC$.

150. The diagonals of a trapezoid whose bases are AD and BC intersect at E. If $AE = 9$ in., $EC = 3$ in., and $BD = 16$ in., find BE and ED.

Suggestion. Let $BE = x$ and $ED = 16 - x$.

151. AB is the hypotenuse of rt. $\triangle ABC$. AE, $\perp AB$ at A, meets BC extended at E; BD, $\perp AB$ at B, meets AC extended at D. Prove that $AE : AB = CB : CD$.

152. $\triangle ABC$ has a right angle at B. From D, any point on AB, DE is drawn perpendicular to AC at E. Prove that $DE : BC = AD : AC$.

153. AB is a common interior tangent of circles C and D, touching $\odot C$ at A and $\odot D$ at B. AB cuts CD at E. Prove $CE : ED = CA : BD$.

154. ABC is a triangular lot having $BC = 40$ ft., $AB = 150$ ft., and $AC = 120$ ft. DE, $\parallel BC$, cuts AB at D, and AC at E. $DB = 25$ ft. How long are the sides of lot ADE?

155. In trapezoid $ABCD$, diagonals AC and BD intersect at O. If base $AD = 2BC$, then $OD = 2BO$ and $OA = 2OC$.

156. AB is tangent externally to $\odot C$ at A and to $\odot D$ at B. AB cuts CD extended at E. Prove CE and DE have the same ratio as the radii of the circles.

157. Diameter AOB of circle O is extended to C. BD is tangent to circle O at B, meeting secant AE at D. $CF \perp AE$ at F.
Prove $DB : AB = CF : AF$.

158. $\triangle ABC$ is inscribed in $\odot O$. $BD \perp AC$ at D. Diameter COE is drawn.
Prove $BD : AB = BC : CE$.

159. In $\triangle ABX$, $AB = 12$ in. and $BX = 16$ in. AB is extended through B to C and XB through B to Y, so that $BY = 12$ in. and $BC = 9$ in. Are $\triangle ABX$ and BCY similar?

160. In trapezoid $ABCD$ with bases AD and BC, diagonals BD and AC intersect at O. If $BO = 3$, $OD = 6$, $AO = 8$, and $OC = 4$.
(*a*) Are $\triangle ADO$ and CBO similar?
(*b*) If $\triangle ABO \backsim \triangle CDO$, what angle does $\angle BAO$ equal?

161. In two similar triangles, the bisectors of two corresponding angles are drawn. Prove that the bisectors have the same ratio as any two corresponding sides.

162. In $\triangle ABC$, $AB = 3$ in.; $BC = 4$ in.; $AC = 6$ in. In $\triangle XYZ$, $XY = 12$ in.; $XZ = 6$ in.; $YZ = 8$ in.
(*a*) Are the triangles similar? Why?
(*b*) If $\angle A = m°$ and $\angle B = n°$, how large is $\angle Z$?

163. In $\triangle ABC$, $AB = 10$, $BC = 12$, and $AC = 14$. In $\triangle XYZ$, $XY = 5$, $YZ = 7$, and $XZ = 9$. Are the triangles similar?

164. Determine three segments that bear to the sides of a given triangle the ratio $3 : 2$. Then construct the triangle having the new segments as sides. Are the two triangles similar?

165. The shadow of a chimney is 36 ft. long. At the same time, the shadow of a pole 2 yd. high is 1.5 yd. long. How high is the chimney?

166. The base and altitude of a triangle are 5 ft. and 3 ft., respectively. If the corresponding base of a similar triangle is 7 ft., find its corresponding altitude.

167. In $\triangle ABC$, $\angle B = 90°$. P is any point on AB, and Q is any point on BC. PR and QS are perpendiculars from P and Q to AC.
Prove $AP : QC = AR : QS$.

⋆ **168.** Point P, outside $\triangle ABC$, is joined to its vertices. Through any point X of AP, XY is drawn parallel to AB, meeting BP at Y. YZ is drawn parallel to BC, meeting PC at Z. XZ is drawn. Prove $\triangle XYZ \backsim \triangle ABC$.

⋆ **169.** $\triangle ABC$ is inscribed in a circle having diameter AC. BD, the bisector of $\angle B$, meets AC at D and the circle at E.
(a) Prove $BA : BE = BD : BC$.
(b) Prove $AD : AB = EC : BE$.

⋆ **170.** Two circles, on opposite sides of XY, are tangent to it at C. Through C, a straight line is drawn, meeting the first circle at A and the second at $D;$ another straight line through C meets the first circle at B and the second circle at E. Prove that $AC : CD = BC : CE$.

⋆ **171.** Circles O and R are tangent externally at B. EBD is a secant through B, meeting $\odot O$ at E and $\odot R$ at D. Prove that BE and BD have the same ratio as the radii of the circles.

⋆ **172.** $\angle A$ of $\triangle ABC$ is a right angle. $DEFG$ is a square, having E and F on BC, D on AC, and G on AB. Prove $CE : EF = EF : FB$.

⋆ **173.** $\triangle ABC$ is inscribed in a circle, of which AD is diameter. A tangent to the circle at D cuts AB extended at X, and AC extended at Y. Prove $\triangle ABC$ similar to $\triangle AXY$.
Suggestion. Prove $\angle Y = \angle ABC$.

⋆ **174.** If E is the mid-point of one of the parallel sides BC of trapezoid $ABCD$, and AE and DE extended meet DC and AB extended at F and G, respectively, then FG is parallel to BC.
Suggestion. Prove $GB : GA = FE : FA$.

175. The tangent to a circle from a point is 15 in. long. A secant from the same point is 25 in. long. How long is the external segment of the secant?

176. The diameter of a circle is 12 in. From a point that is 10 in. from the center of the circle, a tangent is drawn. How long is the tangent?

177. Prove that the tangents to two intersecting circles from any point in their common chord extended are equal.

178. If two circles intersect, their common chord extended bisects their common external tangents.

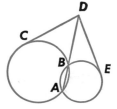

179. Find CD when $\angle C = 90°$:
    (a) If $AD = 3$, $DB = 27$.
    (b) If $AD = 4$, $DB = 8$.

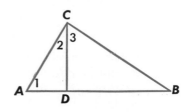

180. Find AC when $\angle C = 90°$:
    (a) If $AD = 3$, $AB = 12$.
    (b) If $AD = 4$, $DB = 5$.

181. Find BC when $\angle C = 90°$:
    (a) If $AB = 12$, $DB = 4$.
    (b) If $AD = 10$, $DB = 6$.

182. The center of a chord that is 16 in. long is 2 in. from the center of its arc. What is the diameter of the circle?

183. If the height of a circular arc is 2 ft. and its span is 10 ft., what is the diameter of it?

184. If the altitude to the hypotenuse of a right triangle is drawn, prove that the segments of the hypotenuse have the same ratio as the squares of the adjacent legs of the triangle.

★**185.** In $\triangle ABC$, $AB = AC$. $BD \perp AC$ at D. Prove that BC is the mean proportional between CD and $2AC$.
Suggestion. Extend CA through A to E so that $AE = CA$. Draw BE and prove $\angle CBE$ is a right angle.

186. Let $ABCD$ be any rectangle. Draw $BE \perp AC$, meeting CD extended at F, and $FG \perp BA$ extended at G. Prove BC is the mean proportional between AB and BG.

187. In rectangle $ABCD$, draw $BX \perp AC$ at X, meeting AD at Y. Draw $YZ \perp BC$ at Z. Prove AB is the mean proportional between AY and BC.

188. In $\square ABCD$, X is on BC. AX cuts BD at O and DC extended at Y. Prove that AO is the mean proportional between OX and OY.
Suggestion. Prove each of two ratios equal to a third.

189. The radii of two concentric circles are 12 in. and 15 in., respectively. How long is the chord of the larger circle that is tangent to the smaller circle?

190. A point is 17 in. from the center of a circle with 8-in. radius. How long is the tangent to the circle from this point?

191. How long is a chord of a circle of radius 10 in. that is 6 in. from the center of the circle?

192. How far from the center of a circle with radius 10 in. is a chord that is 8 in. long?

★**193.** How long must the side of a square be in order that the diagonal shall be 12 in.?

Suggestion. Let x = the length of a side.

★**194.** How long are the sides of an equilateral triangle whose altitude is 9 in.?

195. The hypotenuse of a right triangle is 20 in. long. How long are the other two sides of the triangle if one of the acute angles: (*a*) Contains 45°? (*b*) Contains 30°?

196. If a parallel to the hypotenuse AB of rt. $\triangle ABC$ meets AC and BC at D and E, respectively, prove that
$$\overline{AE}^2 + \overline{BD}^2 = \overline{AB}^2 + \overline{DE}^2.$$

197. If perpendiculars PF, PD, and PE be drawn from any point P inside acute-angled triangle ABC to sides AB, BC, and AC, respectively, prove that

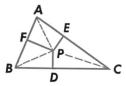

$$\overline{AF}^2 + \overline{BD}^2 + \overline{CE}^2 = \overline{AE}^2 + \overline{BF}^2 + \overline{CD}^2.$$

198. One side of an isosceles triangle is 16 in. and the base is 10 in. How long is the altitude drawn to the base?

199. The legs of a right triangle are 5 in. and 12 in. How long are the segments of the hypotenuse made by the altitude to the hypotenuse?

200. In Ex. 199, how long is the altitude to the hypotenuse?

201. If the bases of an isosceles trapezoid are 12 in. and 20 in., respectively, and the altitude is 10 in., how long are the nonparallel sides?

202. How long are the legs of the isosceles right triangle whose hypotenuse is 12 in.?

203. The equal angles of an isosceles triangle are each 30°, and the equal sides are each 8 in. in length. What is the length of the base?

204. If the altitude of an equilateral triangle is 15 in., how long is a side of the triangle?

Suggestion. Represent the side by $2x$.

205. Let r be the radius of a circle and c the distance from the center of the circle to a point P outside the circle. Write the formula for the length of the tangent to the circle from P, in terms of r and c.

206. Find the formula for the diagonal of the square whose side is of length s.

★**207.** Find the formula for the altitude h of the equilateral triangle whose side is s.

★**208.** Find the formula for the diagonal d of the rectangle whose altitude is a and base is b.

★**209.** The radius of a circle is 25 in. and a chord is 14 in.
(a) How far is the chord from the center of the circle?
(b) How far from one end of the chord is it to each end of the diameter that is perpendicular to the chord?

★**210.** Find the length of the common external tangent to two circles whose radii are 11 and 18, if the distance between their centers is 25.

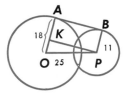

★**211.** If the diagonals of a rhombus are $2m$ and $2n$, respectively, derive a formula for the perimeter p of the rhombus.

★**212.** Prove that the sum of the squares of the distances of any point on a circle from the vertices of an inscribed square is equal to twice the square of the diameter of the circle.

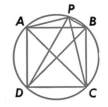

★**213.** If BE and CF are the medians drawn from the extremities of the hypotenuse BC of right $\triangle ABC$, prove $4\overline{BE}^2 + 4\overline{CF}^2 = 5\overline{BC}^2$.

★**214.** If ABC and ADC are angles inscribed in a semicircle, and AE and CF are drawn perpendicular to BD extended, prove
$$\overline{BE}^2 + \overline{BF}^2 = \overline{DE}^2 + \overline{DF}^2.$$

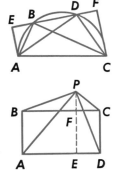

215. If lines be drawn from any point P to the vertices of rectangle $ABCD$, prove
$$\overline{PA}^2 + \overline{PC}^2 = \overline{PB}^2 + \overline{PD}^2.$$

216. If two intersecting chords are perpendicular, the sum of the squares of their segments equals the square of the diameter of the circle.

217. Let K be the mid-point of side BC, and H the mid-point of side AD of $\square ABCD$; let FE, drawn through the mid-point G of KH, intersect BC and AD at F and E, respectively. Prove that FE divides $ABCD$ into equal quadrilaterals.

218. Hyp.   In $\triangle ABC$: $AD = DB$; $AE = EC$; BF and CG are $\perp BC$, meeting DE extended at F, and G.

Con. $\square BFGC = \triangle ABC$.

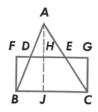

219. In $\square XYZW$, place O on diagonal YW; through O draw $AC \parallel XW$, meeting YX at A and ZW at C; through O draw $BD \parallel XY$, meeting YZ at B and XW at D. Prove $\square AODX = \square BOCZ$.

220. (a) What is the area of the shaded figure at the right if $x = 15$, and $y = 12$?

(b) Make a formula for the area of the shaded surface lying between two squares having the dimensions x and y.

(c) Find the area when $x = 12$ in. and $y = 9$ in.

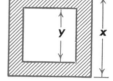

221. What are the areas of the following rectangles:

(a) Alt. $= 4.5$ in.; base $= 6.7$ in.

(b) Alt. $= 3.2$ yd.; base $= 5.8$ yd.

(c) Alt. $= 8.4$ ft.; base $= 21.5$ ft.

(d) Alt. $= 9.6$ rd.; base $= 25.3$ rd.

222. What is the altitude of the rectangle whose area is 336 sq. in. if its base is 32 in.?

223. What are the dimensions of the rectangle whose area is 450 sq. in. if its length is 9 times its width?

224. What are the dimensions of the rectangle whose area is 540 sq. ft. if the sum of the base and altitude is 47 ft.?
(Let $x =$ the base and $47 - x =$ the altitude.)

★**225.** Draw $\parallel$s XY and ZW. Draw $\square ABCD$, having AB on XY, and CD on ZW. Draw $\square MNOP$, having $MN = AB$, MN on XY, and OP on ZW. How does $ABCD$ compare with $MNOP$?

226. What is the base of a triangle whose area is 480 sq. in. if its altitude is 24 in.?

227. What is the area of the rhombus whose diagonals are 10 in. and 18 in., respectively?

228. In an isosceles triangle, find:

(a) The area, if the base $= 14$ and one side $= 25$.

(b) The area, if the altitude $= 24$ and the base $= 15$.

(c) The area, if one side $= 16$ and a base angle $= 30°$.

229. What is the area of the equilateral triangle whose sides are:

(a) 16 in. long.   (b) 20 in. long.

★ **230.** (*a*) *ABCD* is a parallelogram such that *AP* drawn perpendicular to *BC* meets *BC* between *B* and *C* and $BP = \frac{1}{3}BC$. Diagonal *BD* meets *AP* at *Q*.

   (1) What is the ratio of *BQ* to *BD*?

   (2) What is the ratio of △*BQP* to □*ABCD*?

   (*b*) *ABCD* is a parallelogram such that *AP* drawn perpendicular to *CB* extended cuts off $BP = \frac{1}{3}BC$. Diagonal *DB* extended meets *AP* extended at *Q*.

   (1) What is the ratio of *BQ* to *BD*?

   (2) What is the ratio of △*BQP* to □*ABCD*?

   (*c*) Do you get the same answer to both parts of the problem? If not, how do you account for the difference?

★ **231.** Prove that the formula for the area *A* of an equilateral triangle whose side is *s* is $A = \frac{s^2}{4}\sqrt{3}$.

Suggestion. Draw an altitude. Determine its length in terms of *s*. Then find the area of the triangle.

   232. By the formula of Ex. 231, find the area of the equilateral triangle whose side is:

   (*a*) 10 in.   (*b*) 15 in.

   233. The segments of the hypotenuse of a right triangle made by the altitude to it from the opposite vertex are 4 in. and 9 in., respectively. What is the area of the triangle?

   234. What is the area of the isosceles triangle whose base is 24 in. and whose base angles are:

   (*a*) 30°   (*b*) 45°   (*c*) 60°

   235. What is the area of the isosceles triangle whose equal sides are each 20 in. long and whose base angles are:

   (*a*) 30°   (*b*) 45°   (*c*) 60°

   236. If one diagonal of a rhombus is 40 in., and the side of the rhombus is 30 in., what is the area of the rhombus?

   237. A circle whose diameter is 12 in. is inscribed in a quadrilateral whose perimeter is 50 in. What is the area of the quadrilateral?

Suggestion. Draw segments from the center of the circle to the vertices of the quadrilateral. Find the area of each of the triangles formed. Add the areas of the triangles.

★ **238.** Prove that the area of a polygon circumscribed about a circle is one half the product of the radius of the circle and the perimeter of the polygon.

239. If the side of square $ABCD$ is 12 in., what is the area of the shaded part in each square below?

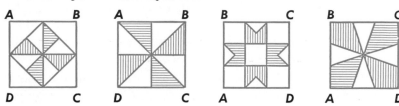

240. Divide a triangle into three equal parts by lines drawn through one of its vertices.

241. Side YZ of $\square XYZW$ is extended to P. Prove $\triangle XWP = \frac{1}{2}\square XYZW$.

242. If diagonal AC of quadrilateral $ABCD$ bisects diagonal BD, then $\triangle ABC = \triangle ADC$.

Suggestion. Prove the altitudes of the triangles are equal.

243. Given quadrilateral $ABCD$. By means of a broken line from A to C separate $ABCD$ into two equal parts.

Suggestion. First draw BD.

★**244.** Point O lies inside $\triangle ABC$, and is joined to B and C. AO extended meets BC at Z. Prove
$$\triangle BOZ : \triangle COZ = \triangle ABZ : \triangle ACZ.$$

Suggestion. Prove each ratio equal to a third ratio.

★**245.** Let the medians AD, BE, and CF of $\triangle ABC$ intersect at G.
(a) Prove $\triangle FBC = \triangle BEC$.
(b) Prove $\triangle BFG = \triangle CEG$.
(c) Prove $\triangle ABD = 3\triangle BGD$.
(d) Prove $\triangle ABC = 6\triangle BGD$.

★**246.** $\triangle ABC$ has $\angle B = 90°$. X is the mid-point of AC. XY, parallel to BC, meets AB at Y; XZ, parallel to AB, meets BC at Z. Prove $XYBZ = \frac{1}{2}\triangle ABC$.

★**247.** If E, F, G, and H are the mid-points of sides AB, BC, CD, and DA, respectively, of quadrilateral $ABCD$, prove $EFGH$ is a parallelogram that equals one half of $ABCD$.

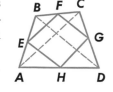

Suggestion. Let FG cut AC at X, and EH cut AC at Y. Prove $EFXY$ is a $\square$. Draw $BZ \perp AC$ at Z.

★**248.** Prove that the sum of the perpendiculars from any point P inside an equilateral triangle ABC to the three sides of the triangle is equal to the altitude of the triangle.

Suggestions. 1. $\triangle BPC + \triangle BPA + \triangle APC = \triangle ABC$.
2. Express the area of each triangle and substitute in equation.

249. If E is any point in side BC of $\square ABCD$, and DE is drawn meeting AB extended at F, prove $\triangle ABE$ equals $\triangle CEF$.

Suggestion. Compare $\triangle FCD$ with $\square ABCD$; also compare $\triangle ABE + \triangle ECD$ with $\square ABCD$.

★**250.** If D is the mid-point of side BC of $\triangle ABC$, E the mid-point of AD, F of BE, and G of CF, then $\triangle ABC = 8\triangle EFG$.

★**251.** If BE and CF are medians drawn from vertices B and C of $\triangle ABC$, intersecting at D, prove $\triangle BCD$ equals quadrilateral $AEDF$.

Suggestion. Compare $\triangle ABE$ and $\triangle BCF$ with $\triangle BEC$.

252. What is the area of the trapezoid whose bases are 21 in. and 35 in., respectively, and whose nonparallel side of length 20 in. makes with the lower base an angle of 30°?

253. What is the altitude of the trapezoid whose area is 400 sq. in. and whose bases are 35 in. and 45 in., respectively?

254. What is the upper base of the trapezoid whose area is 660 sq. in., if the lower base is 50 in. and the altitude is 20 in.?

255. Prove that the line joining any vertex of a parallelogram to the mid-point of one of the nonadjacent sides separates the parallelogram into a triangle and a trapezoid such that the trapezoid is 3 times as large as the triangle.

Suggestion. Join the mid-point with the mid-point of the opposite side.

★**256.** $ABCD$ is a parallelogram. X, Y, Z, and W are the mid-points of AB, BC, CD, and AD, respectively. XZ intersects YW at O. PQ is any line through O, meeting BC at P and AD at Q.

(a) Prove $ABPQ = PQDC$, and $XBPO = ZOQD$.

(b) Is $ABPQ \cong PQDC$? Is $XBPO \cong ZOQD$?

257. In the accompanying figure, if D bisects BC and E bisects AC, $DF = AD$, and $EG = BE$, prove that GCF is a straight line and that $GC = CF$.

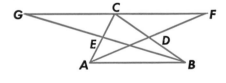

Suggestion. Prove GC and CF each $\parallel AB$; then use §84.

258. An automobile is traveling at the rate of 45 m.p.h. The outside diameter of the tires of the car is 30 in. How many times do the wheels of the car revolve in a minute?

Note. Express the result correct to the nearest whole number.

259. On a circle of radius 10 in., how long is the arc of the side of an inscribed:

(a) Regular hexagon?   (b) Equilateral triangle?

260. Construct a circle whose length equals the sum of the lengths of two given circles.

261. A part of the interior of a circle of radius 8 in. lies between a side of an inscribed square and the minor arc of that side. What is the length of the boundary of this part of the circle?

262. Quadrilateral $ABCD$ is inscribed in a circle of radius 8 in. If $\angle A = 60°$, $\angle B = 110°$, $\angle C = 120°$, and $\angle D = 70°$, how long is each of the arcs between the points of contact if arc $AB = 60°$?

263. The radius of a circle is 6 in. What is the number of degrees in the arc whose length is:
    (a) 2π in.?   (b) 3π in.?   (c) π in.?

★**264.** How many degrees, correct to tenths, are there in the arc of the circle and in the central angle of that arc if the length of the arc equals the radius of the circle?

265. A circle of radius 4 in. is to be filled by six congruent sectors of different kinds of cloth. How many square inches of cloth will there be in each sector?

266. In the adjoining figure, the arcs are semicircles. Prove that the area of the shaded part equals the area of the circle that has BD as diameter, where $BD \perp AC$.

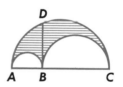

Note. This theorem was discovered by Archimedes.

★**267.** $\angle C$ of $\triangle ABC$ is a right angle. AB, AC, and CB are diameters of circles. Prove that the sum of the shaded crescents equals the area of $\triangle ABC$.

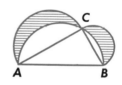

Note. This theorem was proved by Hippocrates. Read about him.

★**268.** In a city park is a circular rose bed. Its radius is 25 ft. It is separated into four parts by paths that are 4 ft. wide. Find the *approximate* area of each of the parts.

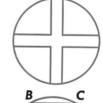

★**269.** Prove that the square inscribed in a semicircle is equal to two fifths the square inscribed in the entire circle.
Suggestions. Let R = the radius of the circle. Compute the areas of the two squares.

★**270.** Prove that the area of the semicircle on the hypotenuse of a right triangle equals the sum of the areas of the two semicircles drawn on the sides of the triangle.

271. What are the circumference and the area of the circle that is circumscribed about the square whose side is 6 in. long?

272. What are the radius and the area of the circle whose circumference is:
    (a) 24 π in.?   (b) 10 π in.?   (c) 9 π in.?

273. What are the radius and the circumference of the circle whose area is:
    (a) 64 π sq. in.?   (b) 81 π sq. in.?   (c) 144 π sq. in.?

★ 274. Find the side of the square equal to the circle whose diameter is 14 in.

275. What is the area of the circle circumscribed about the square whose side is *s?*

276. Inscribed in a circle of diameter 12 in. is a regular hexagon. What is the area of the interior of the circle that lies outside the hexagon?

★ 277. What is the area of the circle circumscribed about the equilateral triangle whose side is 12 in.?

★ 278. What is the area of the circle inscribed in the equilateral triangle whose side is 12 in.?

279. For a patchwork quilt, $1\frac{1}{2}$ yd. of cloth are required for certain pieces that have the form of equilateral triangles 2 in. on a side. How many yards will be needed if these triangles are made $2\frac{1}{2}$ in. on a side?

280. The sides of a triangle are 8, 10, and 12. What are the sides of a similar triangle whose area is 4 times as large as that of the first triangle?

281. What is the ratio of the areas of two isosceles triangles whose vertex angles are 50°, if the equal sides of the one are 10 in. long and the equal sides of the other are 15 in. long?

282. The altitude and base of a certain triangle are 15 in. and 25 in. respectively. Through a point on the altitude 5 in. from the vertex of the triangle, a line is drawn parallel to the base. What is:
    (a) The area of the triangle above this line?
    (b) The area of the trapezoid below this line?

283. If the area of a polygon, one of whose sides is 15 in., is 375 sq. in., what is the area of a similar polygon if the corresponding side is 10 in. long?

284. The area of one polygon is 4 times that of a similar polygon. How does any side of the first compare with the corresponding side of the second?

TEST—TRUE ALWAYS, SOMETIMES, NEVER

*Of the statements below, some are **always true,** some are **sometimes true,** and others are **never true.** Write the numerals 1 to 20. After each write either* A, S, *or* N *according as the statement is* **true always, sometimes,** *or* **never.**

1. Two lines parallel to the same line are parallel to each other.

2. In a plane two lines perpendicular to the same line are perpendicular to each other.

3. The diagonals of a parallelogram are perpendicular.

4. If two chords are unequal, the shorter is nearer the center.

5. Tangents to a circle from a point make equal angles with the chord through the points of contact.

6. The ratio of the altitudes of two similar triangles equals the ratio of two corresponding sides.

7. If two angles have their sides respectively parallel, the angles are equal.

8. In a plane if two lines are cut by a transversal so that the interior angles on the same side of the transversal are supplementary, the lines are parallel.

9. Chords that are equidistant from the center of a circle subtend equal arcs.

10. The altitude from a vertex of a triangle to the opposite side passes through the interior of the triangle.

11. The altitudes of similar triangles have the same ratio as any two corresponding medians.

12. The exterior angles at the vertices of a regular polygon are all equal.

13. The altitude to the hypotenuse of a right triangle bisects the hypotenuse.

14. If the radius of one circle is half that of another circle, the area of the first circle is one half that of the second.

15. An angle inscribed in a semicircle is a right angle.

16. An inscribed angle is less than a right angle if it intercepts an arc that is less than a semicircle.

17. A straight line cuts a circle in two points.

18. The perpendicular-bisectors of the sides of a triangle meet at a point.

19. If one angle of a right triangle equals 30°, the opposite side is one half the hypotenuse.

20. A diagonal of a parallelogram bisects the angles through which it is drawn.

TEST OF ABILITY TO CONSTRUCT FIGURES

In this test, you will be asked to make certain constructions, using figures drawn on this page. After you complete your construction, you will be asked to "measure" a final segment on the scale below, in a certain way.*

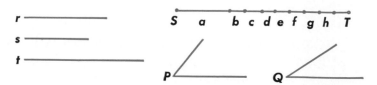

1. (a) Construct $\triangle ABC$ having $AB = r$, $BC = t$, and $\angle B = \angle P$.
   (b) When you are through, take as radius the side AC of *your* triangle. Place one compass point on S on the scale above. Find where the other compass point falls on ST. Then write the letter *of the segment in which your second compass point falls.* Thus, if it falls within segment e, write: (b) Answer is e.

2. (a) Construct $\triangle ABC$ having $AB = t$, $\angle A = \angle P$, and $\angle B = \angle Q$.
   (b) Write the *measure* of your side BC.

3. (a) In the $\triangle$ constructed in Exercise 2, construct the bisector AD of $\angle A$, meeting BC at D.
   (b) Write the measure of AD.

4. (a) Construct the equilateral triangle whose side is r.
   (b) Construct the altitude to one side. Write its measure.

5. (a) Construct the fourth proportional to s, t, and r.
   (b) Write the measure of your result.

6. (a) Construct the mean proportional between s and t.
   (b) Write its measure in terms of the scale above.

7. (a) Construct $\square ABCD$ having $AB = t$, $\angle A = \angle P$, $AD = s$.
   (b) Draw DB. Find its measure on the scale.

8. (a) Construct a circle O with radius s. At point X on this circle, construct the tangent XM to the circle.
   (b) On XM, take segment $XE = s$. Draw OE. Find its measure.

9. (a) Construct a $\odot O$, with radius r. In it, inscribe a regular hexagon.
   (b) Draw and measure the segment that is one side of the inscribed equilateral triangle.

10. (a) Construct the rhombus whose diagonals are s and t.
    (b) Measure one side of this rhombus.

* The device employed to facilitate checking the final result was suggested by its use on an Iowa Plane Geometry Test.

412

1. $\triangle ABC$ is equilateral and P is any point inside it. On PC an equilateral $\triangle PQC$ is drawn so that PQ cuts AC and not BC. Prove that $\triangle ACQ \cong \triangle BCP$.

2. (a) Given points A and B on a line m, and two segments whose lengths are represented by r and s, with s greater than r. By actual construction locate a point C that shall be the distance r from the line m and the distance s from the mid-point of AB.
   (b) How many such points are there?

3. A boat travels north 20.0 miles, then east 8.1 miles and then north 16.0 miles; how far from the starting point is the final position of the boat?

4. A square $EFGH$ is inscribed in another square $ABCD$ so that E is on AB, F on BC, G on CD, and H on DA, and $\angle AHE$ is 30°. The area of $EFGH$ is 100; find a side of $ABCD$.

5. A cathedral window has the form of a regular hexagon surmounted by semicircles with the sides as diameters. The side of the hexagon is 3 feet. Find the area of the window: that is, of the *entire* figure. (Answer in terms of π and $\sqrt{3}$.)

1. In quadrilateral $ABCD$, lettered consecutively, angles ABC and BCD are obtuse, $\angle BCD$ is greater than $\angle ABC$, and AB is less than DC. Prove that $\angle ADC$ is less than $\angle BAD$.
Suggestion. Extend AB and DC to meet at E.

2. AB, the diameter of a circle, is extended through B to C so that BC is equal to the radius. BD is $\perp AB$ at B. CE is tangent to the circle at E, cutting BD at F. AE extended meets BD at D. Prove $\triangle DEF$ is equilateral.

3. Two boys wish to find the height of a light suspended above the gymnasium floor. From a point directly under the light they measure out a distance of 18 feet. At that point, the shadow cast by a vertical pole 9 feet long is measured and found to be 12 feet long. Find the height of the light from these measurements.

4. (a) $ABCD$ is a parallelogram with $AB = 18$, $AD = 12$, and $\angle A = 60°$. Find the area of $ABCD$.
   (b) If M, any point in CD, is joined to A and B, find the area of $\triangle ABM$.

5. $ABCDEFGH$ is a regular inscribed octagon.
   (a) Prove $ABDE$ is an isosceles trapezoid.
   (b) Find the number of degrees in each angle of $ABDE$.

REVIEW OF COMPUTATION

405. The **digits** 1, 2, 3, 4, 5, 6, 7, 8, 9 are used to *represent* the first nine positive integers. They are not the integers any more than were the symbols used by the ancient Romans and Greeks; they are *numerals*.

Thus: The Romans used I, II, III, and IV to represent the first four positive integers; the Greeks, for the same purpose, used α, β, γ, and δ, the first four letters of their alphabet.

The decimal system of writing integers enables us to represent any positive integer by combinations of these digits and the symbol 0.

Just as there are postulates concerning points, lines, and surfaces, *so there are postulates* for the system of positive integers. Addition, subtraction, multiplication, and division of integers are defined by means of these postulates, other kinds of numbers are defined, and methods of computing with them are defined or developed.

We use the digits and the numerals that represent the other integers so much that we refer to them as *if they are* the numbers instead of merely being representations of the numbers. *We shall do so in this book except when it may be clearer to refer to them as numerals.*

You have been taught how to compute with integers, common fractions, and *exact* decimals. A review of some troublesome methods of computing follows.

(a) **To add or to subtract common fractions, change the fractions, if necessary, to equal fractions that have the same denominator.**

Thus:

$$\frac{1}{6} + \frac{5}{8}$$

$$= \frac{4 \times 1}{4 \times 6} + \frac{3 \times 5}{3 \times 8}$$

$$= \frac{4}{24} + \frac{15}{24}$$

$$= \frac{19}{24}$$

Explanation. 24 is the least number that contains both 6 and 8.

To change 6ths to 24ths:

$$24 \div 6 = 4; \frac{1}{6} = \frac{4 \times 1}{4 \times 6}, \text{ or } \frac{4}{24}$$

To change 8ths to 24ths:

$$24 \div 8 = 3; \frac{5}{8} = \frac{3 \times 5}{3 \times 8}, \text{ or } \frac{15}{24}$$

(b) *To multiply a mixed number by any number, change each mixed number to an improper fraction, and then multiply.*

Thus: $12\frac{1}{2} \times 3\frac{5}{8}$

$= \frac{25}{2} \times \frac{29}{8}$

$= \frac{725}{16}$

$= 45\frac{5}{16}$

Explanation. $12 = \frac{2 \times 12}{2 \times 1}$, or $\frac{24}{2}$

$12\frac{1}{2} = \frac{24}{2} + \frac{1}{2}$, or $\frac{25}{2}$

$3 = \frac{8 \times 3}{8 \times 1} = \frac{24}{8}$

$3\frac{5}{8} = \frac{24}{8} + \frac{5}{8}$, or $\frac{29}{8}$

(c) *The number of decimal places in the product of two exact decimals equals the number of places in the multiplier plus the number in the multiplicand.*

This rule is *suggested* by such a product as .5 × .25.
Observe that $.5 \times .25 = \frac{5}{10} \times \frac{25}{100}$, or $\frac{125}{1000}$.

$\therefore \quad .5 \times .25 = .125$

Similarly: $3.2 \times 4.15 = 13.280$

(d) *To divide any number by a fraction, invert the divisor and multiply.*

This rule, for *unit fractions*, is suggested by such a division as $5 \div \frac{1}{3}$. $1 \div \frac{1}{3} = 3$; $\therefore 5 \div \frac{1}{3} = 5 \times 3$, or 15.
This result is obtained quickly by writing;

$$5 \div \frac{1}{3} = 5 \times \frac{3}{1} = \frac{15}{1}, \text{ or } 15.$$

(e) *To divide a number by a decimal, multiply the divisor by the number that will make the product an integer; then multiply the dividend by the same number, to avoid changing the quotient. Now divide the new dividend by the new divisor. Make the number of decimal places in the quotient the same as the number of places in the new dividend.*

Thus:

```
          10.4
2.25∧‾2‾3‾.‾4‾0‾∧‾0‾
          22 5
          ‾‾‾‾‾
            90 0
            90 0
            ‾‾‾‾
```

Explanation. Multiply 2.25 by 100 to change it to an integer. Multiply 23.4 by 100. Place carets (∧) where the new decimal points would be. Place a decimal point and the digits of the quotient above those of the dividend that produce them.

406. The exact population of a city, as 23,162, may be more exact than is needed for some purposes.

Therefore we may say that the population:
(*a*) Is 23,160, *correct to the nearest ten.*
(*b*) Is 23,200, *correct to the nearest hundred.*
(*c*) Is 23,000, *correct to the nearest thousand.*

Each of these last three numbers is an *approximate representation* of the population. It has become customary to call such numbers **approximate numbers.**

The unit of (*a*) is *ten*, of (*b*) is a *hundred*, and of (*c*) is a *thousand*. The number in (*a*) is *more precise* than that in (*b*) or (*c*). (*b*) is more precise than (*c*).

The **precision** of a number is determined by the unit represented by the final digit of the number. The smaller the unit, the more precise is the number.

407. We secured the approximate numbers in §406 by *rounding off a more precise number.*

To round off an integer, change one or more final digits of the integer to zero and:
(*a*) Do not change the preceding digit if the first of the changed digits is less than 5.

Thus: 4716 becomes 4700, correct to the nearest hundred.
(*b*) Increase by 1 the preceding digit if the first of the changed digits is 5 or more.

Thus: 4716 becomes 5000, correct to the nearest thousand.

In the number	the unit is	the *significant digits* are	the number of significant digits is
23,162	1	2, 3, 1, 6, 2	5
23,160	10	2, 3, 1, 6	4
23,200	100	2, 3, 2	3
23,000	1000	2, 3	2

The **significant digits** of a number are the digits that are needed to tell how many arithmetical units there are in the number.

Thus: In .032, the significant digits are 3 and 2.
       In 2.03, the significant digits are 2, 0 and 3.

408. An approximate number can be more or less than the exact number it approximates.

Thus: If 4716 is rounded off to 4700, then 4700 is less than 4716. The last significant digit of 4700 is 7, which represents a number of hundreds. The difference between 4716 and 4700 is *less* than one half of one hundred.

The *numerical difference between an approximate number* and the exact number it represents is not more than half of the unit that is represented by the right-hand significant digit of the approximate number.

Thus: If 3.14 is approximate, the numerical difference between it and the exact number it represents is not more than half of .01, which is .005. The exact number is between 3.14 − .005 and 3.14 + .005.

409. A *quotient often is expressed by an approximate number.*

Thus: $16 \div 3 = 5.333+$, or 5.33, correct to hundredths. The *exact* quotient is between 5.33 − .005 and 5.33 + .005.

410. The **principal square root** of an integer, represented by a **radical sign,** $\sqrt{\ }$, usually can be expressed decimally only by an approximate number.

Thus: $\sqrt{10} = 3.162$, correct to thousandths. (See p. 429.)

Approximate square roots of integers are computed as follows: (See p. 418 for the explanation of Example 1.)

Example 1. Find $\sqrt{456.8}$ correct to tenths.

```
        2  1. 3  7
      4 56.80 00
      4
 40  |   56
 41  |   41
420  |   15 80
423  |   12 69
4260 |    3 11 00
4267 |    2 98 69
              12 31
```

∴ $\sqrt{456.8} = 21.37$ or 21.4

Example 2. Find $\sqrt{2764}$ correct to tenths.

```
         5  2. 5  7
      27 64. 00 00
      25
 100  |    2 64
 102  |    2 04
1040  |      60 00
1045  |      52 25
10500 |       7 75 00
10507 |       7 35 49
                39 51
```

∴ $\sqrt{2764} = 52.57$ or 52.6

Explanation of the computing for Example 1, p. 417.

1. Arrange 456.8 in pairs of digits *both ways* from the decimal point. Thus: 4 56.80 00

2. 4 is the largest square number not more than 4.
Write $\sqrt{4}$ or 2 in the square root. Write 4 below 4 of 456.
First remainder. 4 − 4 = 0. Bring down 56.

3. *First trial divisor.* Write 20 × 2, or 40.
First complete divisor. 56 ÷ 40 = 1+;   40 + 1 = 41.
Write 1 in the square root above 6 of 56.
Find 1 × 41. Write 41 below 56.
Second remainder. 56–41 = 15; bring down 80.

4. *Second trial divisor.* Write 20 × 21, or 420.
Second complete divisor. 1580 ÷ 420 = 3+; 420 + 3 = 423.
Write 3 in the square root above 0 of 80.
Find 3 × 423. Write 1269 below 1580.
Third remainder. 1580 − 1269 = 311. Bring down 00.

5. *Third trial divisor.* Write 20 × 213, or 4260.
Third complete divisor. 31100 ÷ 4260 = 7+;
4260 + 7 = 4267.
Find 7 × 4267. Write 29869 below 31100.
Fourth remainder. 31100 − 29869 = 1231. Since this is less than 4267, 7 is the correct digit for the square root.
Check. $(21.37)^2 = 456.6769$.
∴ $\sqrt{456.8} = 21.37$, or 21.4 correct to tenths.

Find the following indicated square roots, correct to tenths.

1. $\sqrt{759}$ 2. $\sqrt{1406}$ 3. $\sqrt{275.8}$ 4. $\sqrt{5275.6}$

5. $\sqrt{30.25}$ 6. $\sqrt{.7854}$ 7. $\sqrt{15.24}$ 8. $\sqrt{90.07}$

411. An indicated square root is called a **radical**. Before computing the square root, **simplify the radical** by one of the following postulates.

(a) The square root of the product of two or more positive numbers equals the product of the square roots of the numbers.

Thus:
$$\sqrt{63} = \sqrt{9 \times 7} = \sqrt{9} \times \sqrt{7} = 3\sqrt{7}; \sqrt{ab} = \sqrt{a} \times \sqrt{b}$$

(b) *The square root of the quotient of two positive numbers equals the quotient of the square roots of the numbers.*

Thus: $\sqrt{\dfrac{13}{16}} = \dfrac{\sqrt{13}}{\sqrt{16}} = \dfrac{\sqrt{13}}{4}$, or $\dfrac{1}{4}\sqrt{13}$.

412. To simplify a radical.

(a) *Multiply the denominator of any fraction, and therefore its numerator, by the number that will make the denominator the smallest possible square number.*

Thus: $\sqrt{\dfrac{5}{18}} = \sqrt{\dfrac{2 \times 5}{2 \times 18}} = \sqrt{\dfrac{10}{36}} = \dfrac{\sqrt{10}}{\sqrt{36}} = \dfrac{\sqrt{10}}{6}$

Here, 18 is multiplied by 2 to change it to 36. The numerator, 5, also is multiplied by 2 to avoid changing the value of $\dfrac{5}{18}$.

(b) *Factor the numerator into as many square factors as possible.*

Thus: $\sqrt{108} = \sqrt{2 \times 54} = \sqrt{2 \times 2 \times 27} = \sqrt{2^2 \times 9 \times 3}$

$\therefore \quad \sqrt{108} = \sqrt{2^2 \times 3^2 \times 3} = 2 \times 3 \times \sqrt{3} = 6\sqrt{3}$

An approximate value of a radical can be obtained often by using an approximate value from the table on page 429.

Thus: $\sqrt{108} = 6\sqrt{3} = 6 \times 1.732 = 10.392$

$\therefore \quad \sqrt{108} = 10.39$, correct to hundredths.

Find, correct to hundredths, each of the following.

1. $\sqrt{200}$ 2. $\sqrt{240}$ 3. $\sqrt{180}$ 4. $\sqrt{294}$ 5. $\sqrt{363}$

6. $\sqrt{\dfrac{3}{5}}$ 7. $\sqrt{\dfrac{9}{8}}$ 8. $\sqrt{\dfrac{7}{12}}$ 9. $\sqrt{\dfrac{5}{32}}$ 10. $\sqrt{\dfrac{16}{27}}$

413. *Radicals often must be added, subtracted, multiplied, ...*

Like quadratic radicals are multiples of the square root of the same number, as $3\sqrt{5}$ and $4\sqrt{5}$.

$$3\sqrt{5} + 4\sqrt{5} = 7\sqrt{5}$$

$$\therefore \quad 3\sqrt{5} + 4\sqrt{5} = 7 \times 2.236 = 15.652, \text{ or } 15.65.$$

This computation is justified by the distributive law of multiplication with respect to addition, which states that $a(b + c) = ab + ac$, and, conversely, $ab + ac = a(b + c)$.

414. **Multiplication of radical expressions** is based on the postulate that is stated in §411(a) and the distributive law of multiplication with respect to addition.

$$\text{Thus: } (3 + \sqrt{2})^2 = (3 + \sqrt{2})(3 + \sqrt{2})$$
$$= 9 + 6\sqrt{2} + \sqrt{(2)(2)}$$
$$\therefore \quad (3 + \sqrt{2})^2 = 9 + 6\sqrt{2} + 2 = 11 + 6\sqrt{2}$$
$$\therefore \quad (3 + \sqrt{2})^2 = 11 + 6 \times 1.414 = 11 + 8.484$$
$$\therefore \quad (3 + \sqrt{2})^2 = 19.484, \text{ or } 19.48$$

Find the result, correct to hundredths, in each example.

1. $(2 + \sqrt{3})^2$ **2.** $(5 - \sqrt{2})^2$ **3.** $(4 + \sqrt{3})^2$ **4.** $(3 - \sqrt{5})^2$

5. $(3\sqrt{2})(4\sqrt{3})$ **6.** $(5\sqrt{3})(2\sqrt{6})$ **7.** $(3\sqrt{5})(2\sqrt{5})$

8. $\dfrac{8}{4}\sqrt{3}$ **9.** $\dfrac{15}{2}\sqrt{3}$ **10.** $12 - \dfrac{12}{2}\sqrt{3}$

11. What is the value of $\dfrac{6s^2}{4}\sqrt{3}$ when:

   (a) s is 5?   (b) s is 8?   (c) s is 10?

12. What is the value of $\dfrac{a(\sqrt{5} - 1)}{2}$ when:

   (a) a is 10?   (b) a is 12?   (c) a is 9?

415. **Division of radicals and radical expressions** is based on one of the fundamental laws of fractions.

$$(a) \quad \frac{\sqrt{6}}{\sqrt{2}} = \frac{\sqrt{2} \times \sqrt{6}}{\sqrt{2} \times \sqrt{2}} = \frac{\sqrt{12}}{\sqrt{4}} = \frac{\sqrt{4 \times 3}}{2} = \frac{2\sqrt{3}}{2} = \sqrt{3}$$

$$(b) \quad \frac{5}{1 + \sqrt{2}} = \frac{5(1 - \sqrt{2})}{(1 + \sqrt{2})(1 - \sqrt{2})} = \frac{5(1 - \sqrt{2})}{1 - 2}$$
$$= -5(1 - \sqrt{2})$$

This procedure is called **rationalizing the divisor.** To rationalize, multiply the denominator, and therefore the numerator, by a factor that will eliminate all square roots in the denominator.

Rationalize the denominator in each example.

13. $\dfrac{\sqrt{10}}{\sqrt{5}}$ **14.** $\dfrac{\sqrt{24}}{\sqrt{3}}$ **15.** $\dfrac{\sqrt{18}}{\sqrt{6}}$ **16.** $\dfrac{\sqrt{32}}{\sqrt{8}}$ **17.** $\dfrac{\sqrt{28}}{\sqrt{7}}$

18. $\dfrac{2}{\sqrt{3} + 1}$ **19.** $\dfrac{8}{\sqrt{5} - 1}$ **20.** $\dfrac{12}{2 - \sqrt{3}}$ **21.** $\dfrac{15}{3 + \sqrt{2}}$

416. Perimeters, areas, and volumes depend on **lengths of segments.**

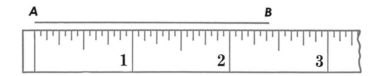

In the figure above, AB appears to be closer to $2\frac{3}{8}$ in. than to $2\frac{7}{16}$ in. We say that AB is $2\frac{3}{8}$ in. correct to 16ths of an inch.

The numerical difference between the actual length and $2\frac{3}{8}$ in. is less than $\frac{1}{2}$ of $\frac{1}{16}$ in., which is $\frac{1}{32}$ in.

An approximate length of $3\frac{5}{8}$ in., correct to 16ths of an inch, means that the actual length lies between $(3\frac{5}{8} - \frac{1}{32})$ in. and $(3\frac{5}{8} + \frac{1}{32})$ in. $\frac{1}{32}$ in. $= .031^+$ in. $= .003^-$ ft.

Therefore if 4 in. is correct to 16ths of an inch, the actual length lies between 4 in. $- .031$ in. and 4 in. $+ .031$ in.; that is, between 3.969 in. and 4.031 in. Each of these lengths is 4.0 in., correct to tenths. Therefore, an approximate length of 4 in., correct to 16ths of an inch, is 4.0 in. correct to tenths. It lies between $(4.0 - .05)$ in. and $(4.0 + .05)$ in.

If 4 ft. is correct to 16ths of an inch, the actual length lies between 4 ft. $- .003$ ft. and 4 ft. $+ .003$ ft.; that is, between 3.997 ft. and 4.003 ft. Each of these last lengths is 4.00 ft. correct to hundredths. Therefore 4 ft., correct to 16ths of an inch, is 4.00 ft. correct to hundredths of an inch.

Summary. *When lengths of segments are correct to 16ths of an inch:*
(a) An integral approximate number of inches is correct to tenths of an inch.

   Thus: 7 in. =   7.0 in., a two-digit number.
            15 in. = 15.0 in., a three-digit number.

(b) An integral approximate number of feet is correct to hundredths of a foot.

   Thus: 6 ft. =   6.00 ft., a three-digit number.
            12 ft. = 12.00 ft., a four-digit number.

417. In the problems in this book, assume that lengths of segments given in inches or feet are correct to 16ths of an inch.

Since approximate numbers only approximate certain exact numbers, results obtained by computing with them only approximate the results that would be obtained if the exact numbers could be used.

Recall that an approximate number like 3.2 represents some number between 3.2 − .05 and 3.2 + .05. *Agree to indicate this by writing* 3.2 ± .05.

418. Adding approximate numbers.

Example 1. Find the sum of approximate numbers 5.2, 4.3, and 7.8.

Explanation. Addition A shows the sum precise to tenths.

Addition B shows that the sum of the exact numbers is between 17.3 − .15 and 17.3 + .15, which is between 17.15 and 17.45, or between 17.2 and 17.5, to tenths. Therefore the sum is not precise

A	B
5.2	5.2 ± .05
4.3	4.3 ± .05
7.8	7.8 ± .05
17.3	17.3 ± .15

beyond tenths and even the final digit is uncertain. However, 17.3 is a good approximation.

Example 2. Find the sum of 27.63, 3.9, and 4.782.

Explanation. 27.63 approximates a number 27.63 ± .005. Similarly 3.9 approximates 3.9 ± .05, and 4.782 approximates 4.782 ± .0005.

Addition C shows that the sum of the numbers is 36.312 ± .0555;

C	D
27.63 ± .005	27.6
3.9 ± .05	3.9
4.782 ± .0005	4.8
36.312 ± .0555	36.3

that is, it is between 36.2565 and 36.3675, or between 36.3 and 36.4. This suggests writing the sum correct only to tenths, which is the precision of 3.9, the least precise of the given numbers.

The sum is readily obtained by the following rule:

When approximate numbers are to be added or subtracted, round off each of the numbers to the precision of the least precise number. Then add or subtract. The final digit of the result is uncertain.

419. Multiplication of approximate numbers.

Example. Find the product of .236 and 3.1.

Explanation. .236 approximates an exact number that is between .2355 and .2365; 3.1, one between 3.05 and 3.15. Therefore the product of these exact numbers must be between 3.05 × .2355 and 3.15 × .2365, which is between .718275 and .744975. Rounded off, these numbers suggest .73 as the approximate product.

A .2355	B .2365
3.05	3.15
11775	11825
70650	2365
.718275	7095
or .72	.744975
	or .74

Observe that the number of significant digits in .73 is the same as in 3.1. The result is obtained readily if .236 is multiplied by 3.1 and the product is rounded off to the number of significant digits in 3.1.

.236
3.1
236
708
.7316
or .73

When two approximate numbers are multiplied, round off the product to as many significant digits as appear in the factor having the fewer significant digits.

Thus: 4.5 × 8.27 = 37.215, or 37.

420. Division of approximate numbers.

Example. Divide 9.317 by 6.2.

Explanation. 9.317 represents an exact number between 9.3165 and 9.3175; 6.2, one between 6.15 and 6.25. Therefore the quotient of the exact numbers must be between 9.3175 ÷ 6.15 and 9.3165 ÷ 6.25. The divisions are shown in Column A.

A 1.51	1.49	B 1.50
6.15)9.31∧75	6.25)9.31∧65	6.2)9.3∧20
6 15	6 25	6 2
3 16 7	3 06 6	3 1 2
3 07 5	2 50 0	3 1 0
9 25	56 65	20
6 15	56 25	

(*Continued on p. 424.*)

The divisions in Column A at the bottom of page 423 show that the exact quotient is between 1.49 and 1.51. This suggests 1.50 as the approximate quotient. This result is obtained readily in Column B on p. 423 by the following rule.

When approximate numbers are divided:

1. **Round off the number that has the larger number of significant digits to one more digit than appears in the other number; then divide to that number of significant digits.**

2. **Round off the quotient to the number of significant digits that appears in the number that has the fewer. The final digit is uncertain.**

Thus: $47.362 \div 12.5 = 47.36 \div 12.5$
$47.36 \div 12.5 = 3.788$, or 3.79.

When finding the square root of a number, carry out the result to one more significant digit than appears in the given number. Round off the square root to the number of significant digits that appears in the given number.

1. Find the sum in each part below.
   (a) $2.47 + 5.08 + 3.92$ (b) $4.2 + 5.36 + 7.309$
   (c) $6.75 + 8.09 + 7.58$ (d) $8.346 + 5.7 + 2.83$
   (e) $.064 + 3.25 + 80.90$ (f) $12.15 + .675 + 8.32$

2. Find the following products.
   (a) 8.5×3.14 (b) 2.38×65.47
   (c) $3.25 \times .7854$ (d) 9.12×1.005
   (e) 3.1416×6.5 (f) $.75 \times 3.8 \times 4.375$
   (g) 3.14×5.8 (h) $\frac{1}{3} \times 15.5 \times 20.42$

3. Find the quotient in each part of this example.
   (a) $26.759 \div 3.142$ (b) $387.6 \div 24.5$
   (c) $8.465 \div 5.3$ (d) $62.57 \div 2.35$
   (e) $72.49 \div 3.4$ (f) $.976 \div .043$
   (g) $45.75 \div 3.14$ (h) $27.85 \div .7854$

4. Find each of the following square roots.
   (a) $\sqrt{34.75}$ (b) $\sqrt{426.85}$
   (c) $\sqrt{2346.87}$ (d) $\sqrt{176.89}$
   (e) $\sqrt{127.5}$ (f) $\sqrt{369.42}$

421. (a) *Letters* are used in mathematics to represent *unspecified numbers*, as h, b, and A in $A = hb$. Such letters, individually, may represent any of a set of appropriate numbers. They are called **variables.**

Thus: Depending upon the problem, h and b above may be any of a set of integers, or of a set of fractions, or of a set of real numbers.

(b) A **number expression** consists of specific numbers (such as 5, 13, $\frac{4}{5}$) and letters that represent numbers, connected by one or more of the signs of addition, subtraction, multiplication, division, . . . , that tell how the numbers are to be used, as

$$2a + ab, \quad \frac{1}{2}h(b + c), \quad \text{and } \frac{4}{3}\pi r^3$$

(c) An **equation** expresses the equality of two number expressions, as $p = 2a + b + c$.

(d) An **identity** is an equation that is true for all possible values of the numbers in it.
Thus: $2(b + c) = 2b + 2c$, for all values of b and c.

(e) A **conditional equation** is true only for one or more of a set of specific values of any variables in it.
Such equations are said to have one or more **unknowns.**
Thus: $3x + 5 = 17$ if, and only if, $x = 4$.

(f) The specific values of the unknown that make a conditional equation an identity are the **roots** of the equation; as 4 for x in $3x + 5 = 17$.

(g) A conditional equation is of **degree one** or is **linear** if the sum of the exponents of the variables in each term is only 1, as $5x - 4 = 21$ and $3x + 2y = 24$.

(h) A conditional equation of the *first degree* that has only one unknown has one and only one root. A conditional equation of the *second degree* that has only one unknown has two roots.
Thus: $x^2 - 5x + 6 = 0$ if $x = 2$ and if $x = 3$.

(i) To **solve** a conditional equation is to find its root or roots.

(j) **Two conditional equations are equivalent** if they have the same roots, as $3x + 5 = 17$ and $3x + 4 = 20 - x$, which have the root 4.

422. Generally, *equation* refers to a conditional equation. An **equation is solved** by using one or more of the following laws.

An equation is changed to an equivalent equation if:

Law 1. *The same number is added to both sides of the equation.*

Law 2. *The same number is subtracted from both sides of the equation.*

Law 3. *Both sides of the equation are multiplied by the same nonzero number.*

Law 4. *Both sides of the equation are divided by the same nonzero number.*

Example. Solve the equation $\dfrac{3}{2c} - \dfrac{2}{c} = \dfrac{1}{4c} - \dfrac{3}{2}$.

Solution. 1. $\dfrac{3}{2c} - \dfrac{2}{c} = \dfrac{1}{4c} - \dfrac{3}{2}$

2. M_{4c} $\qquad \overset{2}{\cancel{4c}}\left(\dfrac{3}{\cancel{2c}}\right) - 4\cancel{c}\left(\dfrac{2}{\cancel{c}}\right) = \cancel{4c}\left(\dfrac{1}{\cancel{4c}}\right) - \overset{2c}{\cancel{4c}}\left(\dfrac{3}{\cancel{2}}\right)$ (Law 3)

3. $\qquad \therefore \quad 6 - 8 = 1 - 6c,$ or $-2 = 1 - 6c$

4. A_{6c}, A_2 $\quad -2 + 6c + 2 = 1 - 6c + 6c + 2$ (Law 1)

5. $\qquad \therefore \quad 6c = 3$

6. D_6 $\qquad\qquad \dfrac{\cancel{6}c}{\cancel{6}} = \dfrac{\overset{1}{\cancel{3}}}{\underset{2}{\cancel{6}}},$ or $c = \dfrac{1}{2}$ (Law 4)

Note. M_{4c} means: Multiply *both sides* of the previous equation by $4c$.

A_{6c} means: Add $6c$ to both sides of the previous equation.

D_6 means: Divide both sides of the previous equation by 6.

Check. Is $\frac{1}{2}$ actually the root of the given equation?

Does $\dfrac{3}{2(\frac{1}{2})} - \dfrac{2}{(\frac{1}{2})} = \dfrac{1}{4(\frac{1}{2})} - \dfrac{3}{2}?$ $\quad \dfrac{3}{1} - 4 = \dfrac{1}{2} - \dfrac{3}{2}?$

Does $\qquad\qquad -1 = -\dfrac{2}{2}?$ Yes.

Solve each of the following equations. Check.

1. $\dfrac{6}{x} = \dfrac{12}{5}$

2. $\dfrac{9}{4} = \dfrac{18}{y}$

3. $\dfrac{3}{5} = \dfrac{z}{20}$

4. $\dfrac{1}{12} + \dfrac{1}{2x} = \dfrac{3}{x}$

5. $\dfrac{5}{3y} - \dfrac{7}{6} = \dfrac{6}{y} - \dfrac{2}{y}$

423. A **formula** is an equation that involves two or more variables, as $p = a + b + c$. In this formula, we may think of p as the *subject* and $a + b + c$ as the *predicate*.

When specific values are given for a, b, and c, then a specific value for p is determined by the computation on the right side of the formula.

Thus: If $a = 10$, $b = 12$, and $c = 15$,
$$p = 10 + 12 + 15, \text{ or } p = 37.$$

p is said to be a **function** of a, b, and c, meaning that a value of p is determined by specific values of a, b, and c.

This same formula can be used to find the specific value of a when values are given for p, b, and c.

Thus: If $p = 36$, $b = 12$, and $c = 16$, then
$$36 = a + 12 + 16, \text{ or } 36 = a + 28.$$
Since $36 = a + 28$, then $a + 28 = 36$.
S_{28} $\therefore$ $a + 28 - 28 = 36 - 28$
$$\therefore \quad a = 8$$

Check. Does $36 = 8 + 12 + 16$? Yes.

424. *Any variable in a simple formula can be expressed in terms of the others; or the formula can be changed into a formula that has a different subject.*

Thus: $p = a + b + c$
S_b, S_c $\therefore$ $p - b - c = a + b + c - b - c$
$$\therefore \quad p - b - c = a, \text{ or } a = p - b - c$$

We have solved the equation $p = a + b + c$ for a in terms of p, b, and c, or we have expressed a as a function of p, b, and c. This formula is useful for solving any problem when p, b, and c are given.

Thus: If, again, $p = 36$, $b = 12$, and $c = 16$
$$a = 36 - 12 - 16, \text{ or } a = 8.$$

1. Solve $p = a + b + c$:   (1) For b (2) For c
2. Solve $p = 20 + b + c$:   (1) For b (2) For c
3. Solve $p = 2b + 2c$:   (1) For b (2) For c
4. Solve $A = hb$:   (1) For h (2) For b
5. Solve $A = \frac{1}{2}hb$:   (1) For h (2) For b
6. Solve $C = 2\pi hr$:   (1) For r (2) For h
7. Solve $B + C = 90$:   (1) For B (2) For C

Example 1. Solve the equation $\dfrac{a}{b} = \dfrac{c}{d}$ for b.

Solution. 1. $\qquad\qquad\qquad \dfrac{a}{b} = \dfrac{c}{d}$

2. M_{bd} $\qquad\qquad bd\left(\dfrac{a}{b}\right) = bd\left(\dfrac{c}{d}\right)$

3. $\qquad\qquad\qquad \therefore\quad da = bc,\ \text{or}\ bc = da$

4. D_c $\qquad\qquad \dfrac{bc}{c} = \dfrac{da}{c},\ \text{or}\ b = \dfrac{ad}{c}$

1. Solve $\dfrac{a}{b} = \dfrac{c}{d}$: $\qquad\qquad$ (1) For c $\qquad\qquad$ (2) For d

2. Solve $m = \frac{1}{2}(b + c)$: $\qquad\qquad$ (1) For b $\qquad\qquad$ (2) For c

Example 2. If $100 = 4x^2$, what is x?

Solution. 1. $\quad 100 = 4x^2\ \text{or}\ 4x^2 = 100$

2. D_4 $\qquad\qquad \therefore\quad x^2 = 25$

3. $\therefore\quad x = +\sqrt{25}\ \text{or}\ x = -\sqrt{25}$

4. $\therefore\quad x = +5\ \text{or}\ x = -5$

3. $A = s^2$ is the formula for the area of a square.
   (a) What is A when $s = 8.0$?
   (b) What is s when $A = 196$?
   (c) Solve $A = s^2$ for s in terms of A.

4. $A = \pi r^2$. (a) Find A when $r = 6.0$ (Let $\pi = 3.14$.)
   (b) Find A when $r = 10.0$. (c) Find r when $A = 153.86$.
   (d) Solve $A = \pi r^2$ for r in terms of A and π.

5. $S = 4\pi r^2$. (a) Find S when $r = 8.0$.
   (b) Solve $S = 4\pi r^2$ for r in terms of S and π.

6. $c^2 = a^2 + b^2$. (a) Find c when $a = 8$ and $b = 6$.
   (b) Find c, correct to tenths, when $a = 10$ and $b = 15$.
   (c) Solve $c^2 = a^2 + b^2$ for a in terms of c and b.

7. $c^2 = a^2 + b^2 - 2ab \cos C$ is a formula from an optional unit of Chapter Eight.
   (a) If $a = 10$, $b = 12$, and $\cos C = .8$, find the positive value of c correct to tenths.
   (b) If $c = 15$, $a = 10$, and $b = 12$, what is $\cos C$ correct to thousandths?
   (c) Solve the formula for $\cos C$ in terms of a, b, and c.

8. $\dfrac{\sin A}{a} = \dfrac{\sin B}{b}$. Solve this equation for a.

No.	Sq.	Sq. Root	Cube	Cube Root	No.	Sq.	Sq. Root	Cube	Cube Root
1	1	1.000	1	1.000	51	2,601	7.141	132,651	3.708
2	4	1.414	8	1.260	52	2,704	7.211	140,608	3.733
3	9	1.732	27	1.442	53	2,809	7.280	148,877	3.765
4	16	2.000	64	1.587	54	2,916	7.348	157,464	3.780
5	25	2.236	125	1.710	55	3,025	7.416	166,375	3.803
6	36	2.449	216	1.817	56	3,136	7.483	175,616	3.826
7	49	2.646	343	1.913	57	3,249	7.550	185,193	3.848
8	64	2.828	512	2.000	58	3,364	7.616	195,112	3.871
9	81	3.000	729	2.080	59	3,481	7.681	205,379	3.893
10	100	3.162	1,000	2.154	60	3,600	7.746	216,000	3.915
11	121	3.317	1,331	2.224	61	3,721	7.810	226,981	3.936
12	144	3.464	1,728	2.289	62	3,844	7.874	238,328	3.958
13	169	3.606	2,197	2.351	63	3,969	7.937	250,047	3.979
14	196	3.742	2,744	2.410	64	4,096	8.000	262,144	4.000
15	225	3.873	3,375	2.466	65	4,225	8.062	274,625	4.021
16	256	4.000	4,096	2.520	66	4,356	8.124	287,496	4.041
17	289	4.123	4,913	2.571	67	4,489	8.185	300,763	4.062
18	324	4.243	5,832	2.621	68	4,624	8.246	314,432	4.082
19	361	4.359	6,859	2.668	69	4,761	8.307	328,509	4.102
20	400	4.472	8,000	2.714	70	4,900	8.367	343,000	4.121
21	441	4.583	9,261	2.759	71	5,041	8.426	357,911	4.141
22	484	4.690	10,648	2.802	72	5,184	8.485	373,248	4.160
23	529	4.796	12,167	2.844	73	5,329	8.544	389,017	4.179
24	576	4.899	13,824	2.884	74	5,476	8.602	405,224	4.198
25	625	5.000	15,625	2.924	75	5,625	8.660	421,875	4.217
26	676	5.099	17,576	2.962	76	5,776	8.718	438,976	4.236
27	729	5.196	19,683	3.000	77	5,929	8.775	456,533	4.254
28	784	5.291	21,952	3.037	78	6,084	8.832	474,552	4.273
29	841	5.385	24,389	3.072	79	6,241	8.888	493,039	4.291
30	900	5.477	27,000	3.107	80	6,400	8.944	512,000	4.309
31	961	5.568	29,791	3.141	81	6,561	9.000	531,441	4.327
32	1,024	5.657	32,768	3.175	82	6,724	9.055	551,368	4.344
33	1,089	5.745	35,937	3.208	83	6,889	9.110	571,787	4.362
34	1,156	5.831	39,304	3.240	84	7,056	9.165	592,704	4.380
35	1,225	5.916	42,875	3.271	85	7,225	9.220	614,125	4.397
36	1,296	6.000	46,656	3.302	86	7,396	9.274	636,056	4.414
37	1,369	6.083	50,653	3.332	87	7,569	9.327	658,503	4.431
38	1,444	6.164	54,872	3.362	88	7,744	9.381	681,472	4.448
39	1,521	6.245	59,319	3.391	89	7,921	9.434	704,969	4.465
40	1,600	6.325	64,000	3.420	90	8,100	9.487	729,000	4.481
41	1,681	6.403	68,921	3.448	91	8,281	9.539	753,571	4.498
42	1,764	6.481	74,088	3.476	92	8,464	9.592	778,688	4.514
43	1,849	6.557	79,507	3.503	93	8,649	9.644	804,357	4.531
44	1,936	6.633	85,184	3.530	94	8,836	9.695	830,584	4.547
45	2,025	6.708	91,125	3.557	95	9,025	9.747	857,375	4.563
46	2,116	6.782	97,336	3.583	96	9,216	9.798	884,736	4.579
47	2,209	6.856	103,823	3.609	97	9,409	9.849	912,673	4.595
48	2,304	6.928	110,592	3.634	98	9,604	9.899	941,192	4.610
49	2,401	7.000	117,649	3.659	99	9,801	9.950	970,299	4.626
50	2,500	7.071	125,000	3.684	100	10,000	10.000	1,000,000	4.642

CUMULATIVE GUIDE TO MASTERY

PLANE GEOMETRY

Directions. Without referring to the page or section, frequently test your knowledge of the definitions, axioms, postulates, and theorems in the following list, as far as the page of the book that has been studied by your class.

1. Be able to complete and to illustrate incomplete statements.

2. Be able to illustrate and to answer the questions asked.

3. Be able to prove theorems selected by your teacher.

For the cumulative Guide to Mastery for Solid Geometry see page 443.

17   (*b*) How many segments equal to a given segment
          are there on a line, from a point on a line?
          (*c*) The shortest line between two points is. . . .
          (*d*) (*Def.*) A **point bisects** a segment if. . . .
          (*e*) How many mid-points has a segment?

19   §10   (*Def.*) An **angle** consists of. . . .
      §11   (*a*) (*Def.*) **Angles are equal** if. . . .
          (*b*) A ray bisects an angle if. . . .
          (*c*) How many bisectors has an angle?

20   §12   (*Def.*) **Adjacent angles** are. . . .
      §13   (*a*) Define (*1*) Right angle   (*2*) Perpendicular lines.
          (*b*) All right angles are. . . .

21   §14   (*a*) Define: (1) Straight angle   (2) Acute angle
          (3) Obtuse angle.
          (*b*) What part of a straight angle is a right angle?
          (*c*) All straight angles are. . . .
      §15   (*a*) (*Def.*) An **angle-degree** is. . . .

22   §16   (*a*) (*Def.*) A **circle** is. . . .
          (*b*) With a given radius from a point as center, there
          is. . . .
          (*c*) A diameter equals. . . .

23   §18   (*a*) (*Def.*) An **arc** of a circle is. . . .
          (*b*) A minor arc is. . . .
          (*c*) A major arc is. . . .
          (*d*) Two arcs are equal if. . . .
      §19   (*Def.*) An **arc-degree** is. . . .
      §20   The number of angle-degrees in an angle at the
          center of a circle equals. . . .

24   §22   Do you know how to draw or measure an angle with
          a protractor?

26   §24   (*Def.*) **Complementary angles** are. . . .
          Each of the ∡ is the complement of. . . .
      §25   Complements of the same ∠ or of. . . .

27   §26   (*Def.*) **Supplementary angles** are. . . .
      §27   (*a*) If two adjacent ∡ have their exterior sides in
          the same straight line, then. . . .
          (*b*) Supplements of the same ∠ or of. . . .
          (*c*) If two adjacent ∡ are supplementary. . . .

28   §28   (*Def.*) **Vertical angles** are. . . .

28 §29 (a) When two straight lines intersect, the vertical. . . .

(b) The total angle around a point in a plane is. . . .

29 §30 What kind of conclusions are suggested by inductive reasoning?

30 §31 Is it safe to draw conclusions from appearances in a figure? Why? Give an example.

31 §32 (a) What kind of reasoning is more dependable than inductive?

(b) Of what does the foundation for such reasoning consist in geometry?

(c) Thereafter, how do we proceed in geometry?

32 §34 (a) (Def.) An axiom is. . . .

(b) Quantities equal to the same or. . . .

(c) A quantity may be substituted for. . . .

(d) State the axiom for: (1) Adding equals (2) Subtracting (3) Multiplying (4) Dividing

(e) The whole equals. . . .

(f) The whole is greater than. . . .

33 §36 The three characteristics of a good definition are. . . .

34 §37 (a) (Def.) A **postulate** is. . . .

(b) (Post. 1) One and only one straight line. . . .

(c) (Post. 2) A segment can be extended. . . .

(d) (Post. 3) Two straight lines can intersect. . . .

(e) (Post. 4) There is one and only one segment equal to a given segment on a line. . . .

(f) (Post. 5) The shortest line between two points is. . . .

(g) (Post. 6) A segment has . . . mid-point.

(h) (Post. 7) An angle has . . . bisector.

(i) (Post. 8) All right angles. . . .

(j) (Post. 9) A straight angle equals . . . right angles.

(k) (Post. 10) All straight angles. . . .

(l) (Post. 11) A circle can be drawn. . . .

(m) (Post. 12) A diameter equals how many radii?

35   (*a*) (*Post. 13*) How do all radii and diameters of the same circle or of equal circles compare?

              (*b*) (*Post. 14*) The number of angle-degrees in an angle at the center of a circle equals. . . .

              (*c*) (*Post. 15*) Complements of the same ∠ or of equal ⦞. . . .

              (*d*) (*Post. 16*) If two adjacent ⦞ have their exterior sides in a straight line. . . .

              (*e*) (*Post. 17*) Supplements of the same ∠ or of equal ⦞. . . .

              (*f*) (*Post. 18*) If two adjacent ⦞ are supplementary. . . .

              (*g*) (*Post. 19*) When two straight lines intersect, the vertical ⦞. . . .

              (*h*) (*Post. 20*) The sum of all the successive adjacent ⦞ in a plane around a point. . . .

40   §41   (*Def.*) (*a*) A **theorem** is. . . . (*b*) Its **hypothesis** is. . . . (*c*) Its **conclusion** is. . . .

      §42   What is included in a formal proof?

45   ★OPTIONAL UNIT A★   Some related Solid Geometry

          If you have studied this unit, turn to the Solid Geometry Guide on page 443, and check the items for pages 46 and 47.

CHAPTER TWO — CONGRUENCE

51   §47   (*Def.*) (*a*) A **triangle** is. . . .

          (*b*) Opposite each side is. . . .

          (*c*) Opposite each angle is. . . .

          (*d*) Each pair of sides includes. . . .

          (*e*) Each pair of angles includes. . . .

51   §49   (*Post. 21*) An arc can be drawn from a point. . . .

52   §50   (*Def.*) **Congruent figures** are. . . .

      §51   (*Post. 22*) Any geometrical figure can be moved. . . .

53   §52   If two △ have two sides and the included ∠. . . .

56   §55   (*a*) Where do corresponding sides of congruent △ lie?

          (*b*) Where do corresponding angles of congruent △ lie?

56   §55   (c) Corresponding sides and ∡ of congruent
             △. . . .

57   §56   **(Fundamental Plan 1)** To prove two segments or
             two ∡ equal, prove that. . . .

60   §58   If two triangles have two ∡ and the included
             side. . . .

63   §59   (Def.) (a) A **scalene** △ is. . . .
             (b) An **isosceles** △ is. . . .
             (c) What are the base ∡ of an isosceles △?

64   §60   If two sides of a △ are equal, then. . . .
      §61   (Def.) A **corollary** is. . . .
      §62   (Def.) An **equilateral** △ is a △ that. . . .
      §63   (Cor.) An equilateral △ also is. . . .

66   §65   If two △ have the three sides of the one. . . .

72   §68   (Def.) The **perpendicular-bisector** of a segment
             is. . . .
      §69   If each of two points is equidistant from the ends
             of a segment, then. . . .

73   §71   Can you lay off on a line a segment equal to a
             segment?

74   §73   Can you bisect an angle and prove it is bisected?

75   §74   Can you construct the perpendicular-bisector of a
             segment?

76   §75   Can you construct the perpendicular to a line at a
             point of the line?
      §76   In a plane how many such perpendiculars can be
             constructed at a point?

77   §77   (a) Can you construct a perpendicular to a line
                 from a point outside the line?
             (b) In a plane how many such perpendiculars can
                 be drawn to the line from a point?
      §79   (Def.) The **distance** to a line from a point is. . . .

78   §80   Can you construct a line that makes a given angle
             with a given line at a point of the line and prove
             your construction is correct?

80   §81   (Def.) (a) An **altitude** of a triangle is. . . .
             (b) A **median** of a triangle is. . . .

CHAPTER THREE — PARALLEL LINES

90   §82   (*Def.*) **Coplanar** lines are. . . .

       §83   (*Def.*) (*a*) Parallel lines are. . . .

              (*b*) Skew lines are. . . .

       §84   (*Post. 23*) In a plane, how many lines are there through a point parallel to a line of the plane?

       §85   If two lines are parallel to a third line, ...

91   §86   What is the procedure for an indirect proof?

       §87   (*Def.*) (*a*) When are alternate-interior, corresponding, and interior angles of two lines formed?

              (*b*) What is meant by a transversal of two lines?

92   §88   (*Def.*) How is an **exterior** angle of a △ formed?

       §89   An exterior ∠ of a △ is greater than. . . .

93   §90   Two coplanar lines are parallel if a transversal of them forms two. . . .

       §91   **(Fundamental Plan 2)** To prove two lines parallel. . . .

       §93   Two coplanar lines are parallel also if a transversal forms two. . . .

       §92   Two coplanar lines are parallel also if a transversal forms two. . . .

94   §94   Two coplanar lines are parallel also if. . . .

95   §95   Can you construct a parallel to a given line through a point and prove your construction is correct?

96   §97   When are alternate-interior angles equal?

       §98   (*Cor. 1*) If two parallels are cut by a transversal, what other angles are equal?

       §99   (*Cor. 2*) By the same hypothesis, what is true of the interior angles on the same side of the transversal?

97   §100   (*Cor. 3*) In a plane if a line is perpendicular to one of two parallels. . . .

       §101   (*Cor. 4*) Two coplanar ∡ are equal if their corresponding sides are. . . .

99   §102   (*Def.*) (*a*) The converse of a theorem is obtained by. . . .

              (*b*) Is a converse of a theorem necessarily true? May it be?

CHAPTER FOUR — THEOREMS BASED ON PARALLELS

108 §104 The sum of the ∡ of a △ is. . . .

§105 (*Cor. 1*) How many ∡ of a △ can be rt. ∡?

§106 (*Cor. 2*) In a plane, how many perpendiculars can be drawn to a line from a point that is not on the line?

109 §107 (*Def.*) (*a*) A **right triangle** is . . . ; its **hypotenuse** is. . . .

(*b*) An **isosceles rt.** △ is. . . .

§108 (*Cor. 3*) The acute ∡ of a rt. △ are. . . .

§109 (*Cor. 4*) An exterior ∠ of a △ is. . . .

§110 (*Cor. 5*) If two ∡ of one △ are equal respectively to two ∡ of another △, then. . . .

§111 (*a*) (*Cor. 6*) If two △ have a side, the opposite ∠, and another ∠ of the one, ...

(*b*) How many other congruence theorems have you had?

111 §112 If two rt. △ have the hypotenuse and a leg, ...

112 §113 (*a*) Any point in the perpendicular-bisector. . . .

(*b*) State the converse. Is it true?

§114 (*a*) Any point in the bisector of an angle. . . .

(*b*) State the converse. Is it true?

114 §116 If two ∡ of a △ are equal. . . .

115 May there be more than one converse of a theorem? When?

116 §117 If one ∠ of a rt. △ equals 30°, the opposite side is. . . .

119 §119 (*Def.*) (*a*) A **polygon** is . . . ; its **diagonals** are. . . .

(*b*) Has a polygon an interior? Why?

(*c*) When is a polygon equilateral? Equiangular?

120 §120 (*Def.*) A **quadrilateral** is. . . .

§121 (*Def.*) A **parallelogram** is . . . ; its **base** is . . . ; its **altitude** is. . . .

§122 (*a*) A diagonal of a ▱ separates. . . .

(*b*) Opposite sides of a ▱ are. . . .

(*c*) Opposite ∡ of a ▱ are. . . .

(*d*) Consecutive ∡ of a ▱ are. . . .

142   §150   When are inequalities of the same order?

143   §151   (Ax. 9) If equals be added to unequals, ...
(Ax. 10) If equals be subtracted from un-
equals, ...
(Ax. 11) If $a > b$ and $b > c$, then a ? c.
(Ax. 12) If unequals be added to unequals of the
same order, then. . . .
(Ax. 13) If unequals be subtracted from equals or
from unequals of opposite order, then. . . .

§152   (a) Any side of a triangle is less than. . . .
(b) Any side of a triangle is more than. . . .

144   §154   If two sides of a triangle are unequal, ...

145   §155   If two ∡ of a △ are unequal. . . .

§156   (Cor. 1) *The perpendicular to a line from a point
is.* . . .

§157   (Cor. 2) *The hypotenuse of a rt. △ is greater.* . . .

CHAPTER SIX — CIRCLES

161   §167   (a) With a given radius and a given center, there
is. . . .
(b) The interior of a circle is. . . .
(c) A point is within, on, or outside a circle if. . . .
(d) (Def.) **Circles are equal** if. . . .
(e) How do all radii and diameters of the same or
of equal circles compare?
(f) How does a diameter divide a circle?

162   §168   (a) Can a circle be constructed through two points?
(b) How many circles, through two given points?

§169   (Def.) A circle **circumscribes** a polygon if. . . .

163   §170   (Def.) A **central angle** in a circle is. . . .

§171   In the same circle or in equal circles:
(a) If central angles are equal, ...
(b) If arcs are equal, ...

§172   (c) If central angles are unequal, ...
(d) If arcs are unequal, ...

164   §173   (Def.) The **chord** of an arc is. . . .

§174   In the same or in equal circles:
(a) If chords are equal, ...

§175   (b) If arcs are equal, ...

182   §203   What is the converse of §202? Is it true?

183   §204   The ∠ formed by a tangent and a chord to the point of tangency has the same measure as. . . .

184   §205   The ∠ formed by two chords that intersect inside the circle has the same measure as. . . .

185   §206   The ∠ formed by two secants or by two tangents; or by a secant and a tangent has the same measure as. . . .

187   §209   Can you construct a tangent to a circle: (a) At a point of the circle? (b) From a point?

CHAPTER SEVEN — SIMILARITY IN TRIANGLES

204   §226   (Def.) The **ratio** of two numbers is. . . .

205   §228   (Def.) A **proportion** is . . . ; the numbers of it are called. . . .

      §229   If r, x, y, and s are proportional, then the product of the means equals . . . ; that is, ...

206   §230   The converse of §229 is. . . . Is it true?

      §231   If the numerators of a proportion are equal. . . .

      §232   If three terms of one proportion are equal respectively to the three corresponding terms of another. . . .

      §233   If r, x, s, and y are proportional, then they are in proportion by alternation; that is, ...

207   §234   Also by inversion, which means. . . .

      §235   Also by addition, which means. . . .

      §236   Also by subtraction, which means. . . .

209   §237   A proportion of geometrical quantities refers to. . . .

210   §239   A parallel to one side of a triangle, divides. . . .

211   §241   In $\triangle XYZ$, if AB is parallel to XZ, intersecting XY at A and YZ at B, write six proportions of segments on the figure.

212   §243   What is the converse of §239? Is it true?

213   §244   (Def.) (a) Two **polygons are similar** if. . . .

214   §245   If two △ have two ∠ of one equal to two ∠ of the other, the △ are. . . .

218   §248   Two △ are similar also if. . . .

CHAPTER EIGHT — TRIGONOMETRY

Note. This chapter is *related* to elementary geometry; it is not elementary geometry. If you study it, prepare a Cumulative Guide to the subject matter that appears on pages 244–258.

CHAPTER NINE — REGULAR POLYGONS

CUMULATIVE GUIDE TO MASTERY

SOLID GEOMETRY

86   SG 18   (*Def.*) The **plane angle** of a dihedral angle is formed by. . . .

87   SG 19   (*Def.*) (*a*) A **dihedral angle** is **right, acute,** or **obtuse** if. . . .
         (*b*) Two **planes** are **perpendicular** if. . . .

      SG 20   If a line is perpendicular to a plane, then any plane that contains it. . . .

      SG 21   Each face of a rectangular solid is perpendicular to. . . .

103   SG 22   (*Def.*) (*a*) Two **planes** are **parallel** if. . . .
         (*b*) A **line and a plane** are **parallel** if. . . .

      SG 23   If two planes are parallel, a line in one. . . .

      SG 24   If a line outside a plane is parallel to a line in the plane, then. . . .

104   SG 25   If a line is parallel to a plane, then the intersection of that plane with any plane through the line. . . .

      SG 26   If two parallel planes are cut by a third plane. . . .

      SG 27   Lines that are perpendicular to the same plane. . . .

      SG 28   If one of two parallel lines is perpendicular to a plane, then. . . .

105   SG 29   If two lines in space are parallel to the same line. . . .

      SG 30   If a straight line is perpendicular to one of two parallel planes, ...

      SG 31   If two planes are perpendicular to the same line, ...

      SG 32   If two planes are parallel to a third plane, ...

133   SG 33   (*Def.*) (*a*) A **polyhedron** is. . . .
         (*b*) A **prism** is. . . .
         (*c*) A **right prism** is. . . .
         (*d*) A **prism** is **triangular, rectangular,** if. . . .
         (*e*) A **parallelepiped** is. . . .

134   (*f*) A **rectangular parallelepiped** is. . . .
         (*g*) A **pyramid** is . . . ; its **lateral edges** are . . . ; its **vertex** is. . . .
         (*h*) A **regular pyramid** is. . . .

134   SG 34   If two intersecting lines are parallel to a plane, then their plane. . . .

          SG 35   If two angles have their corresponding sides parallel and extending in the same directions from their vertices, then. . . .

135   SG 36   (*Def.*) A **section** of a solid is. . . .

153   SG 37   (*Def.*) (*a*) A **trihedral angle** is. . . .
                   (*b*) Its **vertex** is. . . .
                   (*c*) Its **faces** are. . . .
                   (*d*) Its **face angles** are. . . .
                   (*e*) Its **dihedral angles** are. . . .

155   SG 38   (*Def.*) (*a*) Two trihedral angles are congruent if. . . .
                   (*b*) Two trihedral angles are symmetric if. . . .

          SG 39   Two **trihedral angles** are **congruent** if . . . and are **symmetric** if. . . .

          SG 39   If two trihedral angles have the face angles of the one equal to. . . .
                   (*a*) They are congruent if. . . .
                   (*b*) They are symmetric if. . . .

155   SG 40   The sum of two face angles of a trihedral angle is. . . .

          SG 41   If two trihedral angles have two face angles and the included dihedral angle of the one equal to. . . .
                   (*a*) They are congruent if. . . .
                   (*b*) They are symmetric if. . . .

          SG 42   If two trihedral angles have two dihedral angles and the included face angle of the one equal to. . . .
                   (*a*) They are congruent if. . . .
                   (*b*) They are symmetric if. . . .

          SG 43   If two face angles of a trihedral angle are equal. . . .

157   SG 44   (*Def.*) A **polyhedral angle** is. . . .

          SG 45   The sum of the face angles of any polyhedral angle is. . . .

198   SG 46   (*Def.*) A **sphere** is. . . .

          SG 47   The intersection of a sphere and a plane is. . . .

199   SG 48   (*Def.*) A **great circle** of a sphere is. . . .
       SG 49   (*Def.*) A **small circle** of a sphere is. . . .

200   SG 50   Through two points that are not the ends of a diameter of a sphere:
                   (*a*) How many great circles can there be?
                   (*b*) How many small circles can there be?
       SG 51   Through two points of a sphere that are the ends of a diameter, how many great circles can there be?
       SG 52   (*Def.*) The **poles** of a circle of a sphere are. . . .
       SG 53   (*Post.*) The shortest line on a sphere between two points of the sphere is. . . .

201   SG 54   (*Def.*) A **spherical angle** consists of. . . .
       SG 55   A spherical angle has the same measure as. . . .
       SG 56   (*Def.*) A **spherical triangle** consists of. . . .

233   SG 57   (*a*) A plane that is parallel to the base of a pyramid divides proportionally. . . .
                   (*b*) The section made by the plane is. . . .

280   SG 58   (*Def.*) A **regular pyramid** is. . . .
       SG 59   In any regular pyramid:
                   (*a*) The altitude and any radius of the base are. . . .
                   (*b*) How do the lateral edges compare?
                   (*c*) What kind of triangle encloses each face?
                   (*d*) (*Def.*) The **slant height** is. . . .

281   SG 60   (*Def.*) (*a*) A **frustum of a pyramid** consists of. . . .
                   (*b*) The lateral faces of a frustum of a regular pyramid are enclosed by. . . .
                   (*c*) (*Def.*) The **slant height of a frustum** of a regular pyramid is. . . .
                   (*d*) What kind of polygons enclose the two bases?

282   §319   (*Def.*) A **regular polyhedron** is. . . .
       §320   There are not more than . . . regular polyhedrons.

349   SG 61   (*Post.*) The **volume of a rectangular solid** is. . . .

351   SG 62   (*Post.*) (*Cavalieri's Theorem*) If two solids have equal bases and altitudes, and if . . . , they are equal.

352   SG 63   (*Post.*) The volume of any prism equals. . . .

353   SG 64   (*Def.*) A **right circular cylinder** consists of. . . .

354   SG 65   (*Def.*) A **right prism** is **inscribed** in a right circular cylinder if. . . .

      SG 66   (*Post.*) If a sequence of right prisms with bases enclosed by regular polygons is inscribed in a right circular cylinder, by successively doubling the number of sides:

          (*a*) Their bases, lateral surfaces, and interiors. . . .

          (*b*) Their bases have apothems that. . . .

          (*c*) Their radii and altitudes. . . .

355   SG 67   (*Post.*) Any theorem about a prism that is independent of the number of faces is true also of. . . .

          (*a*) The lateral area of a right circular cylinder equals. . . .

          (*b*) The volume of a right circular cylinder equals. . . .

358   SG 68   (*Def.*) (*a*) A **right circular cone** consists of . . . ; its **base** is . . . ; its **lateral surface** contains . . . ;

          (*b*) The **radius** is . . . ; the **altitude** is . . . ; an **element** of its surface is . . . ; its **slant height** is. . . .

359   §391   (*a*) A regular pyramid is inscribed in a right circular cone if its base is. . . . and its vertex is. . . .

          (*b*) If a sequence of regular pyramids inscribed in a right circular cone is formed, having four, eight, sixteen, etc., faces, then:

          (1) Their altitudes. . . .

          (2) Their radii. . . .

          (3) Their slant heights. . . .

          (4) Their lateral surfaces. . . .

          (5) Their interiors. . . .

      SG 69   (*Post.*) Any theorem about a regular pyramid that is independent of the number of faces is true also for. . . .

360   SG 70   The lateral area of a regular pyramid equals. . . .

      SG 71   The lateral area of a right circular cone equals. . . .

362   SG 72   If two pyramids have equal bases and altitudes. . . .

363   SG 73   The volume of a triangular pyramid equals. . . .

364   SG 74   The volume of any pyramid equals. . . .

      SG 75   The volume of any cone equals. . . .

365   SG 76   The lateral area of a frustum of a regular pyramid equals. . . .

366   SG 77   (*Def.*) (*a*) **A frustum of a right circular cone** consists of. . . .

            (*b*) The **upper base** of the frustum is. . . .

            (*c*) The **lower base** is. . . .

            The **altitude** of the frustum is. . . .

            The **elements** of the frustum are. . . .

            The **slant height** of the frustum is. . . .

      SG 78   The lateral area of a frustum of a right circular cone equals. . . . The formula is. . . .

368   SG 79   The formula for the area of a sphere is. . . .

370   SG 80   The formula for the volume of a sphere is. . . .

INDEX

449